"If the last few years have st[o] bring it back, 10-fold. What I lov Dr. Erin Baker first defines, makes the case for, and then shows us how to uncover the Joy in our lives. Using their own journey and numerous case studies, they anticipate our arguments and resistance, making the goal all the more attainable. "

~ Mark J. Silverman,
author of the bestselling *Only 10s 2.0*
and host of the *Mastering Overwhelm* podcast

"*Joy-Full AF* is inspiring AF. As a corporate refugee who initially created a business that filled my bank account but drained my soul, I couldn't agree more that putting joy front and center is a life-changing approach. Erin shares brilliant questions and concepts that'll inspire you to create *your* unique journey to joy-full. I still wear my HILA hat every day. I guarantee you're going to want one, too… "

~ Shelley Paxton,
author of *Soulbbatical: A Corporate Rebel's Guide to Finding Your Best Life*

" This book will prove to be a road map, a wake-up call, or a lifesaver for you. Maybe all 3. Erin is one of the most authentic people I've ever known, fully committed to living a passionate life and advocating for others to do the same. This book is literally an actionable strategy guide for increasing the level of joy in your life, which is actually the main thing we all care about.

It's broken down into real-life consumable and digestible bits. The 4 ingredients of Joy shifted my consciousness immediately, and it only got better from there. If you act upon the wisdom inside, your life will be forever changed. **"**

~ Sean Smith,
speaker, coach, author, poet, actor,
founder of Neuro-Transformational Coaching

" In *Joy-Full AF*, Dr. Erin Baker deftly presents a compelling case for the inclusion of joy in all areas of business. This message that joy is a strategy for success in business is long overdue! The clarity provided around *"Be careful not to chase happiness at the expense of your joy"* alone can 10x your joy level immediately. They have done a fantastic job of taking something as intrinsic as joy that, up until now, has been rather cryptic in the business world, and made it accessible and actionable to everyone. *Joy-Full AF* is your roadmap to having success chase you. **"**

~ Ken Bechtel,
author of *Follow Your YES*

❝ Dr. Erin Baker has a PhD in psychology and a career background as a high-level leader in the world of technology. A coach and consultant to executives and entrepreneurs, Erin is helping leaders bring joy back to their lives and their careers. Let's be honest, all the success, money and recognition you have is meaningless if you're not happy. Joy-Full AF will help you see that joy is not just a result, it's the path to your next level of success. **❞**

~ Rich Litvin,
founder of 4PC and coauthor of *The Prosperous Coach*

❝ Joy is not a frivolous nice-to-have. It's the way that smart leaders avoid creative and physical burnout. Erin's words are a compass for the "meh" that so many leaders are feeling. *Joy-Full AF* is fast-paced, wise, and full of aha moments you'll scribble onto sticky notes. This book feels like a chat with that really smart friend, who always helps you to see what's truly important. Provocative and clever, Erin's words will help you to swap "shoulds" and "supposed tos" for a daily dose of joy. **❞**

~ Dr. Mandy Lehto,
host of *Enough, the podcast*

" In *Joy-Full AF*, Dr. Erin Baker takes us on a journey to pull apart joy, discover what it truly is, and from that true place finally allow ourselves to experience more of it. It's about time someone looked at joy as a measure of success in the same way hope is a measure of how fully you've released an old paradigm. This book will help you befriend joy without making the lack of it fuel for shame—a game-changer for business owners! **"**

~ Catherine Hammond,
Life Transition Guide, award-winning attorney,
and author of *Hope(less)*

" Joy is a vital part of what makes us human. In this book, that is written with care, energy and heart, Dr. Erin Baker shares with us their insights into how you can have more joy in work and life. Allow your skeptical selves to revel in the wonderful world of Joy. Trust me when I say it—you will not regret it. **"**

~ Em Stroud,
clown, author, podcaster and cofounder of Laugh.Think.Play.

"Dr. Erin Baker has written an amazing book that feels like a series of conversations with a new friend who prioritizes your well-being. *Joy-Full AF* made me realize how little I know about joy and then taught me how to cultivate it. Most importantly, its pages empowered me to recognize joy when it shows up in my life and business journeys. This book is a game changer. **"**

~ Addison Brasil,
author of the bestselling *The First Year of Grief Club*

"Thank you, Dr. Erin Baker, for writing the definitive book on one of the world's most ambiguously defined emotions. *Joy-Full AF* is a delightful and, importantly, *actionable* treatise on joy. Baker deftly explains what joy is and isn't, and shows us how we can find more of it in business and in our everyday lives. A scientist by background, Baker takes joy down to the studs and keenly examines its parts — connection, curiosity, creativity, and courage — before ultimately rebuilding it into something we can all embody and experience regularly. (INSERT HUGE SIGH OF RELIEF!) *Joy-Full AF* has inspired me to lead with joy instead of thinking of it like some kind of nice-to-have accessory. Now I see it for what it is: essential. **"**

~ Laurie Shiers,
Creativity Catalyst

❝ No lie—I quoted several things I read in this book the day after reading the first half of it! HILA and magic beans immediately gave me a new, game-changing perspective. And there is one question Erin Baker mentions in the book that energized me to rethink so much about the direction I take my business in. Every entrepreneur needs to read this book (or every aspiring entrepreneur)! In this age of a million gurus teaching you the exact steps or right path, we've all lost sight of the fact that if we do what brings us the most joy, we'll inherently do it better and with more success. **❞**

~ Erin Hatzikostas,
Founder & CEO, b Authentic inc,
and author of *You Do You(ish)*

Joy-Full AF

Joy-Full AF

THE ESSENTIAL BUSINESS STRATEGY WE'RE AFRAID TO PUT FIRST

ERIN BAKER, PHD

Joy-Full AF

Copyright © 2022 by Erin Baker, PhD. All rights reserved. No part of this publication may be reproduced or transmitted in any form or by any means, mechanical or electronic, including photocopying and recording, or by any information storage and retrieval systems, without permission in writing from the author or publisher.

Disclaimer: The advice and strategies contained herein may not be suitable for every situation. This work is sold with the understanding that the Author and Publisher are not engaged in rendering legal, accounting, or other professional services. Neither the Author nor the Publisher shall be liable for damages arising herefrom. The fact that an organization or website is referred to in this work as a citation or a potential source of further information does not mean that the Author or the Publisher endorses the information that the organization or website may provide or recommendations it may make.

Book Design: Dino Marino, www.dinomarino.com

Paperback ISBN - 979-8-9866335-0-3

Hardcover ISBN - 979-8-9866335-1-0

eBook ISBN - 979-8-9866335-2-7

DEDICATION

To my clients past, current, and future.
Your commitment to finding and following your joy,
*and really, finding and following **you***
inspires me beyond words.

And to my wife, Meryl.
Our joy-full AF life,
and my joy-full AF coaching business
exist because of your unflinching
love and support.

Table of Contents

HOW THE F*CK DO WE GET MORE JOY?.. 165

Foreword

by Simone Seol

Let me ask you a question. Which path to happiness were you sold?

When I was a kid, I was taught that, if I studied hard, listened to what my parents and teachers said, and got into a good college, I'd be happy.

So I did that. And I wasn't happy. In fact, I was a tight ball of anxiety.

When I was in college, I was taught that, if I worked hard and put myself on a respectable career trajectory, I'd be happy.

So I did that. And I wasn't happy. In fact, I felt so lost and confused.

When I started my own business, I started repeating the same dynamic. If I follow the right directions, have the right mindset, get the good 'grades' (which, in entrepreneurship, meant money), I'd be happy.

The happiness never came. Neither did the money. In fact, all I got was burnout.

It wasn't until I figured out how to prioritize one secret, subversive ingredient that my business actually started to work, and make me money.

And you guessed it. That ingredient was joy.

The best part of it was, when I started using joy as a compass and barometer for every aspect of business planning, I didn't have to wait until I made more money to feel good.

I remember a particular moment of realizing: "This is it. I made it." It wasn't because of any flashy, impressive milestone I achieved. It was because I actually enjoyed being alive. I liked being myself. I enjoyed my business. That sense of being at home in my own life and pursuits was what I had actually been working toward my whole life, although I didn't know it.

No amount of money or external success could give it to me. Centering joy was what gave it to me.

Since then, I've become a champion of joy in my own way.

That is all to say, Erin and I share a subversive mission. To save other entrepreneurs the years of trial and error we both went through, and set them on the fastest possible path toward a joyful business. We also want to emphatically convey that joy isn't a childish, silly, or "nice to have" extra that you give yourself when you have time for a vacation.

It's essential to you, your customer base, and the world.

It's essential to your creativity, and even your health.

You don't have to try a million other things first, and accidentally stumble on joy as the last stop. You can just skip straight to it, and reap the rewards. And fortunately for us, we have in our hands this friendly, down-to-earth and deeply wise guide of a book to walk you every step of the way.

To be sure, Erin isn't the only person talking about joy. But they may be the only person who answers the gnarly, unspoken questions that few dare to tackle head on:

1. What exactly is joy, anyway?

2. Why can it feel so hard and elusive to find sometimes?

3. And how exactly does one go about creating it?

In answering these questions, Erin clarifies and concretizes what may have felt abstract and nebulous. The four foundational ingredients of joy, introduced in this book, are a revolutionary anchor that enables you to create joy on purpose in any area of life, and in every context.

The greatest gift of this book is that it makes joy actionable and pragmatic. By the time you're done reading it, you might just be feeling a ton of it — even when looking at your business plan.

–Simone Seol is a Joyful Marketing Coach, host of *Joyful Marketing* podcast, and author of *The Fearless Marketing Bible for Coaches*

Introduction

WHY DID I WRITE A BOOK ON JOY-FULL AF BUSINESS?

To be honest, that wasn't the plan.

When I first committed to writing a book, I wanted to write about the power of my favorite word in the English language: And.

At the time, I had done almost thirty episodes of a podcast called *Life in the And*. My guests and small community of listeners were resonating with the concept, so I figured I could reach even more people if I expanded it into a book.

One of my podcast guests was my friend, Niiamah Ashong. He didn't talk about it on the show, but for years he had been contemplating creating a movement called The World Joy Movement. It was perfect for him. Niiamah is an extrovert with an infectious energy and a smile that stretches well beyond his face. He epitomizes joy and joy-fullness. Yet, whenever he talked about his movement, it didn't land for me. Joy wasn't on my radar. It wasn't even in my vocabulary. And I certainly didn't see it as having any relevance to business.

Not long after I hired a book coach to bring my "And" concept to life I realized "Life in the And" as a podcast, and as a potential book, were limiting what I wanted to share. I had so much more to offer that was getting buried.

And quite frankly, I was getting bored.

This was the first of many times in my book-writing process that I lost the joy. (Though I couldn't have articulated that's what was happening back then.) So, I decided to take a step back from writing.

One day, I pulled out a piece of paper and my colored pencils and wrote out a timeline of how my business developed beginning in April 2018.

In green, I listed my successes. The first clients I enrolled several months before I left the corporate world. The day my first group coaching program started. The day I raised my fees far beyond what I thought I would ever make as a coach.

In red, I wrote my failures. When I tried to launch a group, and no one enrolled. When I had a long and painful string of people say no to working with me. Going through a multiple-month dry spell of zero revenue when I thought seriously about giving up entirely on having a private coaching practice.

In blue, I wrote some of the activities that I did in those two years. The time I played the 90-day money game (which we'll talk about in *It's All Fun and Games ... No, Really!*). When I joined one of the communities of coaches — 4PC — that really spurred my growth. Starting a 90-day live challenge on Facebook. Launching and later sunsetting my Facebook community, "The Heart Leader Launchpad."

In pink, I wrote the insights and thoughts I was having at that moment, like how I learned to continue showing up day after day, even during that dry spell when it felt like I was banging my head against the wall.

I realized through the exercise that I had all kinds of things to share about how to have fun, play, step into courage, and move through fear.

But it still didn't occur to me that it was all about joy.

Joy was not in my vocabulary yet. Instead, the colored-pencil exercise sparked an idea for a book called *The 10 Essentials*, set in the business wilderness. After all, aren't we all on an adventure of bushwhacking, climbing mountains, and getting lost? When you go into the real wilderness, you always want to bring supplies for fire, food, water, and extra shelter — The Essentials. I wondered which "essentials" were pivotal to me thriving in business.

I looked back at my colored-pencil timeline and saw several concepts and tools that could be represented by objects. I *love* to experiment. So, I saw a lab coat. One of my favorite concepts in goal setting is High Intentions and Low Attachment or HILA. I thought of it as a hat you put on. Feeling like I had traction with *The 10 Essentials*, I feverishly wrote chapters, confident that I was naming powerful teaching tools and also creating a fun metaphor to teach them through. But I had an underlying nagging feeling that something was missing. I had already written half the book by the time I noticed that despite having one of the most fun and playful concepts for a book that I could imagine, I wasn't having fun or feeling playful. (I'd lost the joy, but I *still* didn't have that word in my vocabulary.)

I procrastinated. I made excuses to do other things. I felt exhausted every time I sat down to write.

When I took a month off from my business in the summer to write and recharge, I only opened Microsoft Word once. I thought, at the time, that maybe I just really needed a vacation and that I'd pick the book back up after.

When I came back, I still didn't want to open Word. I considered many options and it ultimately seemed like the only solution was to shelve the book. Maybe I just wasn't meant to write a book after all.

But the concepts kept coming back into my consciousness. My clients would share how powerful they are. My friends would mention implementing them in their businesses.

One day, my wife, Meryl, and I were driving, and I casually asked her what her business friends were struggling with. She said, "They don't want to hate themselves or their businesses."

Rather than ask her exactly what she meant by that, my brain immediately went to, "What's the positive framing of that statement"? That's when it finally came out of my mouth: Joy.

Meryl's friends wanted more joy in their businesses. And the kicker? That's what I had been trying to write about all along. My business development timeline was a chronology of ways and times I lost joy, AND the ways I brought myself back into it. I had learned to cultivate and curate joy over time.

So, *The 10 Essentials* became *Joy-Full AF*. And I got to writing again using much of the previous book as a starting point.

You'd think it was smooth sailing from there. But it wasn't. I lost joy again. And again. And again. I could not, for the life of me, figure out how the f*ck this was possible.

It took months of trying new structures with my book coach, and exploring even more deeply: *What is joy? What does it mean to be joy-full? And what will make writing Joy-Full AF truly joy-full?*

My conclusions?

For one, I needed to follow *all* the recommendations I was making for you in this book. I needed to have high intentions towards writing a book and low attachment to what it would look like, when it would come out, or even if it would come out. I had to put on the lab coat and experiment with book structures and approaches to writing.

But it required something even deeper than those tools. It required me to ask myself the question: *What does it mean to write a book **my** way?*

I learned over the course of writing this book that my joy gets sucked away every time I try to fit into what I *should* do, and what I am *supposed* to do. I had initially approached book-writing with all kinds of unwritten rules in my head about how to write a book. One was that it I needed a linear narrative. Another was that I must use Microsoft Word.

You see, as I went deeper into what joy is, why we're afraid of it, how we lose it, and how we can create more of it, I realized I needed to break the rules of structure and write in "conversations." I also needed to write in a way that didn't require an organized narrative across chapters. And I needed to not open Microsoft Word! In fact, I needed, as much as possible, to not open any word processors or text editors. Most of *Joy-Full AF* was spoken into my phone and recorded in Otter.AI. It turns out, my brain does much better speaking than writing. When I write, all kinds of mental barriers come up that keep me from saying what I want you to hear. My brain also works better when I can feel connected to other people. Speaking allowed me to feel like I was having a cup of tea or coffee with you, sharing my thoughts, rather than writing into the void.

Conversations were the most joy-full way for me to write this book. They were also the most *me* way.

After the winding road the book took, it felt in some ways like I had stumbled into this format. But in retrospect, I was just *finally* coming home to who I am and what I do best: connect with people through conversation.

So back to the original question — why did I write a book on joy-full AF business? The answer is simply, because no matter how much I went down other paths, JOY was always the message that needed to come out of me. Even though joy wasn't in my vocabulary when Niiamah mentioned his World Joy Movement, it has been an essential strategy in my business. It's been what I've unconsciously (and consciously, at times) created and cultivated. And I've seen firsthand what happens for me when I put joy first.

I'm writing this book for you because I understand deeply all the ways we can have our joy sucked away from us. I've fallen into every single trap that you'll read about in these pages. I've also gotten myself out of those traps through the intentional creation and cultivation of my joy. Now, if you're somebody like me, for whom joy wasn't in your vocabulary, or not until you picked up this book, that's okay. I'm going to teach you a new way to look at joy in your business. It is entirely different than what you might think joy is.

I hope that throughout these conversations I can help you see that joy is your business' lifeblood, and the more joy you seek, create, and cultivate, the more success and fulfillment you'll have. Which will also help you create more resilience to stay in your business for the long haul, no matter the ebbs and flows.

So, strap in, let's get some conversations on joy started.

WHAT'S THE MOST JOY-FULL WAY TO READ *JOY-FULL AF*?

One of the most important things you'll learn about joy here is that it's all about you. It's about learning about and leaning into who you are, what's important to you, and what works best for *you*. In joy-fully writing this book, I leaned into my past life as a user experience researcher and leader at Facebook and Microsoft. When doing one-on-one interviews and focus groups with users, researchers often write down insights and themes on sticky notes. They then put them on a wall and move them around until a coherent story emerges about how the product team should move forward in building a feature or experience. I knew at the outset of writing *Joy-Full AF* that I had the equivalent of sticky note insights to share, but that if I pre-ordained a structure or narrative for the book, I'd miss much of what I wanted to say. But instead of hoping and praying a structure would emerge later, I gave myself permission to write a book of proverbial sticky notes that never told a linear story.

Most conversations were recorded as stand-alone pieces. You'll notice they read as such, rather than flowing like typical book chapters would. Still, there is an order to this book; a narrative *did* emerge. Some conversations were about defining joy. Another chunk was about why it's important to put joy first. A handful covered why we are afraid to pursue joy. The two largest bunches were about ways we lose joy and what we can do to create and cultivate more of it.

Within those larger themes, there were conversations that naturally went together. One set was all about ways we lose joy by looking outside of ourselves for answers. Another few covered the relationship between joy and our bodies. My inner scientist got on a roll and wrote several conversations about collecting data and running experiments as a way to create more joy. I've organized those pieces together and added in some introductions to each high-level concept.

If writing *Joy-Full AF* was all about *my way*, I want to invite you to read the book *your way*.

Are you the type of person who reads cover-to-cover, perhaps even in one sitting? Go for it! Do you like to bounce around looking for content that is most relevant or interesting to you? This book is set up for you to dive into any conversation at random. Do you like to read in bite-sized chunks, savoring each concept or insight? Again, these short conversations are well-suited to that. Several even have reflection questions and exercises to help you fully digest.

Whatever way you choose to read the book, may you do so as joy-fully as possible!

What the F*ck is Joy Anyway?

What the F*ck is Joy Anyway?

If we're going to spend an entire book having conversations on being joy-full AF in your business, we probably should have a common understanding of what joy is.

If you'd asked me to define it before I wrote the book I probably would have stumbled over my words, shrugged my shoulders, and then — because I often want to have all the answers — rationalized my way into something that sounded smart, but didn't feel true.

It turns out I'm not alone in the struggle to put words to an intangible feeling.

I've spoken with dozens of people across ages, professions, and demographics, and asked them, "What is joy to you?" and "How do you experience joy?" Every time, they pause. Again, it's hard to find language for something so nebulous. As soon as they start to work it out in their heads, they have a similar experience of "that sounds good, but I don't know how true it feels." Though there are common threads in how people define and experience joy, I couldn't find a universal, or even unifying, definition.

Joy appears to be something slightly different for all of us.

As a former academic, I couldn't help but get curious about how academics define joy. Surely the experts could come to more consensus than my family, friends, and colleagues, right?

Turns out, the answer is no. I found multiple definitions, none of which gave a me a clear definition of joy. I was struck, however, by a quote from Dr. Robert A. Emmons in the introduction to a special issue in the Journal of Positive Psychology: "Joy may be hard to define, but through the ages, sages have contended that we know it when we experience it, and we know it when we lose it."[1]

We know it when we experience it. We know it when we lose it. **That** feels true to me.

I could have left our definition of joy at that.

But that would have made it more difficult to discuss why we're afraid to pursue joy, how we find ourselves losing it, and what we can do to create more of it.

So, let's at least put some language around joy, using commonalities that seem to ring true for professional researchers as well as laypeople. If you find yourself getting lost in the semantics, come back to your own *internal* sense of joy. After all, that's what this is all about, anyway.

Let's start with an important distinction:

joy ≠ happiness

If you're saying, "Wait, what!?" or you're getting ready to send me an enraged email because Google tells you that the dictionary definition of joy is a "state of happiness" … hear me out. For every definition of joy that includes happiness, there are just as many that separate them.

The academic research is just as divided. Across disciplines, much of the research has focused on happiness with less attention paid to other positive emotions like joy. Within the study of happiness, there are several schools of thought, and many have differing views on if, and how, joy is distinct.

What indicates to me that they are not one in the same is this: When I ask, "What makes you happy?" and "What makes you joyful?" chances are you'll have two very different lists. That was certainly the case when I asked my friends and family these questions.

So then, how do we draw the line between the two? Again, my definitions of happiness and joy rely on a mashup of science and anecdotal experience:

Happiness is a pleasant emotional state created by positive external circumstances, events, or outcomes, like receiving a gift, getting a promotion, or buying a new car. Once the external catalyst has passed, so does our emotional state. Our happiness levels quickly return to what scientists call our "happiness baseline." (We return to this baseline after negative events, too!)

Joy is an internal sense of delight, gladness, or satisfaction.

Joy is more intense and complex than happiness. And we also feel it on a deeper level — for me and many folks I've spoken with, joy is a full-body, multi-sensory experience. It is often accompanied by a feeling of connection to something outside of us, like other people, the greater good, meaning and purpose, or a higher power.

Like happiness, joy can be temporary. We can experience moments that make us yelp and scream — an active and animated joy — like when we reunite with a friend we haven't seen in years. There are moments that make us feel calm and content too — a more tranquil form of joy — like when we watch the sunset over the ocean. But, because joy arises from within us, it has more staying power than happiness. We can experience it at any moment, and we can create and cultivate it over time. (We'll talk in a later conversation about ways you can keep your joy tank full.)

Now, although happiness and joy are not the same, it *is* possible for situations that create happiness to also contribute to our joy. Maybe we reach a goal we've been striving for, like hitting a $500K revenue target or onboarding 1,000 new users to our app. Maybe we get praise from a client about the impact our service or product is having on their quality of life. Or we attend an event that makes us feel connected to something bigger than ourselves (a purpose, community, or cause).

But these situations that create happiness aren't, and shouldn't be, the only routes to joy. For one, they are unpredictable and inconsistent. They're also spiky, creating a high that leaves us almost as quickly as it arrives, leaving us constantly chasing the next one. Furthermore, happiness is dependent on our circumstances or outcomes *going well*. Talk about pressure to never fail!

I maintain that joy doesn't require our emotional experience or our outcomes to be positive. If you've ever felt a sense of satisfaction or delight while working through a challenge, leaning into fear, or even experiencing failure, you know what I mean.

Joy comes from within you; you don't have to wait for positive circumstances or outcomes to create and cultivate it.

Because joy is an intense and complex emotion, I would be oversimplifying its power if I left the definition as "not happiness." Over the next several conversations, we're going to dive deeper into the foundational ingredients of joy and explore what it means to be joy-full.

THE FOUR FOUNDATIONAL INGREDIENTS OF JOY

Three things stood out to me while I explored the meaning of joy for this book.

- It's a rich and deep emotion that we all find hard to define.
- Joy comes in many flavors. Sometimes it's fun, delight, and play. Other times it's deep satisfaction and connection to something outside of ourselves.
- We all define and experience joy differently, though there are certainly some commonalities.

When I looked at those three things together, I saw a natural analogy with cooking. Like many dishes we eat, joy contains multiple ingredients. For any dish we are cooking up, we have our own recipes and preferred ways of preparing it. It's like we are all at a chili cooking competition, but some chilis are vegetarian and others are meat-loaded. There are red chilis and white chilis, spicy ones and smoky ones. And joy isn't a singular dish we create. We have whole cookbooks full of recipes to choose from.

One of my favorite cookbooks is *Salt, Fat, Acid, Heat* by Samin Nosrat.[2] It's more than a book of recipes. It dives deep into what Nosrat dubs the four foundational "elements of good cooking": salt, fat, acid, and heat (temperature, not spice). You don't need to include all four elements in every dish to produce dishes that taste great. For instance, a garden salad doesn't involve heat. An egg scramble may not have an acid. But at least one element will always be present (usually salt), and typically, the more elements that are present, the yummier the dish.

As I began to piece together the parallels between creating and cultivating joy and cooking, I began to wonder, are there salt, fat, acid, and heat equivalents for joy? Are there foundational ingredients for joy that apply to all recipes for joy, no matter who we are?

When I connected with my own experience of joy, I landed on four C-words:

Connection

Curiosity

Creativity

Courage

I wanted to make sure that these were not just features of *my* experience of joy, but common to other people. So, I thought back to those conversations I'd had with friends, family and colleagues. Had those words, or synonyms for them come up for others?

Yes! And, I'd been hearing about all of them in different examples, I just didn't realize it at the time.

I also studied how other experts like Rob Bell[3] (International Speaker on Joy), Simone Seol (Joyful Marketing Coach)[4], and Karen Walrond[5] (author of *The Lightmaker's Manifesto: Work for Change Without Losing Your Joy*) described joy. Each of them was talking about at least one of the four ingredients I'd landed on — both Seol and Walrond spoke about courage, for instance — but none of them talked about all four. (I should note that these four C's are tied together as part of 8 "C" words that describe "Self-Energy" in Internal Family Systems (IFS)[6], a therapy model that can be applied in coaching and beyond, but to my knowledge, IFS has never explicitly tied them as a group to joy.)

The more I studied joy and talked to others about their experiences of joy, I became convinced that **Connection, Curiosity, Creativity,** and **Courage** are indeed the four foundational ingredients of joy. That doesn't mean there aren't other ingredients involved at times too. They just aren't as foundational. (Sugar is a nice parallel in our cooking metaphor. It's in a lot of recipes, but it's not one of the four elements.)

We'll explore each in more depth over the next several conversations. I'll also be sharing throughout the rest of this book how these ingredients can bring you back to joy when it's lost, and how they can help you fill up on even more joy over time.

THE FOUR INGREDIENTS: CONNECTION

"Salt's relationship to flavor is multidimensional:
It has its own particular taste,
and it both balances and enhances
the flavor of other ingredients."

~ Samin Nosrat, *Salt, Fat, Acid, Heat*

If we are looking at connection, curiosity, creativity, and courage as four foundational ingredients to your recipes for joy, the way salt, fat, acid, and heat are for food, I liken connection to salt. Salt is in almost everything. Yes, you can make food without it, but it often lacks flavor and dimension. Salt has its own flavor, but as Nosrat states, it also has the superpower of bringing out or enhancing the flavors of other items in your recipe. Connection is the same way. Connection has its own unique feeling in your mind, body, and spirit. But when you have a sense of connection, it enhances the other foundational ingredients like curiosity, creativity, and courage (and really any other ingredients that you put into your recipe). In a sense, I don't believe we can have a truly joy-full business without some sense of connection.

When I say connection, I think about it on three different levels:

— Connection to something bigger. Perhaps a higher power, God, or spiritual entity. Or perhaps a purpose or calling.

— Connection to others or to the collective. Perhaps it's connection to the people in your life — clients, colleagues, friends, or family. Or perhaps you feel connected to society, or the idea that "we're all one."

— Connection to yourself. How in tune are you with who you are? What's most important to you? What do you most want and need? What motivates you? What beliefs do you hold? What identities do you carry, or roles do you play in your business and life? How well do you know your strengths and geniuses, or how your brain and body work? For instance, I know my brain cannot create ideas in a vacuum. I need someone to ask me questions or give me something to react to before my brain turns on. And my brain can't seem to write the way I'd like to when I do it in Microsoft Word!

"Authenticity" is a buzzword in personal development work. I've been guilty of using it at times, too. I used to say my mission was to create a more authentic, inclusive, and equitable world. That sounds fantastic! And admirable! But also cliché as hell. What, for instance, does authenticity really mean? Most often I see authenticity defined in terms of how you express yourself out in the world. Are you allowing other people to see who you truly are or are you constantly wearing masks?

I see authenticity as something that doesn't need an audience. True authenticity is when we operate in the world from a deep understanding of and **connection** to who we are in mind, heart, body, and spirit. From that **connection**, we can then deeply **connect** with other people. We can also **connect** to a higher power, spiritual place, or purpose.

So really, I don't see the three forms of **connection** as all that separate. And in fact, many people in my circles describe their spiritual **connection** as something that exists within themselves; that is, their self-**connection** practice is also a spiritual practice.

What happens when you have a deep **connection** to yourself? Well, the more you learn about and understand all the ways you tick, the more you can choose *your* way. And that translates into …

When things are hard, you still feel a sense of flow to your actions.

When things are scary, you have a sense of "I've got this."

When it's tempting to go after *shoulds* and *supposed tos*, you lean into your wants and desires instead.

When others want to hand you a map, you trust yourself to create your own.

So how can we create more self-connection? I'm not going to add more clichés to this conversation and tell you to go meditate. (Yes, meditation *is a* way to create connection, but it's also not the only way. Nor is it for everyone.)

One of my favorite ways is to create a map of your internal landscape. Here are a few questions to get you started:

- What's most important to you?
- What are your top five values?
- What do you deeply want or desire?
- What motivates you? Are you more motivated by risk and possibility, or by preventing something going wrong? (Pssst … neither of them is bad!)
- What beliefs, identities, and roles are you aware of?
- What are your strengths and geniuses?
- What do you know about how your brain works?
- What are your natural energy rhythms? Are you a morning person or a night person?
- Do you work better with or without structure?

Once you have a fairly complete picture, ask yourself, "What else do I need to learn about myself?" Connection is an ongoing process. You'll be filling in your map for years to come.

Now, with whatever you do already know about yourself, you can look for where connection is and isn't showing up in your business. What projects, activities, and actions are you taking on from a place of connection? What isn't coming from connection and why not? What are you doing instead? And how is connection related (or not) to your joy?

If you find that much of your business is operating outside of a sense of connection to yourself, it might be overwhelming or scary to think about making a massive overhaul. If you've created your success through actions and activities that are misaligned with who you are, what's important, and/or how you do things, it can be uncomfortable to try another way. Choose one project, activity, or area at a time to make the shift.

THE FOUR INGREDIENTS: CURIOSITY

One of my clients keeps a notecard on his desk that says, "Slow down and get curious." He tells me I said that phrase to him during one of our early coaching sessions together, and he decided to keep it on a notecard as a reminder for himself. It's prominently displayed while he's coaching his own clients.

Another client has a sticky note attached to her computer monitor that says, "Follow curiosity. Have courage." She wrote it after one of our sessions so that upon seeing it she would remember how she wants to show up in meetings, one-on-one conversations with colleagues, and with all the other folks she interacts with in her business.

One day on a call with yet another client (a day she will likely never forget), I asked her to find the silliest hat she owned and wear it as her **Curiosity** Cap in the lead-up to a sure-to-be-frustrating meeting with the CEO of the start-up she worked for. (I would have loved for her to keep it on, but I imagine that might not have gone over so well with the CEO!) She didn't have any hats on hand, but she did have a full-head-covering mask of Olaf from the movie *Frozen*. So of course, I said, "That's perfect!" It made her giggle — the ideal headspace for the meeting she was dreading. She reflected to me after that it was one of the most open, honest, and productive conversations she'd ever had.

I honestly can't remember the last time I coached someone and the concept of **curiosity** didn't come up. You might as well call me the **curiosity** coach!

Sometimes we talk about how my client can get **curious** about themselves.

That might look like these questions:

- I wonder why I feel so much resistance to networking?

- I wonder why I sometimes have tiny volcanic eruptions in meetings?
- I wonder why a part of me keeps insisting that I need to niche, yet another part contends that niching is business sabotage?

Or other times, we talk about how my client can get curious about their clients or colleagues. That can show up as:

- I wonder what's really going on underneath my client's question about what to do next?
- I wonder what solutions my colleague has already thought of?
- I wonder what might be going on for my boss that she keeps chastising people who are highly opinionated?

And other times, we talk about how my client can get curious about the results their actions could produce:

- I wonder what would happen if I tried this approach to sales?
- I wonder what would happen if I raised my prices?
- I wonder what would happen if I dropped half of the projects I am working on right now?

Curiosity can be an antidote for many of our fears, doubts, and challenges in business because we put ourselves in a place of perpetual exploration and learning. Curiosity quiets the inner voices that are critical or judgy of what you (or others) think, feel, or do. It curbs the need to be perfect, to do it right, or have all the answers. It gives you permission to take risks, experiment, and screw up. And it helps you be less socially self-conscious and connect with people more easily.

Curiosity facilitates compassion, creativity, courage, and connection.

Notice those last three are the other foundational ingredients of joy. I'd say that makes **curiosity** pretty great! In fact, we could use it right now. Think about this …

Where could your business benefit from slowing down and putting on your **Curiosity** Cap?

And what's one tiny action you could take purely from a place of **curiosity**?

I'm **curious** (see what I did there?! 😉): what could you create in your business if you used **curiosity** as part of your approach in the long run?

WHY IS CURIOSITY SO F*CKING HARD?

If you read the last conversation (*The Four Ingredients: Curiosity*) and you're totally ready to get curious about everything in your world — yourself, your clients, or colleagues, what actions you can take, what results you might create, or what's possible ...

If you've 100% bought in ... you might skip this conversation ... but if any part of you said, "Erin, I hear you. It's all well and good to say that I should be more curious, but curiosity is *hard*," or "Curiosity doesn't come naturally to me," then stick around. This is the only one of the four foundational ingredients that has a follow-up conversation, and that's because it's the one my clients struggle with the most. I imagine that's one of the reasons some of them keep notecards and sticky notes as reminders on their desks.

When I propose becoming more curious to my clients, I often hear comments from them like the ones I mentioned above. They see curiosity as a skill they aren't good at or one that they must develop. I get where they are coming from. I used to believe that too. What we don't realize is that curiosity naturally lives within all of us — we just may not have accessed it in a while.

As I've explored the four ingredients of joy, I've gotten curious about curiosity ... (pun intended.)

Why do we feel that being curious is difficult?

Where does our belief that it doesn't come naturally stem from?

What makes us hesitant to be curious?

I've come to believe that we are born curious, but we get a lot of messages as we mature that encourage us to tamp that curiosity down. If you were born after 1941, chances are you grew up reading *Curious George*. Or you are at least familiar with the monkey who is always getting into interesting situations thanks to his curiosity. Depending on your perspective, George's curiosity serves him well because he learns about the world, or it works against him because it gets him into heaps of trouble that he's lucky to get out of.

Children are naturally curious. Babies grab jewelry on people's ears and touch faces to explore tactile sensations. Toddlers pick up bugs and chase butterflies. Young kids ask questions incessantly (to the annoyance of adults around them). Curiosity is our innate way of learning about the world, and children display it unabashedly. In fact, we often describe curiosity as "childlike." Little George the chimpanzee is a great example. He breaks rules set forth by adults on the regular. And rarely are the adults, at least in the books I read as a child, joining him in his curious quests. That's because when we become adults, we are supposed to abandon certain childlike qualities and follow the rules. When it comes to curiosity, there are subtle ways we get schooled on squashing it.

Let's start with a cliché: Curiosity killed the cat.

Damn! Curiosity is so bad that it *killed* something. The more that phrase circulates in the collective psyche, the easier it is for us to internalize that curiosity will lead you to trouble. It will put you in dangerous situations. It's clearly not a good strategy!

Cliché notwithstanding, let's also look at the language that we associate with curious people: nosy, lacking self-awareness, childlike. One of my closest friends, Mahrukh, might be the most curious human on the planet. For every single statement you make, she has at least five questions in her head. Because we are not taught how to handle curiosity as adults (let alone how to be curious ourselves), her questions can feel like a lot. They can feel like an interrogation, though that's never the intention. Her insatiable desire to understand — whether it's a person, a story, a situation, or a fact — can seem childlike.

[Can we pause for a second to notice the negative implications around "childlike" and how it has come to connote naivete, immaturity, or silliness!? If curiosity creates joy, but curiosity is childlike in a negative sense, then no wonder we're afraid to pursue our joy!!!!]

I believe Mahrukh's **curiosity** is one of her greatest superpowers. It saddens me to know that others might not agree with me.

Though Mahrukh has been told directly to stow away her **curiosity** or diminish it in some way, that's not the only way **curiosity** falls off the radar. For some of us, it's not that we are actively taught *not* to be **curious**; it's that we aren't actively encouraged to *stay* **curious**. We aren't given the tools and strategies for *how* to bring our childlike **curiosity** into adulthood. We don't know what to be **curious** about, how to assess what is safe to be **curious** about, or how to navigate situations when our **curiosity** has led to unwanted outcomes (such as failure or offending someone). The riskier we consider **curiosity** to be — it killed a cat, right!!?? — the more we train ourselves to choose safety over exploration and learning.

Don't be **curious** about the people in your life.

(You might ask the wrong question or offend them.)

Don't be **curious** about where a path might lead.

(You might fall off a cliff. Find the well-worn path that you can be certain leads somewhere.)

Don't be **curious** about what would happen if you tried that action.

(It's not worth the rejection or judgment you might face.)

As you can gather from these examples, we learn to seek out ways to get the results we want with certainty, risk free. And yet, going back to the last conversation ... **curiosity** is the antidote to so many fears, doubts, and challenges.

Imagine the energetic shift of going from what can I do or what can't I do, to *I wonder what I can do.*

Imagine for a moment that you have a goal to grow a following on Instagram, but you have fears about being visible online:

"What if I say the wrong thing?"

"What if I don't add value?"

"What if people don't like what I have to say?"

"What if people don't like *me?*"

So, you spend a lot of time and energy trying to predict what people need and thinking about what to post.

Now imagine the energetic shift if you approached the goal with curiosity:

"I wonder what will resonate for people?"

"I wonder if people will like what I have to say?"

"I wonder if I can grow a following by being completely, authentically me?"

That curiosity, of course, requires you to lean into risk. And sure, it may kill the metaphorical cat every so often 😉. But just imagine what you could explore, what blocks you could move through, and what new knowledge and learning might be available if you decided to reacquaint yourself with the curiosity you've always had inside you.

Even if you haven't explored it in a while, your curiosity hasn't gone anywhere. You can revisit it. You can foster and grow it over time, building it like a muscle. Curiosity doesn't have to be difficult. And it doesn't have to be dangerous. All it takes to get started is just one instance of shifting the question you're asking yourself out of fear or doubt into "I wonder" or "I'm curious."

Ask yourself, where might you be able to shift the question right now? And what's one area of your business that you could treat like a child in a sandbox?

THE FOUR INGREDIENTS: CREATIVITY

When I think about creativity as fundamental to joy, I picture a five-year-old with red and orange paint all over his hands. It's also splattered on his ears and a drizzle has run all the way down his smock and is dripping onto his shoes. He doesn't care *what* he's painting — he might not even *know* what he's painting — and he's certainly not judging its quality. He's having the time of his life. And his smiles and giggles prove it.

Creativity, like curiosity, is inborn and we most freely express it when we are children. Some kids play "make believe" and other have imaginary friends. Some kids build complex worlds in LEGO®, Lincoln Logs, or Minecraft. (Wait, are Lincoln Logs still a thing or is my age showing? Don't answer that!)

And just as with curiosity, many people have convinced themselves that creativity is difficult and doesn't come naturally to them. Perhaps it's because the word "creative" is often associated with artistic expression. Painting. Drawing. Sculpting. Music. Dance. Poetry. Fiction writing. We judge our own creativity against internal (and sometimes also external) standards of "good" art. If we only look at creativity through the lens of artistic expression — which is often based more on a tangible skillset than creative ability — we are limiting ourselves to studying a few trees in a vast forest. By definition, creativity is simply the ability to *create* something that did not exist before. It could be tangible, like a piece of art, a song, or invention. But it could also be intangible, like a relationship.

The truth is everything in your business is something that never existed before. You are creating ALL. THE. TIME. Perhaps you create a product or service like a course or program. Maybe you create content through blogs, videos, or newsletters. You might create a strategy for finding new clients, growing your community, or broadening your impact. It's possible you are creating relationships with colleagues, clients, and collaborators. Even if you're following a blueprint or a formula someone else has handed you, you are still putting something into the world that has never existed before.

If you've been telling yourself you're not creative, it's time to stop buying into that lie.

We are all creative. We're just not always tapping into the reservoir within.

Just like with curiosity, you can reconnect to the creative spirit you had as a child. You can choose to go back to not caring about the paint splattered everywhere. And you can delight in making shit up and seeing what happens. When you first turn that creativity faucet back on, the waters may not flow the way they used to, not right away. Let it start out as a drip.

Ask yourself: "What's one tiny act of creativity I can engage in today?"

Once you've done that, see if you can get it to drip some more.

What's another tiny act you can do?

Keep aiming for drips and over time, the flow will get easier and stronger.

[Let me bring out my inner psychology geek for a moment on the relationship between creativity and joy. Across multiple studies, scientists have found that creativity enhances our well-being … which in turn, boosts our creativity. There are various explanations for this ranging from biological (higher blood flow to our brain's rewards center), to psychological (better ability to express and process emotions, a greater sense of purpose). How cool is it that we can create a virtuous cycle of joy and creativity?!]

THE FOUR INGREDIENTS: COURAGE

If you ask my friends to describe me, courageous is an adjective that is likely to come out of their mouths. I have done some courageous things in the last decade, including having top surgery to align my body to my internal sense of gender, leaping out of corporate with no idea how to run my own business, and writing and singing a parody of Tina Turner's "Goldeneye" Bond song for an audience of 300 on Zoom at a coaching intensive.

People often mistakenly equate courage with fearlessness, so they see my courage and think I must be fearless. It's really about feeling the fear and proceeding anyway. The truth is, I have been afraid of my own shadow my whole life. I used to let the fear get the better of me. I was anything but courageous. Like in 8th grade when I made it all the way to the front of a very long line for the loop-de-loop rollercoaster at Knott's Berry Farm before completely panicking and doing a walk of shame past hundreds of people. But at some point in my adulthood — I don't remember when — I decided I was no longer willing to let fear to get the better of me. I could see how much it was keeping me from joy-full outcomes. I started to deliberately build my courage muscle.

When I started to work on this book and explore joy more in-depth, I realized joy wasn't just an outcome of courageous action. There's also a joy that courage itself creates, no matter the outcome.

Of the four foundational ingredients, courage may seem like the odd-man-out. That's why I've left it for last. How can having strength and willingness to confront fear, difficulty, and pain be connected to a positive emotion?

Let's start with going back to one of joy's superpowers: It is one of the only positive emotions that we can experience alongside negative emotions.

For one, joy and sorrow are so linked in our cultural lexicon that you can find quotes on Google about them "going hand-in-hand" and being "next door neighbors." We don't just experience joy alongside other emotions. Paradoxically, we can also experience joy *in* them. There can be joy in sorrow. Joy in frustration. Joy in fear. That last one is what makes courage an ingredient for joy.

What makes courage *foundational* and not simply a nice-to-have ingredient, is how much we need a joy-full satisfaction that can only come from taking courageous action. My friend and former teacher, Sean Smith once said at a coaching training, "The most boring thing you can do in your business is set a goal and then easily achieve it." He went on to explain that if you set a goal and then the whole process of getting there is seamless — no fear, failure, obstacles, or challenges — you won't be satisfied with the accomplishment. Yet, seamless is *exactly* what many people seek out.

We are hardwired as humans to avoid pain at all costs. We often focus on avoiding the pain that comes with fear, risk, and challenge, forgetting that there's *also* pain in dissatisfaction. In fact, I believe the pain of dissatisfaction is more far-reaching and long-lasting than the pain we're often avoiding. To be truly joy-full, and truly satisfied, we need to lean into fear. We need to be challenged. We need to face obstacles and overcome them. We need to experience some amount of pain in the journey in order to bathe in the joy of the outcome. (As Brené Brown has said, "When we numb our pain, we numb our joy.")

We need to feel fear.
It's a signal that we are taking risks.

If we're not pushing the comfort envelope at least some of the time, we aren't growing, nor are we seeing possibilities or creating new experiences for ourselves. There is a joy-full satisfaction that we can only experience when we take courageous action and are willing to experience whatever outcomes follow as we go along. To me, that makes courage a juicy AF ingredient to explore in creating a more joy-full business!

TASTE THE RAINBOW

There are tons of words people use interchangeably with joy, but they aren't one-for-one synonyms. To me, they are like different Skittles® giving you one flavor of joy, rather than encompassing the entire rainbow. Here are a few, some of which you'll see sprinkled in throughout this book:

Fun

Delight

Pleasure

Play

Bliss

Glee

Elation

Satisfaction

Happiness

Fulfillment

Meaning

Wonder

Indulgence

Gratitude

Warm fuzzies

Hope

Calm

Alive

The good news is, pursuing any one of them will contribute to your overall joy. The more of them you pursue, the fuller your joy tank gets.

What other flavors of joy would you add to the list? Feel free to keep track as we go along.

I SOUGHT JOY; I FOUND ME

During one of the business masterminds I was part of a few years ago, an improv expert came one afternoon to work with about 30 of us. There was a lot of creative energy in the room that day. It was joy-full AF to take a break from serious coaching to play games with my peers, especially because improv is all about showing up without a plan. The sentences that came out of people's mouths ranged from innovative to truly bizarre!

One of the games we played was The Six-Word Memoir. It is as simple as it sounds: Write your memoir (or what you'd like your memoir to be) in six words.

Because I was in the mood for silly fun, the first words that came to me were, *I did it all for my cat.* I'm pretty sure that's because my cat was sitting right next to me, and I tend to rely on my immediate environment for improv inspiration. But then I thought to myself … yes, we're having fun, but we're also kind of a serious bunch. I was pretty tickled with *I did it all for my cat*, but on the off-chance I was going to be the only person that went down the silly route, I decided to also come up with something serious.

In what felt like a split second, six words flowed: *I sought joy; I found me.* This wasn't some clever phrase my mind came up with. The words landed in my entire body. I had just discovered a deep truth.

Our improv day happened only a few months after I'd realized that I'd been on a mission for joy since starting my business. On the other hand, I'd been (and still am) on a mission to find *me* for much longer. Really, it's been my whole life. As a social psychologist fascinated by all things human, who better to obsess over myself, than myself? I made an instant connection: The pursuit of joy in my business had the unknown (at least, unknown to me at the time) benefit of helping me find *me*.

I sat with that six-word memoir for quite a while after the improv day. I started to wonder if it was actually the other way around. I tried it on for size: *I sought me; I found JOY.*

Yes! That landed in my body too. It turned out that both phrases are true.

When I seek joy, I find more of me. And the more of me I find, the more joy-full I feel.

The moments I feel more joy-full are the times I feel calm, curious, creative, compassionate, connected to myself or something out there in the world, and courageous. (If you're noticing the addition of calm and compassionate, remember that the four ingredients are not the only ingredients of joy and that we all experience joy differently.) It turns out that when I feel one or more of those things, I also feel the most *me*. In those moments, my inner voices like the Critic, Perfectionist, and Controller are quiet. I'm more aware of what's important to me, and what lights me up and makes me come alive. I'm able to partner with my brain, emotions, and body in whatever state they are in. My actions feel aligned and in flow.

I wonder if you have experienced something similar yourself.

What does it feel like when you are joy-full?

What thoughts arise for you?

What sensations do you feel in your body?

What qualities or energies do you feel?

And how does that compare to when you feel most "you?"

Even if your experience of being joy-full and your experience of being "you" differ from mine, I imagine that the truth I discovered for me holds true for you too.

My six-word memoir started out as a personal discovery, but quickly turned into a truth about joy for all of us. The more you seek *you*, the more joy you will feel. The more you pursue your joy, the more *you* you will feel.

Throughout the later conversations, you'll notice a through-line: We lose joy when we abandon ourselves (like when compare ourselves to others, use other people's maps for how to do things, and give in to *shoulds*, *supposed tos*, and what "good business owners do"), and that path back to joy is always about coming back to yourself.

You'll also notice that this book is about much more than joy-full AF *business*. It's also about the beautiful adventure of coming to deeply know, love, and trust yourself!

JOY-FULL AF, NOT JOYFUL AF (AKA THE JOY-FULL AF BUSINESS MANIFESTO)

Now that we've talked more in-depth about what joy is, let's explore what it means to be joy-full. You might be wondering why I've made up a new word (no it's not just to be cheeky!) when there is a perfectly good term already in use.

Don't get me wrong, I'm all about the concept of being joyful. Being joyful makes me think of sunshine, rainbows, beauty, and big smiles (with maybe a few unicorns thrown in for good measure 😉). Doing what's joyful makes me think of pursuing fun, pleasure, and delight. All good things, right? And all things we do need in our business.

But as I wrote this book and began sharing more about creating joy in business with my colleagues and friends, and on social media, I was shocked by people's reactions.

Advocating for a "joyful AF business" was often misconstrued as selling "good vibes only." It was as if the goal implied by "joyful AF" was a perpetual state of positivity, with no room for struggle, challenge, or negative emotions.

I didn't want people seeing *joyful* as an endorsement of toxic positivity (which is the pressure that people feel to keep a positive mindset no matter how dire the circumstance). I'm all in for joy, but I'm not here for toxic positivity.

So, what does it mean to be **joy-full**?

The Joy-Full Business Manifesto

Joy-full is doing the things that make you come alive, even when they are challenging or make you want to pull your hair out.

Joy-full is feeling connected to yourself, other people, spirit, or even a sense of purpose.

Joy-full is being in the vulnerable messiness of your humanity. It's in befriending every part of yourself and letting them all have a seat at the table, even when you wish you could stuff them down or bury them.

Joy-full is being in your genius and playing to your strengths. It's in seeking more ways to align your business to those strengths, while leaving everything else up to other people who can support you, or simply behind.

Joy-full is being courageous, confident, and fully in your power.

Joy-full is allowing, acknowledging, and pursuing your deepest desires. Even when you know you won't be able to have them all come to life.

Joy-full is knowing that joy is an endless resource within you that you can tap into at any time. It does not depend on external circumstances. (Though, of course, external circumstances can create joy too.)

Being joy-full AF is an entirely different experience than being joyful AF.

I stand for creating, cultivating, and filling up on ALL flavors of joy.

If you've been feeling any squidgy-ness about getting on the joy train, perhaps the concept of joy-full will put your worries at bay.

Why the F*ck Do We Need Joy?

Why the F*ck Do We Need Joy?

If I asked you this question in the context of your overall joy, you might tilt your head to the side, furrow your brow, and wonder, "What kind of question is that? We need joy because we need joy. Period." It's a given that joy is a life force. We are always seeking it in the things we do and the people we surround ourselves with. And we never question others who want to load up on more of it. But this book is about business. And chances are, when you read the question, "Why the f*ck do we need joy in *business*?" you won't have the same reaction. It's not a given that joy is a life force for our business.

If joy hasn't been in your vocabulary around business, it's because it's not in the vocabulary of the business world. Most books, articles, and podcasts about business focus on strategies and tactics. Success comes from things like good product-market fit, savvy marketing and sales, strong leadership, and smart decision-making. If there's any mention of the human aspect of business, the focus is almost exclusively on mindset. Emotions like joy (not to mention the rest of our emotional spectrum) seem to have no place in business.

I hate to break it to you, but we don't leave our humanity behind the minute we step into our businesses. As much as you might prefer to switch off your emotions, it's hard to. It's also not good for your health and well-being. Like me, I'm guessing you started your business to have more joy in your life. Joy in life starts with more joy in your business. If you started it for another reason, think about that reason and see if it doesn't trace back to joy. Financial freedom? Joy. Location freedom? Joy. The little voice inside saying to follow your higher purpose? Also joy!

Joy is not just for right now. As you'll see in the next conversations, if you want to be in business for the long-haul, you'll not just need to have joy on your radar — you'll need to put it first.

MISERY ISN'T SUSTAINABLE

Are you successful but secretly miserable? If so, you might be falling into a trap that so many of us do: believing that misery is a necessary evil for creating success.

It's not easy to change course towards joy when we are miserable but successful. Our minds crave certainty, and when we have success, an "effect", our minds search for a "cause" so that we can create that effect again in the future. This means that sometimes we latch onto activities that make us miserable. Our minds credit them with creating our success and target them as essential to replicating that success going forward. We're inclined to believe this is true because it matches the messages we get around "hustle and grind" and "success requires sacrifice" in our culture.

It's easy to see how joy falls prey to faulty reverse logic: If misery leads to success, then joy must lead to … well, everything falling apart. Some of us even tell ourselves there's no other way to run our businesses. We might suspect there is but decide it's too risky to go find out if it's true.

The only problem is, staying miserable is not sustainable.

At best, we might decide that running a business is not for us. At worst, we may find ourselves burned out, experiencing health issues, or even seeing difficulties in our personal relationships.

Which begs the question:

If misery is a recipe for failure in the long-term, why not try joy in the short-term?

Even if things fall apart, all you've done is speed up the inevitable, and possibly even save yourself some heartache along the way. Once I realized that I'd rather have my business fall apart while being joy-full AF than continue creating success through misery, I was much more willing to test the "success is possible with joy" hypothesis!

Most entrepreneurs start their businesses because they want to get paid to do something they love and have more freedom in their lives. But far too many end up stressed out, overwhelmed, anxious, and ultimately in hate with their business. Like me, they get trapped in the *shoulds* and *supposed tos* rather than staying connected to who they are, what they want to do, and how they want to do it. They find themselves overly attached to external goals and making decisions for the short-term that take them away from their joy in the long run. This can look like taking on projects and clients that keep revenue coming in but that don't light them up, rather than putting energy into building relationships that could bring more ideal projects and clients in the door.

The freedom they once dreamed of seems steadily more elusive as they continuously find new ways to shackle themselves to their businesses. You know the expression "golden handcuffs"? Well, I can assure you it's not just something corporations do to keep employees tethered. I have generated a lot of income in my own business by doing things that made me miserable. I've handcuffed myself to my misery, believing my own lie that there is no other path to my income goals. This is why, as we'll discuss in later conversations, part of creating joy is working to shift our focus away from outcomes and back towards the process.

[Just in case you're thinking it: Losing joy is not unique to specific demographics. It happens to beginners and veterans, people working on their first six-figures, and those making seven- and eight-figures, as well as across the spectrum of business types. You can lose joy at any time.]

If you're saying to yourself, "Wait, I'm not miserable, so this doesn't apply!" or "I'm not shackled," you still may be falling into a trap. Instead of misery, you might just feel *meh* — things are going fine and you're far from miserable, but you're a little bored and don't feel very alive in your business. Unfortunately, *meh* is just as unsustainable as misery. There's not enough gas in "meh" to keep the engine running. And it might be a warning sign that you're a step too close to miserable and need to make some shifts before it's too late.

If misery and *meh* aren't sustainable, what is?

I have a sense you might already know my answer to that …

Your joy can come first.

In fact, it *needs* to come first for you to create sustainable, long-term success and impact.

BUT JOY IS

In case it isn't clear from the book's subtitle — *The Essential Business Strategy We're Afraid to Put First* — I firmly believe that joy must be embedded in your business strategy.

Now, I'm not saying you should *only* follow your joy or that everything will be sunshine and rainbows. Of course, you need a product or service that people want to buy and for them to buy it. You probably also need to be good at marketing, or at least hire folks who are. You also need to be financially savvy and lead good people. But even if you have the soundest of business practices, if joy isn't a top priority, it becomes increasingly more difficult to stay in it for the long-haul.

According to the Bureau of Labor Statistics, about 20% of businesses fail within the first two years. Within five years that percentage goes up to 45%. Within 10 years, it's 65% and at 15 years, its 75%. That means that only 25% of businesses make it through the 15-year mark.[7]

What plays into whether a business is still running past those major landmarks? Google Scholar brings up over half a million hits, with research spanning sound business practices, micro and macroeconomics (certainly the rise of Amazon can be attributed to many smaller brick and mortar businesses shutting their doors!), and psychological characteristics of the business owner (like decision-making, ability to pivot in ever-changing markets, resilience, and courage). As far as I could find, no research has been done looking at joy. And as a social scientist, I don't know how it could be studied cleanly, anyway.

Without actual data to back up my belief, why am I so firm that joy needs to be at the center of business?

Let's fall back on some common sense — can you imagine running a business that you feel miserable in for 15 years!!?? Can you imagine weathering the uncertainties inherent in business like ever-changing macroeconomic climates, recessions, pandemics, or wars without a sense of joy?

I cannot.

Whenever I lose joy, just the thought of not being able to endure in the long term without it is enough motivation for me to focus on getting it back ASAP.

Over the years I've met several folks who have been in business for long periods of time. One of the common threads among their diverse experiences is that despite the challenges of business, their work is immensely joy-full. I suspect if I were to ask them, "What's the secret to staying in business so long?" they might not say joy specifically (after all, it's not just me who hasn't had it in their vocabulary), but they might describe what I consider joy: finding fun and delight, following curiosity and creativity, and being courageous to take risks and try new things. I also imagine they would describe a feeling of being connected to something deeper, like a sense of satisfaction or purpose.

To grow and sustain a business, I absolutely believe we should go learn everything possible about making great products and offering high quality services. Our businesses are dependent upon bringing in clients and a commitment to excellent financial practices, as well. We certainly have to be proficient in hiring and forward-thinking in leadership, but I suggest one of the must-haves of business health projection is joy — when you find joy and help your team find joy in all you do, you greatly increase the chances that your business will thrive over the long-term.

IT'S THE WAY OUT OF THE MATRIX

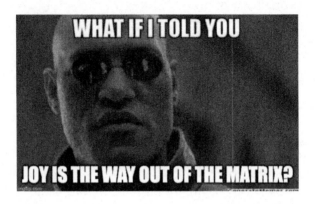

I don't know much about *The Matrix* trilogy, but I do know there is a popular Morpheus meme where people fill in the blank to "What if I told you …" I have that meme in my head as I tell you "Joy is the way out of the matrix."

If you're not sure what I mean by "the matrix", let me illustrate with a story …

"I just don't want to be on Instagram. It's not what makes me come alive."

My colleague, Shaina, spoke these words in a mastermind we both belonged to that was, ironically, all about visibility, and had a heavy focus on social media. We all knew what we'd signed up for, yet her words landed with several of us in the group, including me. She went on to explain that she wasn't looking for us to support her in how to get off Instagram, or how to make Instagram more joy-full for her. She was looking for something deeper: advice on how to stay aligned with her passions and only do activities that light her up. She went on to say, "I'll declare that I'm doing things my way, that I'm stepping out of the matrix, so to speak. Then I'll read an article, or I'll listen to a podcast, or even hire a coach. And before I know it, I'm back in the matrix with a to-do list full of *shoulds* and *supposed tos*. I start to believe that there's a right way to run my business rather than *my* way."

We fall back into the matrix because that's what we were raised in. We're taught that there are right and wrong ways, not that we can find our own way. We're taught who to be, not that we can find who we are … especially not in the context of business. We're taught to look outside of ourselves for the answers, not that we might have answers within us. Without a foundation of self-knowledge and self-trust, the only place to look is towards colleagues or mentors who we hope will tell us what to do and help us remedy our weaknesses.

Shaina's declaration around Instagram, followed by her share about falling back into the matrix, struck a chord with us because it wasn't news. Each of us in that Zoom room had been deep in personal development for years. Each of us had been (and we still are!) committed to being fully ourselves and doing things our way in our businesses. But, we too had been called back into the matrix. We thought we were the only ones who backslid, while everyone else was doing a bang-up job being and doing themselves. (It's amazing what we hide about ourselves, thinking we are the only ones!)

The neat thing is, all of us have choice. If, like Shaina, Instagram doesn't make you come alive … or, like my colleague, Laura, you're an introvert and Tik-Tok drains your energy … or no social media of any kind suits how you like to build relationships … that's okay. No matter how much advice you hear that you *must* be on social media, you have a choice.

The same is true for anything. Podcast. Newsletter. Book. Ads. Conferences. Networking. Any method can work. It's just a matter of finding what brings you joy, and what feels like "yeah, that's a 'me' thing to do." From time to time, you will fall back into the matrix. Its pull is strong; there is no such thing as a perfect or permanent escape from it. When you do find yourself swept back in, remember that the way out can't be found in an article, podcast, mentor, or coach. The way out is through your joy.

Why Are We Afraid to Put Joy First?

Why Are We Afraid to Put Joy First?

In the first part of this book, we talked about joy being more than a positive feeling. It's about bringing all of YOU — who you are, what you care about, how you like to (and best) do things — to your business. Then we explored why it's so important to not only pursue joy, but actually put it first. So naturally, I must have you convinced, and we can jump right into ways we lose joy and ways we can get it back, right?

Not so fast …

Even if your rational mind knows that joy is the life force of your business, your body may feel otherwise. Imagine a project or activity you are doing in your business right now.

What would make it more joy-full?

Now check in with the sensations in your body as you imagine the joy-full path. Does your body take a deep breath of relief?

Or does it brace?

Do you feel calm wash over you or is your heart racing?

What emotions bubble up to the surface?

Excitement? Eagerness? Anxiety? Fear? Guilt?

If your body feels just as on-board with putting joy first as your mind does, fantastic! You certainly could skip this next section. (Though feelings can change, and you may not always feel so aligned about joy. It's good to have some tools to check in. And perhaps you'll learn some new things about joy along the way.)

If your body feels any sort of resistance or trepidation, that's completely normal. You, like me and many of my clients, probably have some automatic associations and unconscious beliefs that steer you away from joy. The good news is those beliefs aren't innate or permanent. You don't have to keep them.

LISTEN ALL Y'ALL,
IT'S A SABOTAGE

It's not just that we're afraid to put joy first. The reality is, many of us don't view joy as something we can pursue or that we can let ourselves *want to pursue*. To borrow the words of the iconic 90s band, the Beastie Boys, "Listen all y'all/[joy] is a sabotage." (Or so we think.)

This brings to mind a conversation I had with Mahrukh, my curious friend from *Why is Curiosity So F*cking Hard?* Mahrukh is a part-time project manager at one of the world's top accounting firms. Don't be mistaken by the label part-time. She isn't working a 20-hour week. She often works more than 40 hours a week, and in her profession, that's still much less than a full-time employee might work. She works this "part-time" schedule because she's a member of the Canadian Women's Cricket Team, which you can imagine requires a sizable commitment. Between the training, practices, and tournaments that demand her dedication, she also hosts a podcast and coaches other folks on how to launch and grow their own podcast. And then much of her remaining free time is spent eating up personal and business development content from people like Tim Ferriss, Gary Vaynerchuk, and Tom Bilyeu, all folks who lean more toward hustle and grind than "find your joy." Mahrukh and I met at a personal development conference put on by business and personal finance expert Ramit Sethi and became close friends after she invited me and two others to create a weekly goals/accountability mastermind group. (Three of the four of us still meet weekly, but we've long abandoned any structure and just connect as friends. Hmm ... I wonder if we've followed our joy here? 😊)

By now, you might grasp that Mahrukh is an ambitious, high-achiever and that she is constantly in 'doing' mode. During one of our weekly meetings, she mentioned a quote that really inspires her: "Chase excellence, and success will chase you." Of course, I wasn't surprised. Mahrukh is clearly chasing excellence in everything she does. The conversation led us to a distinction Gay Hendricks makes in his book *The Big Leap*[8] between your Zone of Excellence and your Zone of Genius. Your Zone of Excellence is anything that you are highly skilled or talented at doing, but that doesn't really bring you energy or joy. You may have been rewarded in the past for these things, through promotions, raises, or business success. So it can be hard, even if they don't bring you joy, to leave them behind in favor of activities in your Zone of Genius. Your Zone of Genius is where everything flows and you feel energized. You are doing the things you are *truly* best at and love doing. And it turns out, those are the things where you can add the most value or make the most impact. Your Zone of Genius is where joy lives.

As Mahrukh and I were talking, I wondered if her chase for excellence was keeping her in her Zone of Excellence. Is she disconnected from her genius? And if so, might that mean she's disconnected from her joy?

I curiously asked her, "Mahrukh, what would happen if you replaced the word 'excellence' in your quote with 'joy' to make it "Chase joy and success will chase you"?

She thought about it for a second before saying, "Yeah." But immediately after, her body said something else. She couldn't get behind that version of the quote.

"What's going on?" I asked her.

"My brain immediately imagined me sitting on the couch, watching Netflix and eating McDonald's. It said to me, 'Joy makes you a lazy motherf*cker.'"

I was fascinated by her automatic association …

Joy is the opposite of productivity.

Joy is the opposite of hustle.

Joy is the opposite of success.

Joy makes you a lazy motherf*cker.

We decided to unpack what was going on for her. I asked, "When's the last time you watched Netflix and ate McDonald's?" (I guessed it wasn't recently.) "Is it possible that your brain automatically went to those joy-full things because you've been depriving yourself of them?"

"Quite possibly," she said.

We chatted further to see what other activities besides Netflix and McDonald's she associates with joy. They were all activities she associates with failure and laziness. (And mind you, they were all false associations. There's nothing inherently lazy about watching Netflix or eating McDonalds. We all need rest and pleasure!) Further, none of the activities were related to her podcast, side hustle, cricketing, or work. It didn't even occur to her to that joy could exist in any of those arenas.

Mahrukh may be an outlier with her level of ambition, but I don't think she's an outlier in how she thinks about joy. We haven't been taught to pursue and include joy-full activities in our professional lives. In fact, we've been taught the opposite. When I think of the lines I've heard or been fed myself, I imagine a dad with mustache, thick-rimmed glasses, and an outdated business suit wagging his finger saying:

Quit playing around. You can't be successful with that attitude. Success requires discipline, training, hard work. If you're not careful, you'll end up working at some dead-end minimum-wage job for the rest of your life. Joy doesn't pay the bills. Work isn't supposed to make you happy. That's what your life is for.

The message many of us were raised with is that joy and success can't go together. We've spent years, and even decades of our lives reaffirming that belief. That is, the more we've created success through grit, hustle, misery, or indifference, the easier it is to believe that the only path to success is the one that denies or keeps out joy. It's not a big leap to then tell ourselves that joy has no place in our business and can actively sabotage us.

Without any evidence of a path to success through joy, we're afraid to pursue it, let alone put it first.

TAKE A MINUTE TO REFLECT:

What are your automatic associations with joy?

How does the idea of "chase joy, and success will chase you" land in your body? If it's uncomfortable, what makes it so?

What are the benefits, in your mind, of pursuing joy? What are the consequences? What are some tiny actions you can take in your business to start testing some of your ingrained assumptions around joy and success?

JOY IS UNCOMFORTABLE

Let's revisit the distinction between our Zone of Excellence and our Zone of Genius that we touched on in the last conversation (*Listen All Y'all, It's a Sabotage*). When we're operating in our Zone of Genius, we're doing the things we're uniquely good at *and* that we love to do. Operating in our genius feels easy, flowy, and joy-full. But, as Hendricks points out, we often resist being in our Zone of Genius, defaulting back to our Zone of Excellence. Why is that?

Doing what feels easy, flowy, and joy-full is *wildly* uncomfortable.

We tend to believe that if something is easy for us, it must be easy for others, too. We don't recognize it's easy *because* we have a special skillset, talent, or strength that makes that activity or way of doing that activity come naturally to us. So, in our minds, our "geniuses" are nothing to write home about. We don't even consider them our genius.

We also tend to discount the value of things that are easy. If you've ever said to yourself, "Wait, I (can) really get paid to do *this?*" chances are you were leaning into your genius. Whenever I have asked myself this question, it's always been followed up by negative feelings. This is naughty. Cheating. I must be a bad person. Or, like my friend, Mahrukh, would say, I'm a lazy motherf*cker.

When we're in our Zone of Excellence, activities are more effortful. But that's where we feel most comfortable. We are trained to be hard-a-holics. Taught that if we're not feeling pain, we're clearly not gaining. And that success can't come without sacrifice.

Our discomfort with ease and comfort with effort are not easily retrained. If they were, we would all read *The Big Leap* and walk away committed to staying in our Zone of Genius for the rest of time. Confession: I've read the book a few times and still struggle to convince myself that my genius is truly my genius, and that operating in that zone is the most valuable way for me to impact my clients and run my business. Many of my colleagues feel similarly. Our discomfort (and comfort) is at a nervous system level. It can feel downright crappy in our bodies to be in the ease, flow, and joy of our genius. It can even feel unsafe enough to trigger us into fight, flight, or freeze responses.

I've been focusing here on the ease part of being in your Zone of Genius, but the same principles apply to joy. We discount the value of things that are joy-full. Sometimes, like in Mahrukh's case, we are convinced that they will sabotage our success. We prefer the comfort and familiarity of our Zone of Excellence, even when we realize that the activities we're doing, or the ways we're doing them, don't bring us joy. And like our resistance to ease is at a nervous system level, so is our resistance to joy.

Let's unpack what's happening in our nervous systems. For one, neuroscience tells us that our nervous systems hold onto unprocessed trauma. Those could be "Big T" traumas like a car accident, sexual assault, or physical abuse, or "little t" traumas like bullying, financial insecurity, or damaging messages from parents, which despite being called "little" are no less impactful to your nervous system than Big T traumas. One of my formative little t traumas occurred when my dad yelled at me in my junior year of high school for getting three As and three Bs during a particularly stressful semester, telling me I was going to work at Burger King the rest of my life. It's taken me years to heal from the fallout of that statement.

Our nervous system also holds on to all the stress and trauma related to the societal systems we live in (capitalism, patriarchy, white supremacy, heterosexism, gender binaries, ableism, and more). The messages we ingest get embedded in us below our conscious awareness. For instance, capitalism and patriarchy reinforce traditionally and exclusively "masculine" definitions of success — revenue, followers, user growth (of an app) — and means of creating that success — logic, reason, "smart" decisions, hard work, and discipline. [In contrast, more traditionally "feminine" definitions of success tend to focus on metrics like the level of personal satisfaction, sense of alignment with purpose, and quality of relationships. The means of creating that success are more about heart, intuition, and going with the flow. We need a healthy balance of both ... not just in our businesses but in corporations of all sizes.]

As we've already talked about, we're not taught to pursue our joy. That's because our societal systems thrive on the premise that we'll keep our joy out. What happens if people start pursuing their joy? Will they no longer be as productive? Will our economies fail?

Whether or not you are aware of it, pursuing joy in your business — whether it's through operating in your Zone of Genius or deciding to build a business based on your desires and passions — is an act of resistance or rebellion to these oppressive systems. And anytime you engage in resistance, it naturally can set your nervous system off. Additionally, if you've had any experiences in your life, especially from your childhood, where you were punished for pursuing your joy, you'll have a nervous system response to rebelling even more deeply ingrained.

So it makes sense why you might choose the safe and comfortable route of doing activities in your Zone of Excellence and/or that require a lot of effort and energy, but don't light you up.

But if you're willing to sit with the discomfort of putting joy front and center ...

If you're willing to lean into the ease and flow of your Zone of Genius even when your brain wants you believe that your skills, talents, and strengths aren't valuable ...

You'll find that joy is the safer and more comfortable path to success.

ZEBRA CAKES, REALITY TV, AND JOY

A few years ago, I served on the leadership team for a multi-day event focused on helping coaches grow their practices. My main role was facilitating small groups to integrate insights from each day's coaching and teachings. I'd been facilitating groups for almost ten years before discovering coaching and hadn't done so in quite a while. Serving the coaching community in that capacity was a no-brainer for filling up my joy tank.

The leadership team met for several weeks leading up to the event. During one of the meetings, we played a game we knew well: What I Don't Want You To Know About Me. Each person shares something vulnerable, that they truly don't want anyone else in the room to know about them. Done properly, it's a great way to create connection and trust quickly in a group.

When it came to my turn, I thought about sharing some "guilty pleasures" like my nearly daily consumption of Zebra Cakes (well, at that point in time) or binging reality TV when my wife was out of town. But instead, I decided to own up to something bigger: "What I don't want you to know about me is that I feel guilty that I get to coach people. I can't believe that I get to sit down with people, ask them questions, and deeply listen. I get to notice things about them that nobody else has, and help them grow as people, leaders, and business owners. It feels like play."

That last sentence was oozing with guilt and shame. Coaching felt like play to me (spoiler alert: it still does), and play, at that point in my journey, was a dirty word. Play meant easy, fun, and child-like, which are all things I had deemed "bad", and certainly the opposite of what a serious professional should feel! You're not supposed to play in your job! At least, that's what I had been taught. Work is supposed to be a hustle. It's supposed to be hard. If it feels like play, you're cheating.

Here I was experiencing the deepest joy of my professional life, and I was beating myself up for it.

I was feeling especially guilty because it was spring 2020. We were in the middle of the global COVID shelter-in-place. People were anxious, angry, and grieving the loss of loved ones. Joy was not in the collective. But here I was, full of joy.

After my share, I was amazed to hear I wasn't alone. Not only did others experience coaching as play, but they also wrestled with their guilt and shame around it, especially in the pandemic.

When we pursue our joy, it feels like play.

It feels easy. Like we're in flow. And we make ourselves wrong for that. We've been indoctrinated in a society where play, ease, and flow are too often equated with irresponsible and lazy (psst...this is a hallmark of internalised toxic capitalism).

So, how do we get rid of the guilt? I don't think we need to. In general, I don't believe in stuffing down emotions. And if we do, we border on toxic positivity more than true feelings of joy.

When the part of me that feels guilty starts making noise internally, I mark it as a good sign that I'm heading toward the joy-full path. I know that it's only raising hell because it's trying to protect me from the judgment that might come from other people, from falling into complacency and laziness, and from following what it thinks is a sure path to existential and/or business doom. I let that inner voice know that I hear its concerns and appreciate it trying to keep me safe. (Yes, I talk to the voices in my head. I highly recommend it, in fact!) And then I let it know I'm going to keep pursuing joy anyway.

When the joy-full activities or joy-full path in your business bring up guilt or shame, I invite you to see those feelings as a compass that you're on the right path.

FOR JOY OR MONEY?

Shortly before the pandemic, I flew to Santa Fe for a four-day meetup of 4PC, a small community of coaches and transformational leaders led by Rich Litvin. I had just started my second year of coaching full-time and I was miserable. I hadn't signed a new client in a few months and although the handful of people that I was in the process of exploring coaching relationships with were great, they wanted coaching in areas that no longer lit my fire (namely, leadership and career coaching in tech).

In my first year in business, I had leaned into building my business through the Prosperous Coach[9] method, created by Rich and his mentor-turned-friend, Steve Chandler. Essentially, the method was a way to cultivate a word-of-mouth and referral-based business through genuine relationships, rather than through social media and traditional marketing tactics. To initially get the word out that I'd shifted from tech leadership into coaching, I relied heavily on existing relationships within my network. I was in the very beginning stages of figuring out who I wanted to coach and on what — there were just so many possibilities under the umbrella of "coaching" — so anytime someone in my network was interested in exploring coaching together, I said "Hell yes!" I coached on everything from corporate leadership to career change, to building a business, to personal goals and dreams.

My Prosperous Coach "strategy" was wildly successful for the first eight months. I was well on my way to replacing my multi-six-figure corporate salary, and according to my mentors, my success was coming way faster than most new coaches. But in moving that fast, I also quickly exhausted my existing network. My revenue went to a trickle in month nine and stayed that way for several months. I was still amid the trickle when I arrived in Santa Fe.

I was freaking out about money as I sat in a room full of leaders who were making multi-six figures and *well beyond*. I felt completely inadequate. I was ashamed that I hadn't yet replaced my corporate salary. (In my mind, it didn't matter that I'd made over six figures in my first year, an accomplishment many coaches don't ever reach, let alone in year one!)

I was also disheartened by who was coming to me for coaching. I'd realized that after coaching everyone on everything, I most wanted to coach mission-driven entrepreneurs and small business owners. But the people coming to me willing and ready to invest in coaching wanted me for corporate leadership or career change. The people I dreamed of coaching weren't in my network. At least not yet.

I believed wholeheartedly that I had a choice to make between making money (coaching people on things I didn't want to coach on anymore) or my joy (coaching the people who lit my soul on fire). I truly didn't believe both were possible. And because I was so worried about being enough in comparison to my colleagues, I was tempted to choose money.

What got me out of the catch-22 I'd created in my mind was a single question Rich asked me in a group coaching session:

"What are you willing to sacrifice, let go of, or give up in order to only work with dream clients?"

I didn't have the answer right away, but on the plane ride home it hit me: If it was true that I could have joy *or* I could have money, but not both, I was going to choose joy.

Woah.

When I got home, I looked at my bank account to see if I really could choose joy. *I could!* (Let me pause here to call out that this was a privileged position for me be in and not everyone has the ability to make this choice.) I made a commitment to myself:

I'm only going to work with clients that bring me joy. Everyone else is a no, no matter how much money they are willing to pay. Yes, I'd like to be replacing my salary. But if I don't make another penny this year, we're not going to go broke. And if I don't make another penny this year,

I have full permission to change course and do something different with my career.

The declaration alone brought me joy. It was uncomfortable to think about making no money and having to face all the good enoughness and comparison fears that were still there. But I knew that I could never run a business long-term if I didn't get lit the f*ck up by it. No amount of money could create longevity if I was miserable.

A few weeks later, shelter-in-place went into effect and COVID times turned everything upside down. Everyone in my circle was panicked about their business. Had I not made that commitment to myself, I might have been too. But I had already come to peace with the idea of not making any money for the rest of the year.

One of the first things I did during shelter-in-place was go Live on Facebook every weekday to give people practical tips for managing the chaos. I also hosted weekly meetups of Facebook community with no agenda but to create connection. It brought me a ton of joy to help people navigate that unprecedented time without expectation.

And wouldn't you know, ideal clients started inquiring about working together. Rather than making no pennies, I ended the year with double the revenue from the year before. Go figure!

It turns out joy and money aren't mutually exclusive, after all.

The Joy Audit

How joy-full is your business right now? Before we dive into the next two sections on how we lose joy and how we can get more of it, take stock of where things are for you right now.

The Joy Audit helps you get clear on what is creating your joy and what is stealing it in different areas of your business. You can answer from a 30,000-foot view of your business, or you can take various elements of your business to do a deeper assessment on (like current clients, marketing activities, projects in progress, your schedule, or programs/products you sell)

In addition to doing the Joy Audit right now, I recommend you do this exercise at least once a quarter, if not once a month. It's quite easy for joy to slip away, so the more regularly you can check in, the better. For a printable worksheet version of this audit, visit ErinMBaker.com.

OVERALL JOY-FULLNESS

- On a scale of 1 to 10, where 10 is joy-full AF, how much joy am I experiencing right now?
- What thoughts, beliefs, emotions, or behaviors are making that number so high? *(Hint: Even if the number is quite low, asking yourself what is making it as high as it is will help you pinpoint what is going well.)*
- What thoughts, beliefs, emotions, or behaviors are keeping it from being higher?

- What concrete actions can I take to increase my joy by just 1 point?

Now go through each of the four C's similarly.

Connection

- On a scale of 1 to 10 where 10 is connected AF, how connected do I feel to myself – who I am, what's important, and how I like to do things?
- What thoughts, beliefs, emotions, or behaviors are making that number so high?
- What thoughts, beliefs, emotions, or behaviors are keeping it from being higher?
- What concrete actions can I take to increase my connection by just 1 point?

Curiosity

- On a scale of 1 to 10 where 10 is curious AF, how curious do I feel about what might happen, what I could learn, or what is possible?
- What thoughts, beliefs, emotions, or behaviors are making that number so high?
- What thoughts, beliefs, emotions, or behaviors are keeping it from being higher?
- What concrete actions can I take to increase my curiosity by just 1 point?

Creativity

- On a scale of 1 to 10 where 10 is creative AF, how tapped into my creativity do I feel?
- What thoughts, beliefs, emotions, or behaviors are making that number so high?
- What thoughts, beliefs, emotions, or behaviors are keeping it from being higher?

- What concrete actions can I take to increase my creativity by just 1 point?

Courage

- On a scale of 1 to 10 where 10 is courageous AF, how courageous are my actions right now? *(Hint: we often don't feel courageous. We feel fear. So measure your courage by what you are doing to stretch yourself and take risks rather than how you feel in doing them.)*

- What thoughts, beliefs, emotions, or behaviors are making that number so high?

- What thoughts, beliefs, emotions, or behaviors are keeping it from being higher?

- What concrete actions can I take to increase my courage by just 1 point?

How The F*ck
Do We Lose Joy
(And How Can We Get it Back?)

How The F*ck Do We Lose Joy (And How Can We Get it Back?)

Every time I ask myself, "Where's the joy?" in my business, I giggle. That's because I immediately flash back to the Wendy's fast-food commercials from the 80s. If you're not old enough to have experienced them — or if you're old enough but have blocked them from memory — let me set the scene. The original commercial features three elderly women peering down at an oversized open-faced hamburger bun with a *tiny* patty sitting on top. One of the ladies leans in, furrows her eyebrows, and asks in a slightly critical tone, "Where's the beef?" She then repeats it to herself twice more, acting a little more exasperated each time, "Where's the beef?" "Heeey, wheeeeeeree's the beef!?"

I'm embarrassed to admit how often that voice pops into my head. In writing this book I asked myself "Where's the joy?" several times before I landed on a process that worked for me. I strive to be joy-full AF in all areas of my life and business. (Some 9 out of 10 people surveyed and 10 out of 10 pets, not bribed with treats in advance, agree that joy oozes out of me in their presence.) So, few people know that in my first couple of years in business, I lost joy on the regular. By "traditional metrics" — you know, the ones the biz gurus say measure whether or not you're "good at business" — I was successful. My coaching practice was usually full, and at times waitlisted. I crossed the magical six-figure revenue threshold that business coaches sell blueprints and formulas for, in my first eight months of business. Apparently, this is warp speed for a business in the coaching world. My income quickly exceeded what I needed to provide for my family. Colleagues told me I inspired them. The sneaky thing about losing joy is that other people don't typically see it happening. And when we're successful by conventional standards, it's often the last thing we want people to know. That makes losing joy also quite lonely. Other than my wife, coach, and a couple of verrrrrry close friends, nobody knew when I was joy-full AF, and when I was just pretending to be, in those first two years. And what few people know now is that I still lose joy at times ...

Hello, my name is Dr. Erin,

I have a PhD in making myself miserable

while doing the very things

— coaching and mentoring people —

that light me up most.

Lovely to meet you.

Sometimes I lose joy because I fall out of touch with myself: What I care about most, who I want to serve, or how I want to run my business. Other times, I become so attached to achieving external outcomes (like revenue) that tunnel vision cuts me off from my curiosity, creativity, and courage to take risks. And still other times, I get so focused on the short-term goals of creating immediate success and avoiding immediate failure that I lose sight of an important truth that we covered in *Why the F*ck Do We Need Joy?*:

Running a business is about playing the long game. And the only way to be in it for the long game is to put joy first.

Over the next several conversations, we're going to explore all kinds of things that might cause you to ask, "Where's the beef ... err joy...?" in your business. Some may feel familiar or obvious to you. Even if you're aware they are potential leaks (or full-on drains) of your joy, it's good to check in with yourself on whether they are showing up in your business right now. Others may be less familiar ... or even feel sneaky. You may even find, once you've read through this section, that I've missed naming joy leaks that you know are true for yourself. The ones I've highlighted here are those I know are most common for me and many of my clients. The truth is, if we all experience joy differently, we all can lose it differently as well. Take note as you go along of what you discover about your joy!

STOPPING YOURSELF
BEFORE YOU GET STARTED
(WHAT YOU THINK IS ESSENTIAL
IS NOT-SO-ESSENTIAL)

Before you start any new activity or project, or set a new goal, what do you need to know?

Pause for a moment to note what automatically came to mind.

What comes to mind for me is that I first need to decide whether it's worth taking on at all (I have lots of ideas for projects and activities that never get past the idea phase). Let's start there.

What helps you decide to take on something new?

Do you weigh how much you *want* to take it on?

Are you calculating whether it's a good strategic move?

Or are you already trying to work out in your head what steps you need to take to get where you want to go?

Keep your answers top of mind as I go to this next question.

Once you've decided that something is worth pursuing, what do you need to know to take your first step?

Do you need to know exactly where you are going?

Or the exact steps for getting there?

As you note your answers, notice whether any of them overlap with how you answered the first question.

We can lose the joy of any journey (before we even embark on it) by needing to have it all figured out.

Three of the most common things we believe we need to know are "Why am I doing this?" (My Big Why), "Where am I going?" (My Big Vision), and "How (down to the very last detail) am I getting there?" (My Map).

(Were any of these in your "need-to-knows"?)

When we mentally label these as essential before we even take the first step, we stop ourselves from pursuing joy-full paths. We also create unnecessary stress and anxiety. There are things we just can't know until we get in motion. I don't know about you but wracking my brain for answers that won't come or having 10,000 equally possible options is joy-less. We also lose out on the joy of discovering what's in store for us along the journey. Though uncertainty can be daunting, there's also magic in not knowing exactly where we're going or what's coming next.

Why is it that we see Why, Where, and How as so essential? We'll dive into some specific reasons for each in the next three conversations, but one thing common to all of them is that we don't want to waste time, money, or effort going the wrong direction. That fear is rooted in a toxic capitalistic and white supremacy cultural[10] notion that our worth lays in how much we produce and how much money we make. We can't afford to wander off course when our value and belonging is at stake! So we do everything we can to maximize the likelihood that we'll succeed and in the shortest amount of time possible.

As we go into these next few conversations, keep in mind those other things you told yourself that you need to know before you decide to take on something and before you take the first step. I suspect that some of these steal your joy and that the reasons why they do are similar to what you'll read the next three sections.

TELL ME WHY
(AIN'T NOTHING BUT A HEARTACHE)

Just because the Backstreet Boys asked you this with their intense eyes and sexy haircuts, doesn't mean you need an answer. You don't need a "why" to pursue anything and insisting on having one can be a joy-ache. (One of my joys is a bad pun!)

When I told people that I was writing a book, the question on everyone's mind was, "*Why?*" Why take on this challenge? Why right now? Did I have burning message to get out in the world? Was there a strategic business reason to put myself out there in book form?

Early in the process my book coach suggested I try writing an introduction to the book centered on why I was writing it. I didn't do the exercise. That's because my answer was simple: I was writing a book *because I wanted to see if I could.* For many years, I told myself a story that I wasn't the sort of person who could write a book. Yet, in mid-2020, I felt pulled to do it. Maybe I wanted to prove myself wrong. Or maybe the bigger *why* for my book — and for the difference I want to make in the world through my business — would emerge during the process of writing it.

It felt edgy for me to say that I didn't have a bigger *why* than *I want to* at the outset of the book writing journey. I was worried that people would think I was foolish for spending time and energy on something that many people see as arduous and only "worth it" if there's a compelling reason for doing so. Or that they'd see me as selfish or greedy because I didn't have an altruistic motive for the journey. I'm sure if I had Googled all the reasons why *not* to write a book, not having an answer to the "Why" question would have been one of the top reasons to just say no. And it might have stopped me if I hadn't reminded myself that I've done plenty of things in my life without a big *why*, including writing songs, playing sports, and even a short foray into visual art. I did those things for the joy — because I wanted to.

I could have made up all kinds of other reasons why writing a book was different, including but not limited to, that I was writing it on my business time. But ultimately, needing a big *why* to justify spending time on a project or activity was just a story I'd made up in my head.

If you follow some of the big business gurus you might know of Simon Sinek's famous TED talk, "Start with Why."[11] He's right, to a large degree, about the benefits of having a why before you figure out *what* and *how*. It can inspire, motivate, and guide your action. If you already know your why for any project, activity, or goal, that's fantastic! But if you don't, I want to assure you that it's not required.

We tell ourselves a *why* is required for three reasons:

1. We think we need to justify how we're spending our time and effort to ourselves and others.

Society assigns value to what we *do* — what we achieve and what output we create. So we feel compelled to only pursue projects, activities, and goals that are logical and benefit others somehow. Doing something purely for the sake of it? Well, that's foolish, selfish, and honestly, downright greedy!

It's easy to believe that until we can articulate a *why* that passes societal muster, we shouldn't go after it. But here's the problem with trying to pass the societal test for what's worth our time and effort: Who the f*ck is "society"? And who made them Grand Poobah of your choices? How many times have you wanted to try something without a clear reason for doing so, but the thought of being judged by your family, friends, colleagues, or some version of Big Brother in your head stopped you in your tracks? Who exactly is making the rules about what passes muster, here? And why the hell should we be compelled to follow them? Who gets to say that "because I want to" isn't a big enough *why*? *And who's to say that you won't discover a big why along the way?*

2. We admire those who have a *why*.

We see people with compelling *whys* all the time. They could be close friends or colleagues, well-known figures in our industry, or celebrities and personalities. We want to be as inspiring and inspired as they are.

3. We often believe a big *why* is necessary.

A *why* will help us stay committed to our goals when times become difficult and we encounter fear or doubt, or our motivation wanes. Although a big *why* can help us face those challenges and those blocks, it's also only one of many tools you can bring out for doing so. And if finding a big why is preventing you from your joy, that sets up a whole new set of challenges and blocks.

In case it's not abundantly clear yet, let me shout it for all the people in the back: IT'S OKAY TO DO SOMETHING BECAUSE YOU WANT TO OR BECAUSE IT BRINGS YOU JOY!

And, between you and me, it's also okay to do something because the real question on your mind is not why, but rather, why not?

WE DON'T NEED NO DESTINATION!

If you read the title of this conversation and immediately heard the line, "We don't need no education!" from Pink Floyd's "Another Brick in the Wall" in your head, you and I might be long-lost friends. And if you didn't, that's okay. I highly recommend you take a break and listen to the song, because the fervency of their singing matches my own when it comes to the idea that we should always know exactly *what* we are creating or *where* we are going. It's completely unnecessary.

When I say *what/where*, I'm not talking about the singular actions we're taking or the small goals we're pursuing. I'm talking about *what/where* with a capital W: The Big Vision. What does our business and life look like three, five, or ten years from now? We believe that if we don't have a big vision for the future, we won't know what actions to take today. We doubt that we can set useful small goals to pursue or that we can create the success that we so deeply desire without that larger focus.

I have been guilty of believing this, too. Two months into my full-time coaching, Rich Litvin invited me onto his then brand-new podcast, *One Insight*. Rather than interview his guests, Rich coaches them. He initially coached me on something very tactical — tools I can use to prevent burnout. And just a few minutes into the show, we had already solved the problem I brought to him. We could easily have wrapped up and called it an episode. But he sensed there was more and asked how else he could serve me. I was a bit surprised that he hadn't yet asked me one of his signature questions:

"Imagine we get on a call three years from today, and you say, 'Holy shit, Rich. This has been the best three years of my life.' Erin, what are you up to in your business and life three years from now that would have you say that to me?"

I'll admit, I was also kind of relieved he hadn't yet asked. The truth was, I had zero clue how to answer him. I was only a couple months into my business, and I had no Big Vision in mind. I didn't know what was possible or what I wanted. I was focused on building up a coaching practice, but I wasn't even sure if that would be the centerpiece of my business or a steppingstone to teaching a course, speaking on stages, or writing books. I was deeply embarrassed to be so aimless. And rather than tell myself, "Oh, Erin it's totally okay, you're at the beginning stages, you'll figure out where you're going along the way," I scolded myself for being clearly incompetent and incapable. My inner monologue was basically: "Erin, you need to get your shit together quickly if you have any hope of being successful."

I had seen Rich ask dozens of other people the question. They all had clarity about where they wanted to go. (I didn't account, however, for how long they'd been in business or working towards their vision. In hindsight, that data would have helped me draw a very different conclusion.) So clearly, I thought, it was just me.

Despite my embarrassment, when Rich offered to continue the episode, I asked him to help me pull out my three-year Big Vision. He refused. My inner teenager was screaming, "F*ck you, Rich." But since we were recording for an audience, and I wanted him to like and respect me, I sat there politely and listened to him as he said, "Your challenge right now is to practice living in uncertainty. There will come a moment when either you go, 'Oh my God, Rich, I think it's this. Can we talk?' or, 'Oh shit, Rich, this really scares me. Can we talk?' But something extraordinary is on the way."

On the inside, I was furious. He wasn't giving me what I desperately wanted. And let's be clear about what I wanted. It wasn't just a Big Vision. It was what the Big Vision would do for me. I wanted a sense of security that the actions I was taking in that moment were amounting to something. And I wanted to be able to tell myself, "See Erin! You just needed a little help from Rich to get there, but nothing is wrong with you after all!"

The reason we think we need a what: We don't want to waste time, money, or effort going in the "wrong direction."

(Pssst ... remember, this is also why we think we need a *why*! Our fear of waste sucks our joy in multiple ways.) The longer we head in the wrong direction, the more risk we think it poses to our longer-term success. So, we want to know, "What's the right path? Where am I going?" as soon as we get into motion. We can end up spinning our mental wheels trying to *think* our way into clarity. Often, we waste more time *not* taking action while we wait for our *what/where* to become clear, than if we'd headed off in *any* viable direction, realized "Nope, this is not where I want to go," and then changed course.

Though I gave myself three to five years to build a business that reliably replaced my income from Facebook and Microsoft, when Rich coached me, I was terrified I was wasting time (while also needlessly draining my bank account). I believed that every single entrepreneur in my world (except me) had a solid *what* and *why*. I also believed having both was "the right way" to run a business. The longer I went without either, the more I felt time was running out. Each day was a grain of sand in the hourglass. And each confirmed that I wasn't smart, capable, or creative enough to run a business.

I hadn't yet learned one of the most profound lessons of any goal pursuit: Our map is not the territory. That is, when we start off on the journey, our perception of where we can go or what we can create is based on our current knowledge and experience — which is inherently limited. There is so much more possible beyond what our experience tells us.

If I'd created a three-year vision in that moment, it would've been based on what I'd seen others do or what I'd done in the past. I couldn't have created a complete or detailed map because I couldn't know in advance what was fully possible for me. I also was missing a key lesson about clarity: the more we stay in active motion, the clearer things become. Going off in a wrong direction can be great information about where to go next.

Three years ago, I couldn't have predicted where I would be today, writing this book and coaching my clients. It took me going down several different paths, correcting and adjusting (and re-adjusting), and building a body of self-knowledge as I went along. In hindsight, Rich's refusal to coach me in that moment was the ultimate act of service.

Now I know that there is nothing wrong with lacking a Big Vision. Even as a business evolves, I don't think there is ever a point when one is necessary. And when you let go of needing one, and later one naturally emerges, that can be a joy-full AF ride.

We can find joy in letting go the need for a concrete picture of what we are creating or moving towards in the future.

We can find joy from leaning into uncertainty and developing a muscle for not knowing more than a few steps ahead.

And we can find joy in bushwhacking our way until we find a clearing.

If you have a Big Vision, or a *what*, I'm not telling you to let it go. One can certainly be useful and nice to have a compass guiding your actions. But if you don't have one, I invite you to sing loudly with me "We don't need no destination!" and to find the joy in that. Have an adventure. Go explore and perhaps find your *what* along the way.

HOW DO I ...

Part of the joy of any journey is figuring out the *how* along the way. So if you're insisting on knowing it in advance, you are missing out on joy in multiple ways.

My friend, Kate, likes to plan every detail when she goes on a road trip. She knows every rest stop, diner, dive, and hotel that she'll stop at along her way well before she gets into the car, and even has backup plans in case of unforeseen interruptions like traffic accidents, inclement weather, or a tired driver. Thanks to technology, Kate can map out a route and exact waypoints to just about anywhere. She really needs to know the *how* of her journeys.

If "*How do I do this?*" crosses your mind almost immediately after setting a goal, you're not alone. Our brains want assurance that our goal is worthy of pursuit. If it's completely new territory for us, or it feels big, overwhelming, or impossible, we think the only way we should say yes to going after it is if we (think we) know *how*. After all, how can we be sure we'll be successful if we're not even sure how to get there? It's not good enough to know only a few of the steps. We want certainty around each of the 100, 1,000, or 10,000 steps we'll need to take to achieve the goal. We want Kate's road trip level of planning, but Kate is mapping based on established highways and points of interest. That makes it so much easier for her to estimate the time and effort it will take to go from point A to point B. She can also fairly accurately anticipate what might delay or derail her plans.

Unfortunately, we want our business journeys to be as easy to plan as Kate's trips. We expect to be on already well-worn paths with easy estimates of time and effort and known obstacles. When we find that the path doesn't exist yet — because we're the first to create a particular product or service, or we're doing something in a new way — we often don't trust ourselves to make our own path. We may decide the goal isn't "worth it" or "smart to pursue".

How many opportunities to go after joy-full goals have you passed by because you couldn't sort out the *how* in advance? I know I've missed out many times! (In fact, even as I write this, I have a big vision for where I want to take my coaching practice in the next few years, but I find the *how monster* nagging me to figure out more of the steps before I commit to fully taking it on.)

Why are we so hell-bent on having the *how* figured out in advance?

I may sound like a broken record here, but again, knowing *how* ensures we won't waste our time, effort, or money going in the wrong direction. We mistakenly believe that if we don't know the entire route (or enough of it) right now, we never will. We can't see the possibility that the path will reveal itself to us as we go along, or the journey itself will create new paths along the way. We also can't see the potential joy that can come from not having it all figured out! The surprises, twists, and turns we encounter when we don't have the entire path figured out can be some of the most adventurous and magical experiences we'll have in our businesses.

Part of the joy of any journey is figuring out the *how* along the way; and really, it's figuring out *your way*. The good and bad news is that the only way to do that is to get in motion and learn what works and what doesn't. Yes, you'll risk wasting some time, money, or effort, but you'll also get clearer and clearer as you go. You'll have doors open to you that you never imagined would, just because you happen to be in the right place or time.

Let's bring Kate back for a moment. By sticking to a pre-made plan, she might not notice the flyer at a gas station advertising a show by her favorite indie musician. All she'd need to do is stay in that town overnight instead of driving through. Or she might miss out on the chance to try a pop-up BBQ joint that becomes nationally recognized because she'd already committed herself to stopping for tacos three miles down the road.

Insisting on knowing the *how* can be a kill joy.

Not knowing the *how* yet can stop you from pursuing things that you're passionate about or really want to go after. It can also create more stress along the way if you don't have all the answers right now and you aren't sure they're ever coming. On the flip side, leaning into, "I don't know how" can be an incredible source of joy. We'll talk even more about the joy-fullness of the unknown in later conversations.

WHO DO I NEED TO BE?

This question is so popular in the coaching industry that it's almost a cliché. It's a question that often follows someone stating a goal or vision that they are moving towards.

"I want to be a best-selling author!" says the client.

"Who do you need to be in order to become a best-selling author?" asks the coach.

I'm going to be blunt. I hate this question with the heat of 10,000 suns. It's a subtle, insidious way to reinforce that who a person is in this moment is not enough, and that to achieve their dreams, they must become someone else. Now this question isn't explicitly asking people to look around at others for answers of who to be or what to do. But ultimately, we are social creatures and that's what we do. Like the client who wants to be a best-selling author and looks to emulate their heroes. We whip or shame ourselves for who we currently are or what we do, while pedestalizing people who already have the personal qualities or professional accomplishments we desire.

It's not just poor coaching questions that nudge us to look outside of ourselves. Gazing outside for validation is baked into the fabric of society. There is no curriculum in our formal education that teaches us how to look inside ourselves for answers or to build self-trust. Even if we are bombarded with messages to "be your authentic self" (like when I worked at Facebook and was told to bring my "whole self to work"), many of us have been rewarded for fitting in more than standing out. We come to believe over time that others have the right answers (after all, didn't it feel like our teachers all had them, even on subjective matters like creative writing?), and they must know something that we don't. For all the "be authentic" messaging, we get even more messaging from family, friends, teachers, the media, and society at large that reinforces the idea that there are right ways to be and do. Most of the messages are so subtle that we don't realize they are running the show.

Our tendency to look outside ourselves is so automatic that sometimes when we do look inward toward what we want, or how we might do things, we draw a blank. Even if we have some inklings, it can be terrifying to follow them. *What if who I am or how I do things is wrong? Then I'll really know I'm not enough.* It's safer, therefore, to stay in the comfort zone of following other people's rules.

"Who do I need to be?" is not just a coaching question I hate. It's also the theme of the next four conversations on ways we look to others that leak our joy. This is one of those places in the book where you might find additional ways you look outside yourself that I haven't mentioned. To be honest, I could have written the whole book on this theme. Joy is about deeply connecting to you. There's a multitude of ways to lose that connection. The good news is: The more aware you are of your potential joy leaks, the quicker you'll notice them and be able to plug them up!

"JUST FOLLOW MY 10-STEP BLUEPRINT!"

Blueprints.

Formulas.

Step-by-step strategies.

Word-for-word scripts.

No matter what business you're in, someone out there is dying to sell you on *their* path to success. Sometimes, they've followed the path themselves and are convinced that other people can replicate their success. But just as often (or perhaps even more often), the person selling the blueprint or formula hasn't implemented any of it themselves. They are merely a marketer selling something that someone else has told them works. In other words, they are selling you something that someone else sold them.

I regularly get messages through LinkedIn and Instagram from people who are ready to help me get more leads (HUNDREDS per month!), hit my first $10K or $20K month, or scale to six- or seven-figures. Rarely have these folks been in my shoes as an independent coach. Nor have they created the kinds of results in their own business that they are trying to sell me on some program for. These messages tend to come in waves, which tells me when a new cohort of marketers have graduated from the many programs that teach them how to sell blueprints and formulas to coaches.

Other people's maps are everywhere.

It's so tempting to follow them! The uncertainty we face in business can be excruciatingly uncomfortable. And these solutions promise to take our pain away.

We want to know the right way to:

... design our services or products

... find a profitable niche

... market to our niche

... build a client base

... grow a social media following

... write a book

... make more money

As if there's a *right way*.

This need to "get it right" is ingrained in us from an early age. Our one-size-fits-all education system (especially in the United States) grades us on the extent to which we have the right answers or do things the right way. It teaches us to look outside of ourselves to teachers and experts for facts and information on who we are supposed to be and how we are supposed to behave.

So naturally, when perceived experts offer up blueprints, formulas, or word-for-word scripts, even guarantees, we can convince ourselves that they know better than we do. We feel like we shouldn't trust ourselves or the path we have taken on our own. Why would we take the risk of failing while doing it our way when someone else's right way is right in front of us and they say it'll be wildly successful?

Well ... I hate to break it to you ...

There is no right way.
There's only your way.

Just because a person has found success with a certain set of steps, it doesn't mean those steps will work for you. Each of us has a unique context: age, gender identity, race, wealth, location, business background, life history, personality, strengths, etc. If no two people are the same, then no two paths can be the same either!

[And even if, by some miracle, you could find someone with your *exact* context, there is still no guarantee their blueprint or formula will work. There's only so much we can control in our world, especially when our business outcomes depend on the behavior and decisions of other humans!]

Of course, our joy is drained any time a blueprint, formula, or script doesn't work. But the more insidious way they suck our joy is in cutting us off from our connection with ourselves and our creativity. When we look outside of ourselves, we don't learn about or tap into our own strengths and geniuses. We don't explore how our brains work or how we like to do things. We don't give ourselves a chance to develop self-trust or to realize that we *can* create success by following our own map.

Now, let me clear: blueprints, formulas, and scripts aren't all bad. You don't have to isolate yourself from all experts and bushwhack a path entirely on your own. Unless, of course, that's what works best for YOU. That's not what works best for me. I struggle without some sort of reference point or set of ideas to work from. To shift metaphors, if someone hands me a blank canvas, I won't know what to do with it. My creative juices need something to respond to. So, I am better looking at lots of examples of how people have done something and then getting curious about how I want to do it.

If you do want to look at how others have gone about a particular thing, take blueprints, formulas, and scripts with a grain of salt. Especially any that come from marketers who haven't implemented any of what they are selling. The gold is often with people who have been on a journey like yours, but instead of trying to get you to follow their footsteps, they help you figure out what, if any, parts of their path might work for you.

I WILL TEACH YOU TO BE RICH

Every time I try to mimic somebody else in my business, I lose my joy. If you're familiar with the book "I Will Teach You to Be Rich" by Ramit Sethi, that's not who I'm talking about in the title. Though Ramit does sell people "proven scripts", so he's somewhat relevant to the idea of this conversation. The Rich I'm referring to is Rich Litvin, who you met in *For Joy and Money* and *We Don't Need No Destination!*

Rich is known for his powerful language and presence. When coaching people on creating new clients, he offers suggestions on what and how to have conversations. Though he likely doesn't intend for them to be scripts, many people take them as such. Early on in my career, I did exactly this. I figured that I didn't know what to say, so I might as well follow his lead. And of course, if he was giving them to me, *surely* they must work. Even the times when I didn't have a script pre-handed to me by Rich, I'd ask myself "What Would Rich Do?" and something that sounded a lot like him would come out.

The problem was, every time I tried to channel my inner Rich in a conversation, it felt awkward, achy, and difficult. His language — and the power and presence it was meant to convey — wasn't authentic to me. It stands to reason that if being and doing you is joy-full, then trying to mimic someone else feels quite the opposite. And to be honest … it also didn't "work." It's not that Rich's language was wrong. It was just wrong for ME. (And I believe, wrong for anyone not named Rich Litvin.)

We often believe that experts, mentors, and gurus have the answers or know what's best. After all, if they didn't, they wouldn't be experts now would they! Every time I tried to do things "Rich's way", what I was subconsciously telling myself was that whatever way *I* would have done it was wrong. Most of the time I didn't even consider what my way might be. And even if I did, I certainly didn't give myself permission to try. I'd tell myself something like, *"Erin, look Rich has a multi-seven figure business. He clearly knows better than you. That's why you joined his coaching community."*

It wasn't just Rich that I mimicked in my early coaching days. Along with being part of Rich Litvin's community, I was also part of Sean Smith's coaching community, and I worked intensively one-on-one with Christina Berkley. As I absorbed myself in their teachings and mentorship, I found myself also asking "What Would Sean Do?" and "What Would Christina Do?" Rich, Sean, and Christina all had different businesses, but there was enough overlap that I started to create a mental picture about what a successful coach looked, felt, and sounded like. Who should I coach? What should I coach on? What prices should I charge? How should I build an audience of potential clients?

In those early days of working with the three of them, I never once asked myself, "What Would *Erin* Do?" As I soaked up their knowledge and expertise, I never considered what I uniquely brought to the table in experience. Or what I had to teach that they didn't. I automatically assumed that any unique knowledge, skills, or expertise I had was irrelevant.

Hoo'boy was I wrong about that! I mean, I have a PhD in social psychology, for Pete's sake! I don't know *everything* there is to know about how our minds work, but I do know a lot. I know about our emotional system and why it's important for us to feel all our feelings. I know how motivation and goal-setting works, and what barriers we often encounter in accomplishing our goals and dreams. I also know what social psychology research the personal development industry is misinterpreting, and conversely, what research findings are solid enough to apply outside of experimental labs. And yet, here I was looking to Rich, Sean, and Christina to tell me what I needed to know about human behavior to best work with my coaching clients. *cue face palm emoji*

I was also discounting what I learned during my five years in the tech industry. User Experience Research — which was the majority of what I did in tech — has all kinds of parallels to coaching. It's all about asking good questions to gain insights. Often you look underneath what people are saying and doing in a research study to understand what they really want and need. Across multiple people, you find patterns that then help you make decisions about what products to build or how to make existing products better. In coaching, you ask good questions, helping your clients gain insights. Often you look underneath what they are saying and doing to understand the real problem or challenge they are facing (or even to discover the root of that problem). And as you get to know your client, you notice patterns that help them make decisions about how to move forward with their goals and dreams.

On top of being a researcher, I learned a lot about business during my time in tech. I know how to take a product from non-existent to present on the phones of billions of people (I was part of the team that launched Facebook Stories to the world). That is, I know every step in the process of making a product or service "go live," from initial ideation to exploring and narrowing ideas, to testing a beta version with a handful of people, to launching more broadly. My knowledge and expertise is not something many coaches in my industry — including my mentors — have. Yet somehow it didn't occur to me that it was relevant, let alone a significant differentiator.

I was trying so hard to fit into the box in my mind of "what a successful coach and coaching business looks like," that I repeatedly told myself a lie that I didn't have anything special to bring to the table. The more I told myself that story, the more I was subtly convincing myself that "me" wasn't enough and that figuring out my flavor of coaching and running a business by leaning into my strengths, geniuses, and expertise wasn't going to be nearly as productive as following the advice or examples of others.

And the more I believed that, the more miserable I was. Notice where you might be subtly (or not-so subtly) putting someone else on a pedestal and convincing yourself that success requires you to become more like them. There is no joy in that. (And often no success either!) There's only joy in being you and doing things your way. (And if you're not sure yet who you are, what you care about, and how you do things, there's immense joy in the discovery process, too!)

LOOK AROUND, LOOK AROUND ... AT WHAT OTHERS ARE DOING RIGHT NOW

You might notice at this point that one of my joys is titles that reference songs or pop culture. This one might be obscure if you're not steeped in Broadway's *Hamilton*. There's a line early in the play where one of the Schuyler sisters sings, "Look around, look around, at how lucky we are to be alive right now." I can't help but sing that "look around" piece of the tune when I think about this next way we lose our joy.

Now that I've let my inner Broadway star have a moment to shine, let's get into it ...

How often do you look around at what other people in your industry are providing their customers? It might surprise you to hear me say that doing so isn't inherently problematic. It can be useful to get creative inspiration by seeing what else is out there. If someone puts a blank canvas in front of me and tells me to paint something, my mind will go as blank as that canvas. I mostly don't generate my ideas naturally from within. My best bet is to gather a bunch of examples as a springboard. Sometimes I'll take pieces of different ideas and combine them in a way that feels good for me. Other times, I'll see what someone else is doing and have a completely new idea spark from that. If that's how your creativity works best, too, go with it!

Joy comes from working with your brain, not against it.

But know that looking to others can turn into a sneaky leak of your joy tank.

When you look around at other offers, you might find several people offering a particular service. For instance, if you're a copywriter, you might see fellow copywriters selling end-to-end copywriting services for everything under the sun that requires words (social media, websites, email lists, even ghostwriting books). The more people you see offering that service, the more it can feel like, "Well, that's what everyone is offering. I guess I should too."

I've felt a similar pull as a coach. "Coaching" is an abstract concept that encompasses a wide range of activities that someone might do with a client. When I look toward the coaches who are most visible in online spaces (like Instagram and Facebook communities), my brain could easily pick up the message that I should:

- Coach on very tactical problems like social media visibility, marketing and funnels, offer creation, or step-by-step guidance to building a business

- Have one very specific coaching offer or program, rather than a menu

- Coach a lot of people on very short-term contracts (6 months or less)

As a business coach, I do love working with people on some of the more tactical business things. But we do so in the context of pursuing joy, and really in the context of my client being deeply connected to who they are, what lights them up, and how they do things. Much of my coaching starts at a deeper level and works its way up into tactical actions. Whenever I start feeling the pull of dropping the deeper coaching work in favor of selling tactical solutions, I know it's time to stop looking outside of myself for ideas and come home to my self-connection.

What tips the scale between looking around at others in a way that feels creative and joy-full, and looking at others that slowly leaks joy from the tank?

In my experience, it comes down to trust. If we believe that when we create offerings from our joy, people will enroll or buy, it's easy to stay in a joy-full place as we gather external ideas. But if self-doubt, comparison-itis, and/or societal programming about success are running in the background, we have a more difficult time resisting the pull to follow what others are doing. We can convince ourselves that *they* must have the answers or secrets. The more we give into that pull, the more leaks we get in our joy tank.

You might be thinking, "Well okay, Erin. I get the message to not follow what other people are doing at the expense of my joy. But what if nobody wants what I have to offer? What if the reason so many other people have similar offers (like end-to-end copywriting) is because that's what people want?"

I've thought similar things too. But I've also realized an important truth:

If I want or need something, somebody else does, too.

On a planet of nearly 8 billion people, it's next-to-impossible for me to be a unicorn that wants or needs something that no one else does. When I create something from my joy, I naturally create something *I* would want or need. And because I'm not a unicorn, someone else will want or need it too, likely way more folks than I imagine. (Maybe I'm just not reaching those people yet. But that's an entirely different problem.)

If I'm not a unicorn, neither are you.

As I mentioned, this joy leak can be subtle. It's a good idea to make a regular practice of checking in with yourself on how you are using inspiration and ideas from others. Notice when you are telling yourself stories about what you should be doing or what success looks like. See what reassurance your inner voices need for you to come back to connection, curiosity, creativity, courage.

COMPARISON IS A THIEF OF JOY ... OR MAYBE NOT

Teddy Roosevelt famously said, "Comparison is the thief of joy." I (much less famously) said, "Comparison is the thief AND source of joy," on my podcast *Life in the And* a few years ago.

In many respects, Teddy was right. When we compare ourselves to people who are further ahead of us or better off in some way (what scientists call Upward Social Comparison), we can easily end up feeling shitty. If we only made that much money, had that size house, drove that fancy a car ... then we would be successful, good enough, or worthy. When we compare ourselves to people who are behind us or less well-off (Downward Social Comparison), we can end up feeling pity for them. Shitty and pity are not joy-full!

One of my colleagues, Jessica, has made jaw-dropping amounts of money in her coaching business. She's been in business just a little longer than me. She speaks openly about her income on social media and often when she does my social comparison pangs arise, and I feel the joy seeping out of my bones. Without fail, several other colleagues message me saying they feel the same thing. Each of us have a very different business than Jessica. Each of us also have different goals and priorities that affect what revenue we bring in each year. Yet, we can't help but fall prey, even if briefly, to joy-thieving thoughts like, "Ugh, I'm clearly not a good enough coach and entrepreneur. And I'm never going to be," Or "Gosh, Erin what's wrong with you that you aren't making as much as her! You suck."

A couple of years ago, I was feeling particularly shitty about myself after reading one of Jessica's posts. She had made $500k that year. My brain immediately went to "you're behind," "not powerful enough," "a failure." Amidst my brain spiral, I read a Facebook post by another colleague, Christine, about how she had been up since 3:30 a.m. stewing about a coach friend. She was asking herself questions like, "How did they propel themselves to success so quickly? How are they more powerful than me? Are they actually, or is that a front?" I knew from the context that she wasn't talking about Jessica. Something whispered to me, "Erin, she's talking about YOU." I immediately dismissed it, telling myself that was quite an arrogant thought. Besides, Jessica's post clearly showed me that I'm neither successful nor powerful. I left a heart reaction on Christine's post and said to myself, "Just be grateful you aren't the only person sucked into the comparison trap."

Within a few minutes, a private message came in from Christine: "FYI you were the friend I was stewing about! Though you know I have nothing but love for you!"

Wait, what!? Here I was telling myself I'm not enough because I hadn't made the money Jessica did and someone else out there was telling herself that same thing because of me. I was letting someone else's success steal my joy rather than recognizing that my success was extraordinary too.

Christine's message, along with my reaction to it, hints at how comparison can also be a *source* of joy. More on that shortly.

So, what's the solution to comparison thieving our joy? Can we just simply stop comparing ourselves to others, as a sea of personal development articles on the internet suggest? Unfortunately, no. Social comparison is just about as automatic as breathing. We humans need to know how we are measuring up. We like to have a way to orient and evaluate ourselves, and to know what direction to go. The problem is, we don't always have the answers we need inside ourselves. So we look to others for information that might be helpful. It doesn't matter what our personal circumstances are — the wealthiest, most successful people in the world make comparisons. We make them so frequently and quickly that we aren't even always aware when we're doing so.

The solution is not to get rid of comparisons, but to learn what to do when they pop up. Once you become aware that you are making a comparison, here are some questions to ask yourself.

Does this matter to me?

Sometimes we make comparisons based on things that don't matter to us. I live in the smallest house on my street by a large margin. I could look around and feel shitty about that. Except that my wife and I feel like we have plenty of space — sometimes even more than we can keep up with. I don't want a larger house.

Ironically, the same thing was true for my comparison to Jessica's income. That year, my income was much less important to me than having a coaching practice full of clients I loved working with, launching and hosting my podcast *Life in the And*, and managing my mental health through the COVID-19 pandemic and 2020 US election season. If you're wondering why I got down on myself for something that wasn't all that important to me, it's because for a moment I lost connection with my internal guidance and allowed societal definitions of success and worth to dictate how I felt about myself. Remember how I said that comparisons are almost as automatic as breathing? Sometimes that's because we have been so inundated with messages from family, friends, teachers, the media, culture, and society about what success and worth look like that they have become embedded in our psyche.

When you catch yourself making a comparison, come back to connection. Ask yourself: What do I want? What's important to me?

It takes some intention to unwind our own desires and goals from the ones that have been placed on us by external sources. The more you stay connected, the more quickly you realize a comparison isn't relevant, and the less likely it will be to suck your joy.

When you do find a relevant comparison, that is, you answer "yes" to "does this matter to me?" move on to the next question.

Is this reasonable?

If I told you that I suck at basketball because I'm not as good as LeBron James, what would you tell me? That's an unreasonable comparison, Erin! Lebron James is an extreme example, but this is what we're doing without realizing how absurd the comparison is. We look at people who are masters of their craft, or have been in business for ages longer, or have a previous skillset that gave them a head start, and decide that they are the measuring stick (that we couldn't even come close to measuring up to).

Let's go back to Jessica. When I said she was a couple of years ahead of me in years in business, I was counting full-time. She was a part-time coach for several years before that. She steadily built her business while staying in her corporate career until she got to a point where she could reliably replace her income. I leapt out of corporate to build a business. We started our full-time work in very different places. And, that corporate career of hers? She spent decades in sales and knew exactly how to market herself and her programs when she started out on her own! Her $500K figure was not just a result of more time in business, she also brought expertise to the table. I came to coaching and entrepreneurship from a research background, first in academia and then in tech. I had to start from the basics in terms of learning how to talk about what I do and for whom!

So, what *is* a reasonable comparison? Look at people who are at the same place you are on the business journey. Maybe that's in years in business. Maybe that's in experience they had coming into business. And if there's nobody exactly where you are, ask those who are ahead of you what it was like when they were in your spot.

Be careful, though. Even when you do find a relevant and reasonable comparison, it can still suck your joy. You're not done asking yourself questions just yet!

How am I feeling toward this other person?

Remember I said comparisons can make us feel shitty or pity? Pity is a joy-sucking emotion. When we compare ourselves to someone who is not as far along as we are, we have a choice about how to feel. We may think that pity will make us feel better about ourselves. But what that unconsciously does is tell us that when we are the ones less far along, we are to be pitied. Yikes. A more positive, joy-creating emotion is gratitude. You have to be intentional about where you focus your gratitude, though. Gratitude for "not being where they are" is almost as destructive over the long-term as pity. Gratitude for being "exactly where I am" is an opening for joy.

Pity is not the only joy-sucking feeling we can have towards the person we are comparing ourselves to. When someone is ahead of us, we can feel envy. With envy, there is an important distinction to draw: malignant versus benign envy. Malignant envy is a feeling that the other person does not deserve their advantage or status and that you'd like for it to be taken away from them. That doesn't mean you actively wish ill on them, but you certainly might feel some schadenfreude if something were to happen to them. Benign envy is, well, more benign. It occurs when we believe the other deserves or has earned their status and we'd like to get to their level too. Benign envy can inspire and motivate us. It can bring us back into curiosity and creativity ("How do I get there too?") and help us gain the courage to move through fears and blockers on our path.

Just because you have dropped irrelevant and unreasonable comparisons and are choosing gratitude for where you are and benign envy for where you want to be, doesn't mean you are guaranteed joy. There's still one more question to take yourself through …

What am I making this mean about myself?

This one is tricky. By definition, comparison is about, "Where am I and what does this mean?" Yet, there is a difference between "What does this mean?" and "What does this mean *about me?*" Even though we already deemed Jessica's revenue both an irrelevant and unreasonable comparison, for simplicity let's stick with that example. If I ask myself what it means that she made $500K that year, several things come to mind. It means that she was consistent on social media. That she knew exactly what she offered and to whom. And most of all, that making $500K is possible in an industry where most coaches rarely make more than $40K. If I ask myself what it means *about me* that I didn't make $500K that year, my Inner Critic runs amok listing my deficiencies. I am not successful, competent, powerful, or good enough.

The truth is, what someone else has accomplished never means anything about you.

There are no universal benchmarks of success. Nor are external markers that we traditionally equate with success indicators of your competence, intelligence, or power. I know many phenomenal coaches who make very little money and many not-so-phenomenal coaches who make a great deal. And, despite a society that is obsessed with what we "do", your value is inherent. Nothing you achieve or don't achieve can take that away. You are enough *as is*.

Let's return to the notion I talked about on *Life in the And* that comparison can be both a thief and source of joy. Comparison is a *thief of joy* when you make comparisons that are irrelevant or unreasonable, or when you make a comparison mean something about you. Comparison can be a *source of joy* when you are connected to what you *want* to achieve, rather than what you are supposed to. When you can look to others in a similar place on the journey and be inspired and motivated by them. And most of all, when you can be grateful for being exactly where you are and know that if means absolutely nothing about you to be ahead or behind others.

CONSISTENCY IS *ALSO* THE THIEF OF JOY

Comparison is not the only "C" that is a thief of joy in the entrepreneur world. So is Consistency, though the internet would tell you otherwise. Just a quick Google of "consistency in business" unearths dozens of articles about why it's the key to success. One article goes so far as to say, "even the best business plans will fail without a dedication to consistency."

Here's the funny thing about those articles: There isn't even consistency about what it means to be consistent.

Some examples:

- Be predictable in your brand and/or message. Find an angle or lane and stick with it!

- Show up on a fixed schedule (like every day on Instagram, every Wednesday at 7 a.m. in email boxes). Your client/audience needs to know when they can expect to hear from you.

- Always have a plan for where you're going and how, and have the discipline to follow through on it.

- Have a coherent suite of services and products aligned with your brand.

These all have their merits. But they also have some severe, joy-draining limitations. Let's look at each of them, and how we can take them from thief to source of joy.

Be predictable in your brand and/or message. Find an angle or lane and stick with it!

It's time for one of my favorite phrases: "Yes, AND." Yes, it's helpful for people to be able to easily understand or articulate what your business and message is all about. And perhaps the larger your brand, the more important it becomes to stay narrow and consistent. But for most solopreneurs and small businesses, pigeonholing yourself into a single lane does not allow for your message to grow and evolve as YOU do. Stagnant is the opposite of joy-full!

You'll recall that in 2020, my brand was all about the power of the word *AND*. If I had stuck with that message in the name of consistency, I'd be bored to tears, and you wouldn't have this book in your hand! Because I gave myself permission for ME to be my brand and for my message to evolve, what I'm sharing now is richer and all the more relevant to you.

If you're concerned that you'll lose your audience if you change, I'm happy to report that almost everyone in my community came along for the ride when I did. Some people even commented on how my willingness to evolve and pivot gave them permission to do so as well.

Show up on a fixed schedule. Your clients/audience needs to know when they can expect to hear from you.

I started my weekly email newsletter in early 2021 with the intention to show up in people's inboxes every Wednesday. I've heard from several people that they look forward to my newsletter each week. Now, if I asked them how many times I've skipped a newsletter OR during what time period I sent newsletters bi-weekly instead of weekly, I know their answer would be "I have no friggin' clue." (To be honest, I don't remember either!)

I skip weeks when I can't find something I want to share with my audience. I skip weeks when my body and brain are on the struggle bus. I skip weeks when my schedule is too full to dedicate enough time to writing. If I force it any of those times, my newsletter would be a joy-drain for me — certainly, on those weeks, but perhaps even on the whole.

Rigid consistency / perfect attendance is a thief of joy.

However, what I call self-led consistency can be a source of it. Self-led consistency is when you have the intention for a consistent practice (like showing up every day on social media or once a week in an inbox), but you give yourself full permission to bend and weave with the needs of your brain, body, or schedule. Consistently showing up over the long haul is more important than whether you have "perfect attendance" in the short run.

My commitment to consistency is to show up *mostly* weekly for many years to come. I have to admit, thinking about still connecting with people through a newsletter several years from now brings me a ton of joy!

Always have a plan for where you're going and how, and have the discipline to follow through on it.

The "be consistent" message in this one is all about follow-through. Yes, if you have a long pattern of starting and stopping things, and you know that giving up early is getting in the way of your success, then it makes sense to create a plan and find some support to hold you accountable.

Forcing yourself to have a plan that you follow no matter what is a recipe for not committing to anything at all. This type of consistency is like asking yourself to have a crystal ball. It would be essential to know exactly what goals you are going after, how you intend to achieve them, and have absolute certainty that your plan is the correct one. (Cause, after all, you're going to muster the discipline to see it through!)

I believe the most joy-full "strategy" is having High Intentions and Low Attachment to an outcome (we'll cover this concept in-depth in *Put on Your HILA Hat*). In brief, this means that you hope to reach the goal and will take action towards it, but you also have no attachment to how or when you get there, or whether you get there at all. HILA allows you to stay with a "plan" only as long as it still makes sense to do so, and pivot to different or better things when it doesn't.

Have a coherent suite of services and products aligned with your brand.

Okay, I must admit that coherence can be a pretty good thing. Chances are, if you sell scented candles, coaching, and cryptocurrency, I am going to be suspicious of the quality of any of the three 😉. Even if you're a coach that offers business, leadership, and relationship coaching, I might prefer to find someone who focuses just on business when I'm looking for that support. But then again, if you do a great job illuminating your expertise in all of them, or even how they are all related, I might change my tune. And just because that's *my* preference does not mean it will be the preference of your people.

It's a joy-suck to force yourself to be "more coherent" or hold yourself to impossible standards of what "coherent" looks like, at the expense of sharing more of your gifts and passions with the world.

Where is consistency sucking your joy?

Where is consistency creating it?

And how can you define consistency for yourself in a way that creates even more joy?

THE UNWRITTEN RULES

What unwritten rules are you following in your business? I say *unwritten* because they aren't etched on a stone slab, inked on some scroll nailed to a tree, codified in a book, or plastered on social media. The unwritten rules are in our heads. They're stories we've told ourselves about who we're supposed to be and how we're supposed to do things. That's not to say these rules are fabrications. We glean them from our social world. Sometimes we have been told a specific thing and we turn it into a rule ... like "post on social media at 9 a.m."... but other times our brains have filled in a gap or made an inference. For example, if I see a colleague responding to every comment on every post in their Facebook group, I might infer that's a rule of successfully running a community.

We have unwritten rules *everywhere* in our businesses. In fact, we have them in every part of our lives, and we are often blissfully unaware of how often they are driving the bus. (And how much them driving the bus is draining our joy.)

I used to have a lot of unwritten rules about how I was supposed to show up on Instagram (and to be honest, they *still* get me sometimes). When I first moved over from Facebook to Instagram as my main business platform, it was like when I learned how to speak Spanish. A lot was familiar but just different enough that I couldn't quite speak it fluently. So I asked myself, "What are the norms here? How do people do things?"

Generally, it's not a bad thing to pay attention to social norms. We are social creatures, after all! But I suggest we never stop questioning their necessity, and whether we can follow them and still show up in authentic, joy-full ways.

Here are some of the unwritten rules that drove my Instagram bus. (Because we follow these rules as if they are carved in stone or published in a gilt-edged volume, just for the joy of it, I'm going to write them in that language. It also makes me giggle thinking about just how seriously I used to, and sometimes still do, take these rules!)

1. Thou shalt beautifully design all posts. Become a Canva pro.

2. Thou shalt always add value. Otherwise, don't take up space.

3. Thou shalt only post "mic drop"-level quotes or statements. If they aren't that great, don't post.

4. Thou shalt have a coherent "brand". Stick to only a few lanes of content so you are predictable and people can easily articulate what you are about.

5. Thou shalt have a visually pleasing and coherent post grid. People don't want to see an ugly display while they are window shopping.

6. Thou shalt do Reels. They must be entertaining AF. That's the only way to grow your community.

7. Thou shalt post EVERY DAY. You're either ALL IN or ALL OUT.

8. Thou art required to share your life, not just your business. People want to know that you are a human. (But don't share too much, lest people think you're a narcissist!)

9. Thou shalt not say things you see other people saying. Nobody likes a copycat. And they WILL know that you are one.

Just look at these rules. To have to think about rules, whether consciously or unconsciously, every time I showed up on Instagram — no wonder I was miserable! Every post or Story, I was worrying, asking myself, "Am I doing it right?", "Am I supposed to/allowed to be doing this?", and "What will people think of me?"

I also remember thinking, "Well, I want to have a social media presence, and Facebook is too limited, so I better get used to being on Instagram. Surely the only way people will be able to receive my message is if I learn how things are supposed to be done here." Let me tell you, when you are trying to "get used to" or "fall in line with" a certain way of being or doing things in a space, there is no joy. And people can *feel* that on the other end. Ironically, the more I tried to make my business appealing through following my unwritten rules, the less appealing it was.

Here's the thing … I made up ALL of those unwritten rules. Yes, there were people conforming to all the rules I had on their own social media accounts, but that didn't mean they were actual rules or that I couldn't be successful doing it another way. In fact, I joined a program from a coach who writes all her posts in her iPhone Notes app. She followed NONE of my rules.

So once you uncover your unwritten rules, what do you do with them?

Well, to start, break one at a time and see what happens. Unsure if there is a hard and fast rule, or just a norm people follow that really isn't necessary? Test it! You can also rewrite your rules. Whether consciously or not, you're always going to be following a set of rules (or principles) in how you do things. And they're going to be made up in your head. So why not create ones that serve your joy?!

Here are my new rules of Instagram:

1. Show up whenever you damned well feel like it.

2. Screw the formatting shoulds. Share however feels good to you. Only prettify a post or do a Reel if you WANT to.

3. Share whatever your heart wants to. The mundane. The silly. The vulnerable. The valuable. If they think you're a narcissist, they're not your people.

4. F*ck perfection. You're a human. The people who want to see your stuff are too.

5. If it isn't joy-full, don't do it.

I posted these new rules on Instagram, in part to hold myself accountable and in part to give other people permission to rewrite theirs. I felt instantly free. Over the next several weeks, I noticed a huge shift towards joy, ease, and flow in the way I felt about social media.

Posting those rules on Instagram also helped this book get in your hands today. Just like I had unwritten rules around Instagram, I had another set of rules for writing a book:

Don't be too smart. People won't be able to relate to you.

Don't be too snarky. People won't take you seriously.

Don't swear too much. People will think less of you.

Be smart. You have a dang PhD!

Be snarky. People love that about you.

Swear as often as you damn well please. You know when it's an appropriate emphasis and tone, and when it's not.

Writing with a set of completely contradicting unwritten rules was not a recipe for joy! When I applied some of my new rules of Instagram to writing this book, everything shifted for me.

EXPLORE SOME OF YOUR UNWRITTEN RULES

My Unwritten Rules of _____

* Choose one area of your business to focus on. Write down any rules you can think of about who you are supposed to be or how you are supposed to do things.

How the Rules Affect Me

* For each rule, write down the feelings, actions you take or don't take, and/or the results you get when following that rule.

My New Rules of _____

* Create any rule that will help you show up joy-fully in this area of your business.

Note: you don't need to replace your unwritten rules one-for-one. Notice that I had nine unwritten rules for Instagram but only five new rules. For me, the fewer rules I follow the better!

SHOULDING ON YOURSELF

Before working with me, Joe had a successful product and user experience consulting business, working with a handful of start-ups. He spoke regularly at conferences and led workshops. He also built up quite a library of videos and blog posts on social media. When we met, he not only wanted to transition from consulting (where he would hand people the answers) to coaching (where he could encourage people to find answers within) he also wanted to get rid of any activities in his business that were no longer lighting him up (and that weren't aligned to the type of coaching he wanted to do).

Pretty early on in our work together, Joe realized that workshops related to design and user research practices needed to be on the chopping block. As were his one-off consulting sessions where people would rent his brain for an afternoon. He also decided (and the pandemic made this easier for him) that speaking at conferences, wasn't high on his priority list.

As he was cutting out activities, we also explored what activities would bring him joy while allowing him to start growing his coaching practice. He immediately landed on virtual coffee chats with interesting people in his network. He loved being able to reconnect with people he hadn't spoken with in a while and getting introduced to fascinating people one and two hops away in his network. Virtual coffee dates were also a great way for him to practice speaking his new business direction into the world.

Within a couple months of cutting out joy-drains and focusing on joy-full virtual coffees, Joe found himself with a full client load of people he was delighted to be coaching. But despite everything going well, he came to me one session with low energy.

Amidst his full client load, continuing to do YouTube videos — a holdover from his consulting days — had become a giant drag. Though it had been easy for him to cut workshops, speaking, and one-off consulting gigs, he hadn't been able to convince himself he could drop YouTube. We hadn't spoken much about that part of his business, so I decided to get curious. What kinds of videos was he making? What were they doing for his consulting business? What were they doing for his coaching business now? He answered that the videos hadn't been much of a lead generator when he was consulting, and they definitely weren't generating any leads for his coaching.

When I asked him, "Then why do them?" it became clear that Joe was trapped in a "should." He believed, based on what he'd been seeing from other coaches in this industry, that regular thought leadership, whether through YouTube videos or LinkedIn blogs, was necessary for him to be successful in coaching.

He went on to share that it wasn't just videos he was thinking about. He'd also been noodling on the idea of finishing his second book. As he spoke about it, I could tell that his noodling was not coming from a joy-full place. I could tell his *shoulds* were also stealing the joy he would have otherwise been feeling about having a full coaching practice.

Since Joe was caught up on what he thought makes coaches successful, I asked him what had made *him* successful, not just in building his coaching practice over the previous few months, but also in creating a successful consulting business years before. The insight hit him instantly. His face lit up and the rest of his body took a deep sigh. Personal relationships and word-of-mouth. The network he'd been joy-fully reconnecting with was created and cultivated by him. Connection is one of his geniuses.

In that moment of insight, I didn't need to ask him what it might look like to follow his joy. He already knew the answer. He shelved the book idea. He let his social media person know that he no longer needed her help — which, to his surprise, allowed her to explore new opportunities with other business owners! And he went back to focusing on meeting fascinating people.

A couple of months after giving himself permission to not create video or written content, Joe came to a session and said, "You know what, Erin? I'm getting excited about creating content again. I like to write, and I'm excited about getting back into it. I may even want to do videos again at some point." When Joe dropped the *shoulds*, it gave those activities enough breathing room for natural *wants* to shine through.

Not every *should* that gets dropped will turn into a want, but some will. For Joe, as long as content creation in any format was a *should*, he couldn't find joy in it. When it was no longer something he held over his own head, he allowed for a natural writing desire to re-emerge.

Sure enough, he started writing content on LinkedIn. One of those pieces of content led him back to a speaking gig. But now he was speaking on something he was really excited about. Will he write a second book? Only if it becomes a want. Will he do videos again? Only if that, too, becomes a want. The more Joe leans into his natural desires, the more aligned opportunities will come his way.

If there is something in your business that you're telling yourself you *should* do, it's probably not true. There are no *shoulds* in business (except perhaps paying your taxes 😉). Anything that you are *shoulding on yourself* will drain your joy. I can guarantee you if it's something that other people are going to see or receive from you, they will feel your lack of joy. When you focus on your wants and desires, and lean into activities that light you up, your joy will be felt by others. Like Joe experienced, opportunities and doors will open.

EXPLORE YOUR SHOULDS

Make a list of everything you *should* be doing in your business. Write each item as "I should …"

Now go through the list and look for any that you wish felt like a want, not a *should*. Circle those.

Any *should* without a circle, cross off. Those are officially off your list of business to-dos. For anything that is a vital part of your business, like taxes, this is a great opportunity to practice asking for help or outsource completely.

Now, for each circled *should*, asked yourself, "what needs to happen in order for this *should* to become a *want?*" (It could be dropping it for now, changing how you're approaching it, asking others to do it with you. Get **curious** about what might shift it. Get **creative** with your solutions.)

Once you know what needs to shift, make a concrete plan for shifting it. (Example: "I'm going to stop doing X for 3 months and revisit then whether it has become a want.")

ARE YOUR GOALS
STEALING YOUR JOY?

Goals are such a big topic within business that we're going to spend the next several conversations focusing on them.

Within the field of social psychology, one of the biggest areas of study is human motivation and goal pursuit. One of the differentiators between coaching and psychology is that coaching is more outcome-oriented. So you'd think that as both a social psychologist and coach I'd be a big fan of goals. The truth is, I have mixed feelings.

I don't think they are always necessary. And when we do set them, there are quite a few traps we can fall into that actively drain our joy, or at best, limit the amount of joy we can experience. At the same time, to feel satisfied we need direction and to see measurable progress. Goals are not the *only* way to meet those needs, but they can be great ones … if we know how to avoid the traps!

"HOW MONSTERS", INNER CRITICS, AND THE KILLJOYS OF LONG-TERM GOALS

Before we dive in, let me be clear on how I define long-term goals. I see them as anything you're looking to achieve at least one year, if not many more years, into the future. Usually, long-term goals are bigger than short-term goals, and require more effort and commitment. Some of my past long-term goals were playing college basketball (Nope, didn't even come close!), getting a PhD (Yep, got that one!), becoming a manager at Facebook (Yep, got that one too!), and becoming a senior leader at a company (Nope! I was on that trajectory but left corporate long before I got there.)

Pursuing a passion, vision, or big dream over a longer period can be joy-full in and of itself. Long-term goals are also a great compass. They guide our actions, decisions, and even short-term goals. They keep us focused in a world full of distractions and quick fixes. And they help us stay resilient during the inevitable twists, turns, and troughs of business and life.

But ... long-term goals can also get in the way of our joy.

There are loads of reasons for this. For one, they can be overwhelming, keeping us from moving forward. The bigger the goal, and the more distant the finish line, the fuzzier and more abstract it feels. Since we are wired to resist uncertainty, your inner defenses are likely to come online to keep you safe. The "How Monster" (the internal voice that wants to know all the exact steps to get there before you commit) is likely to come out screaming. Your Inner Critic is also likely to come knocking, telling you all the reasons why you are incapable of reaching the goal. If the long-term goal is just a little stretch beyond what you believe is possible, the How Monster and Inner Critic are a good sign that you are growing. But if the goal is *too* much of a stretch, you'll likely experience "self-sabotage" along the way. It's not really you sabotaging yourself like you may have previously been lead to believe. It's just your inner system going to extremes to keep you safe.

Long-term goals also get in the way of our joy when we believe we need to have them. As we talked about in *We Don't Need No Destination!*, we don't always know what we want to achieve in the distant future, and that's a-okay. I certainly wasn't feeling joy-full back when Rich Litvin refused to help me find my big dream on his podcast. There's no joy in wracking your brain to find a long-term goal if you don't naturally have one in mind. There's also no joy in telling yourself that a long-term goal is necessary for you to be a valid and worthy entrepreneur. And there's definitely no joy in making up a long-term term goal to go after just for the sake of having one!

To tell you the truth, I have just as little idea of where my business is going now as I did back when Rich interviewed me. I've learned in the years since that for the most part, long-term goals are complete killjoys for *me*. So I rarely pursue any.

On the rare occasion I do set a long-term goal these days, I always give myself permission to be committed to it until it no longer makes sense to be so anymore. One of the challenges of long-term goals is that we are making a commitment that "future me" needs to keep from the vantage point of "today me." Who we are, what we care about, and what's happening around us (in our family, business, community, and the world) are always changing. Long-term goals can stop making sense as our current reality evolves.

Sticking to a goal because we've already put time and effort into pursuing it is a recipe for misery. (It's also an example of the "Sunk Cost Fallacy".) It's a recipe for missing out on potential magic. If we're too focused on the goal we're already pursuing, we may not see all the proverbial road signs leading us somewhere more aligned with who we are now.

Still, even if we know there is another, more joy-full path available to us, we can sometimes convince ourselves to keep going, so that we don't come off as flaky or lacking follow-through. (Who exactly are we trying to keep up appearances for? Almost always, it's ourselves. We're afraid of the internal lashing we'll give ourselves for "giving up", especially if we already believe we aren't the sort of person who can follow through on our goals.)

So, should you model after me and mostly give up on long-term goals? Not necessarily. Remember joy-full business is about doing things *your way*. If abandoning long-term goals feels joy-full for you, great! If going after big and longer-term goals feels joy-full, great! And, if you're in-progress with long-term goals, you might benefit from checking-in on whether they are still joy-full to pursue. This next exercise is designed to do just that.

LONG-TERM GOAL CHECK

Long-Term Goal: _____

When did I set this goal?

Who was I back then? What was happening in my life?

Why was it important to me, at the time, to set that goal?

Who am I now? What's happening in my life?

What's important to me?

Is continuing to go after my goal aligned with Today Me?

    [If yes] When will I check in again?

    [If no] Do I want to drop the goal altogether or shift it towards something more aligned?

        [If drop] What steps, if any, do I need to take to wrap up working on the goal?

        [If shift] What needs to shift? And what steps do I need to take to make those shifts?

GOAL TRAP #1 -
HEADING TOWARD DESTINATIONS
ON OTHER PEOPLE'S MAPS

Even if you've decided, like me, that long-term goals are killjoys, chances are you haven't given up on goals altogether. Short-term goals can give us a sense of direction, at least for the time being, and help us measure progress and growth. That said, there are several joy-sucking traps we can fall into when it comes to what goals we go after.

Unless you are bushwhacking through a vacuum in the space-time continuum, you will inevitably be exposed to other people's maps and destinations. In fact, just by reading these conversations, you are being exposed to my map.

Any time you hear an expert, guru, mentor, teacher, or even a colleague talking about goals, you may be convinced that their goals are "good" ones to pursue. These goals might be truly in service of the people talking about them (or to someone else out there), but they aren't necessarily in service of *you*. Sometimes goals people talk about are completely arbitrary. Other times, they're based on what some abstract entity called "the industry" has decided marks success. (In the coaching "industry" everything was about making six-figures in revenue for a while, and now the fashionable goal is scaling to a whopping seven-figures.) And even other times, the goals are about products or services they are selling to you directly:

Land your first TEDx talk. It's the best way to build a following of millions.

Facebook and Instagram are dead. If you want to grow your business, it's time to switch to TikTok. (And by the way, here's my course for doing so for $297.)

Make $200K a year as a coach without running a single ad.

These are real examples of social media posts that have come across my feed. They tell me that one of my goals should be to build a big following — though one post tells me to do it through TEDx and the other says TikTok. They also tell me that $200K should be my financial target.

Sometimes destinations on other people's maps will be explicit, like in the examples above. Other times, they will be more subtle. A person may not directly tell you goal to have, but as you observe their business, you infer that their goals should be on your map.

Inés created a 7-figure business in her first few years. I should scale my business.

David charges $50K a year for coaching. I should raise my fees.

Mark's book sold 60,000 copies. I should set that as a target for my book.

Again, these are real examples. They were all destinations I once thought I should set my sights on.

Whether the destinations are handed to you explicitly or you've picked up on them subtly, you'll know you're in Trap #1 when "should" or "supposed to" starts coming out of your mouth. As we've already discussed in *Shoulding on Yourself* …

Should is a siphon of joy.

GOAL TRAP #2 - GOING AFTER POSSIBLE GOALS

How often have you heard …

"Be realistic."

"Be practical."

"Do what's smart."

"Focus on what's reasonable."

OR

"That's impossible!"

Maybe you haven't heard any of these from other people (though most everyone I know has, often from someone close like a family member, teacher, or mentor,) but I would venture to guess you've said one or more of these *to yourself.*

When we talked about courage as one of the four ingredients of joy, I mentioned that Sean Smith once said to me, "The most boring thing you can do in your business is set a goal and then easily achieve it."

One of our biggest sources of joy comes from reaching and stretching beyond what we thought was possible. Chip and Dan Heath describe it well in their book *The Power of Moments*[12], "We feel most comfortable when things are certain; we feel most alive when they are not." (Aliveness is one of those Skittles® flavors we talked about earlier in *Taste the Rainbow*!) Reasonable, realistic, practical, and smart goals keep things safe, certain, and too comfortable.

At some point, certainty is
no longer in service of your joy.

Wait! I hear the record scratch in your head right now. *Didn't Erin just write about how goals that are too big with finish lines too far in the future are joy-suck in Goal Trap #1? That too much uncertainty is bad for us? How can they be talking about leaning into uncertainty now?*

You've caught me. I wanted an excuse to bring back that favorite word of mine: AND. **Courageously** stepping into uncertainty can create immense joy AND it can put our nervous system into massive flare ups. There's a sweet spot for every one of us, where uncertainty goes from feeling uncomfortable to feeling unsafe for our systems. (We'll talk about this sweet spot more in *Uncomfortable Versus Unsafe.*)

When I advocate for setting goals that are unreasonable, impractical, or even feel impossible, I'm not advocating for setting big, hairy audacious long-term goals. Smaller, more short-term goals can also feel impossible! (I could feel it's impossible to sell out my next group coaching program, or to get booked as a guest on one of my favorite podcasts.)

I'm *also* not advocating for setting goals that are way beyond what you or your nervous system is capable of right now. For me, one guidepost is a stretch that feels just on the other side of possible. Adrienne Mishler of the popular YouTube series *Yoga with Adrienne* calls it "finding your appropriate edge." Landing a publishing deal for my second book might feel impossible, but not so ridiculous as to flare my system. But becoming as well known as Brené Brown or Glennon Doyle might be a whole different story!

Now, I'm not saying that you should avoid realistic or possible goals. Wins can boost your confidence. (And sometimes you need the resources, whether monetary or emotional to be able to move forward joy-fully.) But if you find yourself bored or joyless with your goals, chances are you're playing too much in the realm of possible and could use a stretch.

GOAL TRAP #3 - CHASING HAPPINESS

Raise your hand if you've ever said … "When I reach goal X, I will be happy"? I know I have!

When we defined joy, I explicitly called out the difference between joy and happiness. If you've wondered why it was important to make that distinction, it's because of this goal trap.

Recall that we've defined happiness as a pleasant emotional state caused by positive outcome or circumstance. So achieving a goal could be a source of happiness. We're not lying to ourselves when we think, "When I accomplish this goal, I will be happy." The problem is, happiness is fleeting. Once it dissipates and we move back to a general baseline of happiness, we chase the high again by dangling another carrot in front ourselves. In other words, setting a new goal. Psychologists call this the Hedonic Treadmill. No one wants just a temporary high. Yet, when we chase happiness, we don't necessarily see that's what we are settling for.

It's easy to get tunnel vision when we chase happiness. We are so focused on the feeling that is to come in the future, that we forget to tune into the feelings we are having right now. (Which means we're not tuning into joy, nor are we deliberately creating it!) We can even tell ourselves that any misery we're experiencing on the way to a goal is a worthy sacrifice, in order to have the happiness payoff later.

Be careful not to chase happiness at the expense of your joy.

Joy doesn't rely on you reaching a destination or accomplishing a goal. Or on any other circumstance, for that matter. It's a resource within you that you can tap into at *any time*. And you can cultivate more of it over time. As you continuously fill your joy tank, it expands to hold even more. You can be joy-full in success, joy-full in failure, and joy-full at any step along the way.

So rather than chase goals that will make you happy at some later date, instead set goals that feel joy-full now, and will continue to be every step of the way.

GOAL TRAP #4 - CHASING ENOUGHNESS

In my opinion, chasing the feeling of enoughness is the most insidious of all the joy traps because it hits us in our most tender and vulnerable spots. That's why I've saved it for last.

When we say, "When I reach X goal, then I will be … ", happy is not the only word we use to finish that sentence. We have all kinds of things we hope achieving a goal will do for us:

When I make $150,000 a year in my business, I will be able to call myself a successful massage therapist.

When I get selected for a TED talk, I will know my story is valuable and therefore I am valuable.

When I receive venture capital funding for my start-up I will know I am a capable innovator.

I believe avoiding this trap is impossible. We need positive self-worth for our mental and emotional well-being the way our bodies need food, water, and sleep. No matter our current sense of self-worth, our brains always reach for ways to either increase or preserve our enoughness. Achieving goals is one of the ways our brains try to do this. Even if we're able to recognize this as a faulty strategy, in a society that judges and values people for what they do, it can be difficult to permanently override our automatic association between value, worth, and achievement.

We may not be able to completely avoid this trap, but we can recognize when we've fallen into it and learn how to pull ourselves back out.

Trap #4, then, is about what are brains our convinced our goal will do for our self-worth. "When I achieve this goal, I will be _____." Fill in the blank: successful? capable? competent? good enough?

Really, these all boil down to chasing our enoughness. If I am successful, I am enough. If am capable, I am enough. If I am competent, I am enough. You get the idea.

The problem with this strategy is that if we believe *achieving* the goal will grant us enoughness, the flipside must also be true: *failing* to reach the goal signals that we are not successful, capable, competent, worthy … or enough. Talk about pressure to never fail!

Though we might think that avoiding failure is avoiding judgment from others, we're really (understandably) avoiding feeling embarrassed and ashamed of ourselves. We don't want to face the lashings of our Inner Critic, who can be quite good at convincing us that we're a shitty human being!

You'll never be enough.

Who did you think you were to try to do that?

You're pitiful.

You might as well give up now. Loser.

Everyone thinks that you're incompetent. You might as well accept that.

When we have our whole self-worth riding on accomplishing specific goals, we clench to them. We become needy. We get tunnel vision. We become risk averse. We get hell-bent on reaching that destination, even if it makes us miserable in the process.

There is no room for joy when you are chasing your enoughness.

TAKE A MINUTE TO REFLECT:

What goals would you set if you knew that reaching them meant nothing about your success, capability, or competence?

What goals would you set if you knewthat you were enough no matter what?

FALLING INTO MULTIPLE TRAPS AT ONCE

The traps we've covered in the last few conversations are not mutually exclusive. In fact, in my experience, it's common to fall into multiple at once (or even all four of them). We can set a goal that feels reasonably attainable (Trap #2), based on what someone else has gone after, or has indicated is a measure of success (Trap #1), and clench to that goal because we've decided that reaching it will mean that we're successful (Trap #4) and that we'll be happy (Trap #3).

What an epic joy-suck to take someone else's definition of success — which is personal to them at best, and completely arbitrary at worst — and tell ourselves that we aren't successful unless we meet it.

Let's use revenue to illustrate. It's one of the most universal goals of entrepreneurs AND one I constantly see siphoning joy (my own included). As I mentioned in *Just Follow My 10-Step Blueprint!*, coaches are flooded with messages about creating their first six-figures, or even scaling to seven-figures.

When I first started coaching, there was a revenue number that seemed to be commonly tossed around in multiple peer circles. I quickly I anchored into it as a marker of success (Trap #1). It was also basically what I was making at Microsoft, so replacing my income felt reasonable (Trap #2), like a real marker of whether I was a competent, capable, good enough coach and entrepreneur (Trap #4), and a recipe for happiness (Trap #3).

I didn't once ask myself ...

"What level of revenue do I *want?*"

"Do I need that amount of money to live the life I left want? The one I left corporate to create?"

"Is that amount aligned with the kinds of activities I want to be doing in my business?"

"Is it aligned with the effort and time I want to be putting into my business?"

I also didn't consider if revenue was a primary goal of mine, or if there were other, dare I say, more joy-full goals I could focus on that would lead to a comfortable income.

I became so needy, clenching around replacing my corporate salary that I made all kinds of misery-inducing choices. I took on clients who were less joy-full to work with. Don't get me wrong, I love most human beings, but sometimes people aren't ready for the depth of work I do. And certain areas of focus in coaching are more exciting for me than others. I said yes to people and focus areas that I knew weren't a fit. I also took on too many clients, prioritizing money in the bank over what my energetic capacity could handle. To make matters worse, I often designed creative coaching agreements to make it more affordable for people to work with me (like meeting monthly rather than biweekly), which meant I was tapping myself out energetically AND *still struggling to meet my revenue targets.*

I also designed several coaching programs that I thought would be easy yeses for folks but that didn't totally light up my heart and soul to deliver. One of those programs was The Launch Accelerator for new business owners. The program itself was well-designed (or so said my peers at the time) and was a "*good business decision.*" But it wasn't a joy-full decision for me. And my energy around marketing it and enrolling people showed it. I didn't get a single taker.

I've since become aware of all four traps I can fall into with goal setting and have been more intentional with checking in on what feels joy-full to pursue, rather than what will make me "successful", "good enough", and (momentarily) happy.

Now that you know about these traps, the next exercise will help you get clear on which, if any, you are falling into, and how you can pull yourself back out of them. I get that this could be overwhelming. You DO NOT need to do all your goals at once.

Choose which one (or two) feels good or important to work with right now. You can always come back to others later.

GOAL TRAPS CHECK-IN

My Goal_____:

Did I come up with this goal or learn it elsewhere? If I learned it from someone else, is it a goal I want to keep?

How realistic or possible is this goal?

If it feels possible, then: Is this a goal I want to stretch on?

[If yes] What would feel like a good stretch? (Check in with your body to make sure the stretch doesn't feel overwhelming to your nervous system.)

[If no] There's nothing else to do. Keep on keeping on.

If it already feels impossible, check in with your body: Does this stretch feel uncomfortable but something I can lean into, or does it feel overwhelming to my nervous system?

What am I making achieving this goal mean about me? What does it actually mean?

To what extent is my happiness riding on achieving this goal? How can I let go of that need and focus more on my joy?

If it's too much, how can I dial back the goal to something that feels safer in my nervous system?

MORE MORE MORE

"I could be doing more!" If there's one phrase that's on repeat in the heads of most business owners I know, it's this one.

There is always so much more we could be doing in our business. In a world with thousands of options and pathways to success, that statement is *technically* true. The problem is, we often translate that into "There's so much more I *should* be doing."

Over the last several years, most of my coaching clients have come to me through word-of-mouth and referral. I could continue to rely on my current clients to refer new ones, but I don't want my clients to be solely responsible for my business success. Don't get me wrong — I love referrals! But I also prefer for them to be a delight, rather something I'm wishing and hoping will happen to keep my business full.

So if I want to bring more clients into my coaching world, I have several options:

- Go to in-person events in Ann Arbor and Ypsilanti.
- Go a little further down the road to in-person events in Detroit and its surrounding metro area.
- Attend conferences and trainings, virtually and in-person.
- Host a podcast. (Which I did for a while with *Life in the And* and *Shift-Starters*.)
- Build a following on social media. (Which I've started to focus on more recently.)
- Cultivate a community through email. (Which I do! I write a weekly newsletter.)
- Write articles for *Forbes*, *Entrepreneur*, or other large media publishers.
- Do a TED talk.
- Get on the speaking circuit.

And those are just a *few* of the options. When I tell myself that I need to be doing more than a couple of these strategies — or when I tell myself I'm not doing any one strategy enough — I quickly lose joy.

My need to do more is rooted in fear. There's so much information out there about what strategies are THE ticket to success. I've seen business gurus say, "If you're not doing a podcast, what are you doing with your business?" I've seen others say the same about social media. On the flip side, I've heard people say, "You know what? Social media is a volatile thing. The algorithm is always changing and not always in your favor. And what happens if social disappears one day? You're better off having an email newsletter."

When I'm not taking a step back and asking, "What path feels most joy-full?" I can get lost in a sea of options, and I can easily end up with the thought, "I should do all of them. That way I can cover my bases in case any one of them doesn't work."

Then when I try to do too much, I burn out. I don't want to do any of it. And when I do the work anyway, my energy is not loving, caring, or joy-full.

Where are you convincing yourself that more is better? Where are you risking overwhelm, burnout, or failure by doing too many things? What would happen if you chose to focus on just a few things at a time instead?

HELLO, IT'S ME,
YOUR NERVOUS SYSTEM

Let's revisit part of our definition of joy for a moment (see *What the F*ck is Joy Anyway?* for a refresher): It's a *full-body* experience. Our bodies, and more specifically our nervous systems, have a large role to play in our joy — in how we feel it, create it, and cultivate it. And when we ignore or override our bodies, we crowd out joy.

Throughout most of human history, the mind-body connection was a given. It wasn't well understood, but it was a premise of all medicine and healing. However, during the 17th century, the "Western world" began to see the mind and body as separate entities and started referring to the body as if it were more machine-like. Thanks to colonialism, that notion of mind-body separation spread and became the dominant paradigm for a large part of the world. As part of this, society came to reward thought over emotion, logic and reason over intuition, and intellect over instinct.

That said, the tides are beginning to turn. Eastern medicine, spirituality, and mindfulness practices are becoming more mainstream. Western medicine is beginning to adopt healing modalities like acupuncture that were once written off as junk. Neuroscientists are discovering more and more about how our nervous system affects everything from bodily functions (like digestion) and drives (like hunger) to our thoughts, feelings, and behaviors.

Although science's understanding of the mind-body connection continues to improve, society has not yet shifted from over-rewarding thought, logic, reason, and intellect. Most of us have been raised to distrust our bodies and ignore its signals. We believe our bodies are supposed to function like machines, letting us produce consistently across time (day-to-day, week-to-week, month-to-month, and year-to-year). We even idolize people we perceive as being machine-like (like pro-athletes). I've even seen messages, particularly in weight loss and exercise circles, that we need to be at war with our bodies and that we can bend them to our will if we have the right mindset. Did you hear that!? At war! Bending to our will! YIKES!

If paying attention to your body is not on your radar ... or maybe it *is* in your everyday life but not in your business ... you're not alone. Business culture is just a reflection of the dominant ideals in society. Listening to our bodies and befriending our nervous systems is a foreign concept. But, if we don't tune in, not only is there no space to create and cultivate joy, we can actually find all kinds of ways to lose it.

Like so many themes in this book, I could have written an entire book on the relationship between joy, your nervous system, and business (and perhaps I will someday). These next three conversations will help get you started tuning in.

WHEN YOUR BODY SAYS NO, BUT YOU STILL GO GO GO

I'm writing this conversation in March 2022. The Ukraine has been invaded by Russia in an unprovoked attack. Everything in my brain is telling me to stay the course — to keep working. I'm not watching the news. I'm recording this conversation in Otter.AI instead. But everything in my *body* is telling me, *take care of your emotional health right now, do things that are soothing, you don't need to be hitting arbitrary deadlines.*

This is a conversation I have with myself all the time, even though I know my joy seeps away when I insist on operating in a linear way, overriding the natural rhythms and flows of my body.

Most of us, at least in the United States, are indoctrinated into the 9-to-5, Monday-to-Friday work week. In the academic world I was raised in (both of my parents were professors) and then joined briefly as a PhD student, the indoctrination is even more extreme: There is no such thing as down time. "Publish or perish" means that working evenings, weekends, and all through breaks in classes is the norm. Summer was the time to catch up on work, not to rest.

After finishing my PhD, not working weekends at Facebook felt like a downshift from the hustle and grind I was accustomed to. Except that the norm there was to be on ALL the time Monday through Friday. I often started my workday when I jumped on a company shuttle from San Francisco to Menlo Park at 6:30 a.m. I'd close my computer when I jumped off the shuttle at the end of the day, sometimes at 7 p.m. or later, but I would often be drawn into Messenger conversations on my phone until bed.

The idea of "listening to my body" simply didn't exist in academia or the corporate world; at least not when I was there.

When I started my business, deprogramming from the 9-to-5 (and really the always-on mentality) was a struggle. There's a popular "sound" on TikTok that says "I didn't want to work a 9-to-

5, so now I work 24/7." Though I wasn't quite that extreme, I was joining the ranks of many entrepreneurs who struggle to turn off. As I set up my schedule, I didn't ask myself, "When am I at my best?" or "How can I build wiggle room into my schedule to account for life happenings or how my energy shifts day-to-day and week-to-week?" or even, "How many hours do I really need to be working in a week to accomplish my business and personal goals?" It's taken me several years of making small shifts to create a business that runs on the rhythms of my body. First I built a schedule around when I am most alert and productive. Then I got rid of most deadlines. Every deadline in my business is made up. I'll never wake up after missing a deadline to find that my business has fallen apart. I can always push things out by a few days, weeks, or sometimes months. And trying to stick to deadlines can prompt me to override my body's needs. (By the way, some people do very well with deadlines. I'm just not one of them!)

After making schedule and deadline changes, I dug deeper. I reconsidered my beliefs about what makes a "good" entrepreneur. I began unwinding the internalized capitalistic notion that my self-worth is tied to my productivity and abandoned the notion that productivity happens only in a linear way. I decided that there is nothing wrong with me when I have to take a day off because my anxiety has flared up. Or when I take long pauses on writing my book because my creative juices aren't flowing. Likewise, I came to understand that I'm not "less than" because don't want to pack my schedule just to make more money and I work best going deep with only a handful of clients at a time. I had to let go of the notion that a valuable thought leader posts on Instagram every day. (My creativity comes in waves, and my posts do too.)

When I listen to my body and allow myself to follow the waves of my energy, my coaching is more masterful. My writing is more creative. I can do less but create more impact.

The same is likely true for you too — you've just been taught not to trust your body! Every creature on earth operates in cycles, including us. We have times of day that we're more energized and others when we're not. We go through seasons, lasting from days or weeks, to several months or years. People who menstruate literally go through a cycle every month that impacts everything from energy to creativity to mood.

How often are you ebbing and flowing with your cycles? Are you allowing yourself to be productive when your energy is high and rest when your energy is low? Are you attuned to the way your body ticks? Or are you trapped, like many people, in the beliefs that society has handed you about productivity?

Your joy depends on you listening to the rhythms of your body. And though it may feel uncomfortable as you begin to tune in, over time, I know you'll find yourself more productive and doing higher quality work.

GOING TO BATTLE AGAINST YOUR NERVOUS SYSTEM

Is your nervous system a friend that you lovingly attend to, or a foe that you try to defeat, override, or ignore?

If this question has you wondering what this has to do with joy in your business, read on. It's likely you've been paying too little attention to your nervous system, your body's command center that has influence over your automatic responses, thoughts, feelings, and actions. This is true for many of us whose success is derived from our intellectual abilities, as well as those who've been taught to ignore physical and emotional signals in favor of logic and reason. I like to call this "living from the neck up."

Most professional settings are over-rotated towards intellect, facts, logic, and reason. Emotions are a distraction at best, completely unwelcome at worst (since we're talking about societal systems, I should note this is a hallmark of white supremacy culture). The same focus tends to show up in business culture. Even the personal development world tends to be neck up, focusing on how to shift your mindset. A popular mantra in coaching is "Change your thoughts, change your life," and it is stated similarly in Cognitive Behavioral Therapy (a very thoughts-orientated treatment modality that can be helpful for some people in specific applications). There are certainly times when it makes sense to be in our heads — to lean on logic and reason, or focus on changing our thoughts. But if that was appropriate all the time, then we might as well be floating heads in jars (like in the cartoon Futurama) instead of full-bodied humans! There's so much more going on below our necks than we realize — and more than we allow ourselves to feel or tune into! In fact, there are more neurons in the rest of our bodies than in our brains. Science is only beginning to scratch the surface of understanding how our nervous systems work and how we can best listen to them.

Even if you haven't paid much attention to your nervous system in the past, you've certainly experienced it in action. Consider the scenario where you're on stage delivering a talk to a waiting crowd. Your palms might sweat. Your heart may race. As you begin to speak, your voice might sound jittery or even crack. That's all your nervous system reacting to what it perceives as a threat.

Whenever we face a threat — whether it's social like being laughed at or booed on stage, or physical like being followed down a dark alley — our bodies will respond in one of four ways: fight, flight, freeze, or fawn.

To illustrate how each of these 4 Fs can show up in your business, let's shift to another example. Not everyone speaks on stage, but most of us do engage in social media, whether for business or pleasure. Imagine you've made a post or video on your favorite platform and someone leaves an angry comment disagreeing with you.

If your nervous system goes into *fight*, you might "yell" at the person or insult them in a written response. Later, you might make a new post from an angry or defensive stance to pre-emptively deal with future antagonists or trolls.

In *flight*, you'll likely feel anxious or nervous, and have an urge to run and hide. You might delete the post, or if the flight urge is extreme, end up deleting your social media account altogether. If you do stay online, the next time you go to post, you might find yourself overthinking the post's photo and caption, hoping to be as inoffensive as possible.

In *freeze*, you might stare at your computer or phone, searching for something to say in response to the angry comment, but completely blank out.

And in *fawn*, you're likely to immediately apologize to the person for what you've said. You might even change your opinion to match theirs.

Your nervous system can also go into multiple modes. I used to go into a combination of flight and freeze on social media before learning how to recognize and soothe my nervous system's response. In all 4 Fs, your nervous system both responds in the moment, and also shapes your future actions in similar situations. The fear/threat response is a joy-suck that keeps on sucking, until you learn to be in tune with your nervous system.

Chances are your nervous system is in one of the 4 Fs in your business more often than you're aware. You may have been led to believe that you have a mindset block rather than a nervous system challenge. Maybe you've been told not to trust your nervous system, and that you should bypass what it's telling you.

Befriending your nervous system creates more space for joy.

By listening to our nervous systems (we'll cover one of those ways next in *Uncomfortable versus Unsafe*), we can learn when it's time for courage and when it's time to say no. And by having compassion for the ways our nervous system is trying to protect us, we can begin to work through fears, beliefs, and traumas that might be holding us back from activities and projects that will bring us a lot of joy. For instance, once I began to understand my nervous system's response to social media, I was able to self-soothe and self-coach, and courageously put myself out there more. It took a couple of years of coaching and therapy specifically geared at my nervous system — I had a lot to work through! — but now showing up on social media is more connective and joy-full than I ever imagined possible.

BEFRIENDING YOUR NERVOUS SYSTEM

Here's an exercise you can do when you feel stuck, afraid, anxious, or physically agitated. It will help you identify what is happening below the surface so you can come back to joy.

What is the circumstance? (Make this as neutral as possible. Example: Someone commented on my Instagram post that my opinion about the phrase "Change your thoughts, change your life" is wrong.)

What thoughts am I having about this circumstance? (Name the most prevalent thought. Example: I'm stupid and clearly am not suited to being a thought leader.)

What feeling am I having? (Name the most prevalent feeling. Example: shame.)

Where am I noticing this thought or feeling in or around my body? (Example: There's a lump in my throat. It feels like a steel ball clogging everything up.)

(Now focus all of your attention on that sensation. As you focus, begin to ask that sensation questions like it is another person sitting in a chair next to you. If this feels a little strange, I get it. I was a skeptic until I realized that I could learn a lot by talking to my body!)

Is there anything you want me to know about why you're here right now?

What are you afraid might happen to me? What are you protecting me from?

What do you need from me right now? Reassurance? For us to take a deep breath? A new thought or belief for us to try out?

In some cases, your system might ease or soften just by paying attention to it, allowing you to move forward. In others, it will ask you for soothing or deep breaths. And in others, it will say, "Hey, I need you to put on the brakes. Today is not the day to move forward." Honor whatever your system says it needs. Despite some of the popular rhetoric about our bodies being unreliable narrators, I personally believe they are wise well beyond what our conscious minds can comprehend.

UNCOMFORTABLE VERSUS UNSAFE
(WHEN TO LEAN INTO COURAGE
AND WHEN TO LEAN OUT)

Being in business requires us to stretch and challenge ourselves. Joy requires that too. Courage comes into play here. If you spend any time reading personal development articles or hanging out in the company of self-help enthusiasts, chances are you'll come across mantras like "Feel the fear and do it anyway" and "FEAR = False Evidence Appearing Real." Interpreting these without a critical gaze can leave us feeling that all fear should be met with courageous action. I'd like to challenge that.

Yes, sometimes we need to feel the fear and do it anyway. Yes, sometimes we perceive a threat or danger that isn't actually there. Leaning into fear to get to what we desire on the other side of it can be immensely joy-full. But sometimes it's quite the opposite. Sometimes it creates misery. *Sometimes it even does harm.*

My therapist introduced me to a powerful distinction a couple of years ago: feeling uncomfortable versus feeling unsafe.

This distinction is not something that happens in our heads. Instead, it happens in our bodies. There might be something we want to do that cognitively, seems like it should be fine. We might tell ourselves our fear is just a fear, and that doing it anyway should be no big deal. And yet, our bodies might have a very different opinion.

During my first year in business, one of my coaches encouraged me to go live on Facebook for 90 days straight. The goal was for me to get comfortable sharing my thoughts and opinions more broadly than just with my clients and coach peers. At the time, I wasn't sure exactly what I had to offer that wasn't blatantly obvious or that others weren't already saying. In my coach's mind, there was no better way for me to find out than to hit "Go Live" and share whatever was top-of-mind, pouring it out stream-of-conscious style, each day. In principle, she was right. One of the best ways to get clarity on anything is to take messy action. And there's also something about speaking out loud that aids that clarity in a different way than writing.

My head was completely on board with the challenge. My friend, Inés, who you will meet in *Put on Your Lab Coat AND Feel Your Feelings Too*, once told me that the only way to know your message is to speak it over and over again. Her words continuously played in my mind. My body, on the other hand, was *not* on board. I was filled with dread. I had many Facebook Friends who had previously been my colleagues from when I worked there. I already had mind drama about what those folks thought of me leaving tech to become a coach, and now I was going to talk about coaching with them!!??? SHIT. I also had Facebook Friends that met me during my academic life, including several members of the PhD committee that evaluated my dissertation and greenlit me to be called Dr. ... Hoo'boy! What were *they* going to think of me? First I left academia for Facebook, and now I'd left that to become a coach!!?? What if I shared my social psychology knowledge wrong? What if I shared things that were pseudoscience or spiritual garbage? Would they consider me a disgrace to the academy? Would they think I didn't deserve my PhD?

Those fears were just scratching the surface of what was happening internally. Deeper down, I was worried about showing up in people's News Feeds *every day*. Back then, that was way outside the norm, at least on my feed. *I'll be taking up too much space. People will think I'm too much. They'll think I'm arrogant or egotistical. I'm going to lose people from my life.*

But in an effort to "feel the fear and do it anyway," and also to avoid showing my coach any weakness, I convinced myself that I *had* to do the challenge. I brought my head back into the equation as a cheerleader, reminding myself that I wanted to be more visible, and that action would indeed create clarity.

The first few days of the challenge were brutal. I had a panic attack every day either before or after I went live. Sometimes both before *and* after. I'd burst into tears and my whole body would shake. One of those days I curled up in a ball, writhing on the floor because there was so much energy going through me. All the while, I kept telling myself that I needed to push through. That this challenge was not a big deal. I never once considered reaching out to my coach to tell her what was going on. I was mortified that she'd lose all respect for me if she found out what a scaredy-cat I was.

In essence, I was shaming myself and my body for its response to being visible on social media. I carried that shame until I offhandedly shared about the Facebook Live challenge with my therapist, an expert in Somatic Experiencing (a body-based therapeutic modality), a couple years later. That's when she shared the distinction about feeling uncomfortable versus unsafe.

She confirmed that when your nervous system feels uncomfortable, that's not necessarily a sign to slow down or put on the brakes. In fact, it may be a sign that you are heading in the right direction of growth or learning. In those circumstances, it makes sense to, as Brené Brown says, "Choose courage over comfort." However, she went on to explain that if your nervous system feels unsafe, it's having a trauma response. Continuing to push through anyway is overriding that trauma response and *potentially creating even more trauma*.

The tricky thing about feeling uncomfortable versus unsafe is that we can't always be sure of the difference. Remember, our conscious minds are good at telling us stories about what is and isn't dangerous. In my Facebook Live challenge, my mind thought everything was safe. Even if I had known the distinction, my mind might have convinced me that what I was feeling was uncomfortable. But the fact that I was having daily panic attacks to the point of being curled up on the floor says otherwise. Was my body responding to all the fears I was consciously aware of? Fears of being judged by my Facebook colleagues or academic mentors? Fears around taking up space and being seen as arrogant? I don't know.

We can't always determine what our body is responding to. But we can know that our body is telling us to stop.

And we can honor that signal without judging or shaming it. However, that action doesn't have to feel unsafe forever. We can dial back whatever we're doing to find actions that *are* safe, even if still a bit uncomfortable, as we build up tolerance toward doing the original action. For me, that might have been sending videos to a handful of trusted friends and colleagues every day rather than blasting my entire Facebook feed. We can heal the beliefs and traumas that are causing our nervous system's alarm bells to go off in the safety of therapy or a trauma-informed or trauma-trained coach.

(Note: trauma-informed or trauma-trained is important here. Coaches can unintentionally do more harm than good if they don't have proper knowledge and training.)

So, as you take courageous action, be sure to check in with your nervous system. If you feel a bit uncomfortable, lean in. But if any part of you feels unsafe at any point, lean out.

There's no shame in getting in motion thinking it's a little uncomfortable and then realizing, "Nope, this is unsafe," and pumping the brakes. As soon as you know that, look for another route to where you want to go or find a way to dial back the extremity on the route you are taking. And seek support! Every bit of healing you do makes more space for joy!

FOCUS ON THE PRESENT ...
BUT NOT *TOO* MUCH

Hold on to your socks ... I'm about to say something sacrilegious: Focusing on the present can steal your joy.

I know, I know. Didn't I tell you to let go of future-focus in *Goal Trap #3 – Chasing Happiness* in favor of experiencing joy now? And what about all the articles and Instagram-perfect quotes and memes that tell us how much future-tripping and past-dwelling is stealing our joy?? Heck, didn't the Buddha say, "Do not dwell on the past, do not dream of the future, concentrate the mind on the present moment"? To a large extent, what I said is true. As is the wisdom of Instagram, and of course, the Buddha. But it's also overly simplified.

We need the past, present, *and* future to thrive. Nothing's all bad, and nothing's all good. Sure we can get trapped in the past, but there are also psychological benefits of nostalgia — including increasing our optimism and deepening our sense of connectedness. And sure, we can spend so much time planning for and thinking about the future (which we often hope will be better than today) that we're missing out on the joy of the present. But thinking about our future selves also helps us to do healthy things like plan for retirement and pursue long-term dreams and goals. Assuming long-term goals are a joy-full pursuit for you (see *"How Monsters", Inner Critics, and the Killjoys of Long-Term Goals*). There are lots of psychological and nervous system benefits of being focused on the here and the now ... but it can also make us short-sighted.

In business, we often want results ... now. We want cash flow, revenue, great clients ... now. We want to know if an action, activity, or project is going to be a success or failure ... now. If we're overly focused on now, we can forget that business is a long-game. Not every seed that gets planted will grow into something right away, or at all. (We'll talk more in-depth about this in a later conversation called *Fe-Fi-Fo-Fum ... Plant Some Magic Beans.*) Not every goal we set can be worked toward or achieved in the short-term.

When we expand our mental horizons beyond the here and now, we can *create more* joy in the here and now.

And technically we can double dip, experiencing joy now and again when something comes to fruition in the future. Before we talk about expanding our mental horizons, let's explore how overly focusing on the present can steal our joy.

When we are focused on immediate results, we only take actions that we believe will produce them. For instance, when I was first building my business, the only local meetups I would attend were ones that I thought would be an opportunity to meet potential clients. If I didn't have a business-based reason to attend something, I wouldn't. I felt like I didn't have time to be playing around with meetups that wouldn't pay-off in the short-term. But that meant I wasn't looking for meetups that would fill my joy tank. I'm curious now about how much I missed out on because I had my blinders on. I was trapped in thinking about what "I should" go to. And I'm sure that my energy at those events was off too. Nobody is attracted to someone who clearly has an agenda to find clients, even when it's an energetic, rather than spoken, agenda.

We also tend to worry more about short-term failures when we are overly present-focused. If we're not seeing our business as a long game, any failures we experience in the here and the now feel like a much bigger deal. We might even see them as a sign we should give up or quit.

So why do we get trapped in the here and now in our businesses? Besides the messaging that pedestalizes present-focused thinking, we also feel like the present is more certain and controllable than the future. We have to trust and surrender to the unknown if we take actions or do activities that have an indefinite timeline for results. That can feel *wildly* uncomfortable.

Now, I'm not saying that you need to shift completely away from present-focus. In fact, we can be both present and future-focused at the same time, creating joy in the here and the now, as well as potentially in the future.

There will be times when immediate results are necessary. Not every business has the privilege of going months without revenue or cash flow. When you need cash, focus on that! But you can also expand your horizons for the future by choosing more joy in the present. That is, including in your overall strategy any actions, activities, and projects that bring you joy right now and also might help you on the path toward longer term goals ... or turn into interesting opportunities in the future.

In early 2022, I hosted a Magic Bean party, purely for my own joy, on Zoom. (You don't need to have read *Fe-Fi-Fo-Fum ... Plant Some Magic Beans* to get this example). I shared it in my newsletter and posted about it several times on Instagram. My friend, Michelle, saw all my posts, but only decided to say, "Hey, send me the link. I'll be there," hours before the event. Afterwards, she messaged me to say that she had talked herself out of coming for days. In her words, she didn't have a business case to attend. It was only hours before the call that she realized, "Wait, 'because I want to' is business case enough!" She had a lovely time and even connected with a new friend or two. Will those turn into anything business-related down the road? Who knows. I know that at least one new person follows her on Instagram now and loves her content. The joy of connection was energizing and bled over into other activities Michelle did in the coming days. Whether she can see it (or ever will see it) chances are, filling up her joy tank helped her business.

Where might you be keeping out joy by only doing what you believe will either pay off right away or stave off failure?

What are some steps you can take to allow a bit of future-focus to guide your actions and activities?

Where can you decide that joy is a business case enough?

CUTTING OFF, EXILING, OR STUFFING DOWN "PARTS" OF YOU THAT "DON'T BELONG IN BUSINESS"

We are multifaceted humans. We contain a multitude of "parts" — thoughts, emotions, beliefs, qualities and characteristics, personality traits, identities and roles that make up who we are. If you've ever said, "A part of me feels X, but another part of me feels Y", you're already somewhat familiar with this concept.

We all have certain parts of ourselves that we deem "good" or acceptable — these are parts of us that we believe are allowed in any context. One of my "good" parts is my highly intellectual part. I see it as beneficial to my success, so I allow it to show up in my business, relationships, hobbies, and even my alone time. That intellectual part is always welcome to the party. Another part that I welcome no matter the context is my loving part (for obvious reasons 😊).

We also all have parts of ourselves that we deem "bad" or unacceptable. These are parts of us that we try to suppress or get rid of. I have an anxious part that can take me out for an entire day, and a shy part that sometimes stops me from putting my message out into the world. If I could only find a way to bury them for good …

And then there's a middle ground where some parts are welcome in certain contexts or situations, but not in others. A part of me loves to rap at karaoke. Warren G, Coolio, and Eminem are my specialities. I love to perform, and sometimes relish in the attention I get when I'm being silly. That part was not always welcome in my professional world. In fact, I was mortified at the possibility that my PhD advisor would find out I did karaoke every Friday during grad school because I didn't want him to think that part of me existed.

Our beliefs about which parts are always good, always bad, or acceptable in certain contexts but not in others, rarely come from within us. Sometimes we've inferred a message from the media or society at large, like what being a professional looks and feels like. Sometimes, we've been explicitly told by parents, teachers, friends, or mentors what is and isn't allowable. Perhaps a part of you emerged when you were young, but someone told you to put it back in the proverbial box. Or it came out in a situation where it wasn't all that useful and you decided to stuff it away completely. It only takes one instance of being told a part of you is wrong or seeing that a part of you is incompatible with a situation for you to extrapolate and decide it's unacceptable to everyone and in all situations.

In our businesses, we tend to allow only a limited range of parts of ourselves to come to the table. But, it's unlikely that those parts are the only ones that can help us be successful. You likely have parts that you're actively suppressing because you see them as detrimental to your business, but they'd be surprisingly beneficial to bring out. Until you experiment with ones that feel safe to try, you won't know. You're just operating on an untested belief.

One of my clients was known as a free spirit from a very young age. Her free spirit part took her on all kinds of wild adventures in her teens and twenties. But when she began to build a name for herself in corporate — and then considered stepping out into entrepreneurship — she tried to keep that free spirit part as buried as possible. She was worried that if any little piece of her free spirit got out, people wouldn't respect her or see her as professional. But, keeping her free spirit locked away also meant that she was burying some creativity and spontaneity that could make her work more impactful. So we explored how her free spirit could have a naturally valuable role in her work and then slowly experimented with bringing it out and seeing the results. She was promoted and took on a much larger role in the organization just a few months later. Was it because of her free spirit part? We can't know. But what we do know is that her work was much more joy-full with her free spirit welcome at the table.

In the spirit of my client's free spirit, let's go back and visit my karaoke rapper part. Could it have a natural role in my business? Absolutely! We live in the TikTok and Instagram Reel era. People crave edutainment. Social media is the perfect playground for my karaoke rapper to have a little fun on occasion. I don't foresee myself going down the route of becoming a full-blown video content creator, but when I need a little creative spark or want to delight myself, my karaoke rapper is ready to play.

Now just because I've welcomed in my karaoke rapper and my client welcomed in her free spirit, doesn't mean that you need to welcome in every part of you to your business. And it doesn't mean that every welcome part needs to always be present. It's natural and healthy for parts to show up when they are useful; the key is learn to leverage them when they are beneficial and letting them step aside when they aren't.

PARTS CHECK-IN

What parts of you are you holding down like a kick-board under water?

How is holding those parts down contributing to or draining your joy?

Which parts could you get curious about bringing back in?

How can you playfully experiment and explore what kind of role they might play for you in your business?

~~LOVE~~ JOY AND BASKETBALL

If you ask anyone who knew me growing up, they'd say that I was born with a basketball in my hand. I have no clue where my love of the sport came from. It certainly wasn't my parents. They never played, and to my knowledge, they didn't watch sports on TV. One of my earliest memories is of the 10-foot basketball hoop in the courtyard at my preschool. While everyone else was riding tricycles around the courtyard, I wanted to be throwing a ball at that hoop.

Maybe the mere presence of a hoop at my preschool made enough of an impression on young me to inspire my love for the game, but part of me believes I was born with it. Growing up, Michael Jordan was my hero. I watched all six of the Bulls' NBA titles. I watched the original Dream Team win the gold medal at the Barcelona Olympics in 1992. Though I couldn't have a hoop in my driveway, I had a mini-hoop that hung off my bedroom closet door. I loved jumping from my bed for a slam dunk, mimicking Jordan's form, even down to his signature tongue hanging out. In my parents' building at the University of Arizona, I turned every recycling bin I could find into a basketball hoop until they got a mini-hoop (like the one in my bedroom) for their department's lounge.

When I joined my first youth basketball league in 3rd grade (the earliest I was allowed to participate by the Powers-That-Be), I was the only girl ("girl" because that's how I was gendered growing up, though now identify as nonbinary). None of the boys liked that a girl was playing with them. Several of them, including the coaches' sons, teased me mercilessly. But I didn't care. My love of basketball was too strong. Throughout elementary school, I joined enough leagues and programs to be playing basketball multiple days of the week. Sometimes it was everyday but Sunday. Basketball was all I thought about. It was all I wanted to do.

In middle school, I went to every summer basketball camp I could. Overnight camps at University of Arizona, University of Michigan, and Michigan State University. Day camps at various places in northern Michigan. As I got exposed to other girls playing basketball, I realized that I was pretty good. I can't tell you that I was the best player to ever walk the earth, but I was good enough to make the "All Star Team" at all the overnight camps. When I was finally eligible to join the middle school basketball team in 7th grade, I was the only non-8th grader on the A team (we had A, B, and C teams). I was also one of the best players on the team, if not the best. The same was true the next year. I knew the likelihood of playing college basketball was slim, but I thought I just might have a shot.

Everything changed my freshman year of high school.

Most of my life, I played a position called shooting guard, which, if you're not familiar with basketball, means that I played far away from the basket. I had a good shot and a long range. I wasn't always the tallest player. I also wasn't the strongest. I was 110 pounds and could barely bench press the bar. So I wasn't fit to play positions like center or power forward that were almost always for the tallest and strongest players. But somehow, when I got to freshman year of high school, I was taller than all the other girls my age. I hadn't grown. All the older girls on the JV and varsity team (many of whom I'd played with on the A team in middle school) were still taller than me. But the freshman girls were unusually short as a group, and among them, I was a tower.

So, my freshman team coach, Coach Flores, deciding entirely based on my height, moved me out of my natural role of shooting guard to center. I was devastated. I didn't want to play center. I loved shooting from far out. I loved trying to figure out how to be quicker than my defender, even though I wasn't the quickest person. I loved being able to run around the whole court. The center's job was to stay near the basket and bully people around them to score. It wasn't fun for me at all. Despite this, when we played other schools, I was decently successful at center, scoring a handful of points every game. When our team scrimmaged against the JV and Varsity teams, I got beat up. I pled with Coach Flores to move me back to shooting guard, but he wouldn't do it.

Moving out of my natural position wasn't the only thing that changed everything my freshman year. My parents took me to New York City for a conference and family holiday during Thanksgiving week, just as basketball season was getting into gear. The trip had been planned for months, but it turned out I missed two or three practices. As "punishment" for missing practices, I both lost my starting spot as center *and* had to sit out a game completely when I got back. Frustratingly, I was never able to earn my starting spot back or Coach Flores' trust. In his mind, I wasn't dedicated enough. And though I never missed another practice that season, he continually searched for evidence of my lack of dedication. I wasn't the fastest runner on the team. To Flores, I was lazy. I wasn't the strongest on the team. To Flores, I didn't push myself hard enough. No matter how much I tried to get back in his good graces, he found ways to tell me that I just wasn't as good at basketball as I thought.

Any gains I'd made with Flores during the season were wiped out when summer rolled around. My family spent every summer at a cottage in Michigan (we primarily lived in Arizona). So I wasn't around in the summer to participate in unofficial, non-mandatory summer practices and open gyms. That wasn't okay with Coach Flores. I thought I made a fair compromise by staying in Tucson the first few weeks of summer to attend some of the most important events. My parents had already left for Michigan and at 15 without a driver's license, I stayed with a friend and her parents transported me to all things basketball. Me staying back for a few weeks wasn't enough for Flores, though. The fact that I was going to Michigan to be with my family at all was, according to him, evidence that I didn't really care enough about basketball.

The message was loud and clear: If I wanted to play this sport that I loved more than anything ... that I ate, slept and breathed from the time I was a toddler ... I needed to forfeit the position I was strongest at, and play one that I didn't love. I also had to give up going to Michigan in the summers. Which meant giving up family *and also* summer camp — which was the only place I truly felt safe and welcome at the time. And as if it couldn't get any more crushing, the message was laced with, "you're just not as good as you think you are."

It would have been one thing if Coach Flores had been coming from a place of, "You're really talented and have potential to play in college, but this is the reality of what it takes to do so. And I'm here to support you every step of the way." Though it would have been difficult, I imagine I would have been all-in on that. But instead it was coming from, "You don't have what it takes."

At the beginning of sophomore year, I made the excruciating decision to quit basketball. I gave up my first love in favor of summer camp, family, time at the cottage, and really, not feeling like crap all the time.

I thought I'd never find anything I loved as much as basketball … and then I found coaching.

Why am I telling this story in a book on joy in business? Because that story became *the story* for me. When I started my coaching business, what I was told about basketball became what I believed about my coaching and my business:

Your strengths and genius don't matter. If you want to be successful, you'll have to play how you're told to, not how you want to.

*You'll have to make sacrifices. If you're not fully dedicated **at all costs**, then why are you wasting time going for it at all?*

*Don't even believe that you're good at what you do. You're **never** as good as you think you are.*

It wasn't just basketball that led to the self-doubt and not-enoughness I carried into coaching and my business. The narrative that started in basketball was reinforced several times over the next few decades. One of those times was in my PhD program. My advisor specialized in a theoretical framework I wasn't thrilled about, but I was excited to work with him because of what research questions he was applying the framework to. Unfortunately, it turned out that he had no intention of helping me find what I was naturally interested in or curious about. So I spent four years being told that if I wanted to play this game called "academic job", I needed to give up my natural curiosities and strengths. Hell, I was so busy doing his research that I didn't have the time and space to even discover what they were. (Spoiler alert: that was one of *many* reasons I didn't go down the academic path.)

Early in my time at Facebook, my beliefs about who I needed to be in order to be successful were reinforced again. I was hired as a Quantitative User Experience Researcher because of my expertise in running surveys and analyzing data. But the department I was placed in when I arrived at Facebook didn't know what to do with me. Most of the teams that I was supposed to provide research support for hadn't been exposed to much quantitative research before. The qualitative researchers, who did more interview-based work, were each assigned to a specific team of product managers, engineers, and designers to work with, but I was supposed to float around and work with different teams as needed. That model didn't work well at all. I wasn't embedded enough in the teams to know what decisions they were making that could be supported by a survey or data analysis. They also didn't know enough about quantitative research to reach out for my support. I confided in my manager that I felt lost. I didn't have many projects to work on and I wasn't sure what my role was. She assured me all was okay.

Around that same time, my dad passed away suddenly. I took an emergency flight home to Arizona to deal with some legal issues quickly. As an only child to divorced parents, I was the executor of the estate. It took me several weeks of work time to sort through everything. At the same time my house in San Francisco flooded. (I don't know how that happens while living on a hill in San Francisco, but sure enough, it did!) My wife, our pets, and I were displaced from our house for over a week, and the repairs took much longer. So for the first six or eight months of my Facebook career, I was not being used for my natural skills and abilities while also dealing with grief, legal issues, and a disrupted home life. I would have worried about my performance review, except that my manager assured me all was well.

So, naturally, I was shocked when I sat down for my first performance review and my manager said, "Erin you got a 'Meets *Most* Expectations' and you're going on a Performance Improvement Plan (PIP). We even took into account that your dad died." If you're not familiar with corporate speak, a PIP is often a "Get in shape or we'll tell you get out" warning. She went on to tell me, just like Coach Flores, all the ways in which I wasn't as good as I thought I was. Apparently, in my anxiety to find a role for myself I had said things to colleagues that came off as dismissive of qualitative research. But rather than being given a chance to fix the damage directly with my colleagues shortly after it happened, I wasn't even aware there was damage until it was on my record.

As part of trying to save my job during the PIP, I gave up my "natural position" — quantitative research — and learned qualitative research. I also learned, like I did in basketball, to put my family priorities last. I was able to stay at Facebook and become successful over the next few years, including moving into management, but thanks to the message from my first manager, I never allowed myself to think I was good at what I did.

Fast forward to 2018 when I started my business. The beliefs that started in basketball and had become more ingrained over the years, were running the show now, but I wasn't conscious of them just yet.

I'd become a basketball center, construal-level theorist, and qualitative researcher ... what was the "giving up my natural position" equivalent going to be in my business?

I'd started my business partially to spend time with family and have more space for hobbies ... running through my head were questions like "How soon would I have to admit to myself that to be truly successful I was going to have to put my business above all else?", "How could I make sure that I never ever got to a point of believing that I was good at what I do?" and "How could I ensure I stayed in a perpetual state of feeling not enough so that I'd never have to hear, 'You're not as good as you think you are' from anyone ever again?"

Recall from *Joy is Uncomfortable* that we experience joy when we are in our Zone of Genius. Starting with being moved to center from shooting guard in high school, I got message after message that if I wanted to keep doing what I loved (basketball, psychology, research at Facebook), that I needed to give up my Zone of Genius. So of course, I didn't even consider what my natural strengths and geniuses were. I looked around at other people to see who I was supposed to be and what I was supposed to do. I also listened to people who were eager to give me their opinions on who I should be and what I should do. Not a recipe for joy!

I got message after message that I wasn't dedicated enough and that I wasn't as good at what I was doing as I had thought … that led to me working too hard and coming from a place of harsh self-criticism and desperation to prove myself. Also not a recipe for joy!

The beliefs that were instilled in me from my childhood, and got reinforced throughout my adulthood, were keeping me from my joy as I leapt into business. It took me years of growth work through coaching and therapy to make the connection between my experience in basketball and how I show up in my business. Now anytime I see a belief driving the bus in my business, I try to find the source and re-write the narrative from older, hopefully wiser, me.

What are some of the core stories and beliefs that you hold? They may be ones that have been with you so long that you've just accepted them as true or they may have come from life-shaping events.

Which of them are keeping you from stepping fully into who you are and doing what's most joy-full?

How long have you been carrying them with you?

Are they true? If yes, can you be *absolutely sure* they are true? If not, what new beliefs do you want to try on instead?

How can following joy become a compass for rewriting those beliefs?

How the F*ck
Do We Get More Joy?

How The F*ck Do We Get More Joy?

Let's go back to one of the distinguishing features of joy: It's a resource that comes from within us. We always have access to it, and we can also create and cultivate more of it over time.

I picture us all having a joy tank. From that lens, the previous section of the book was about ways joy seeps, leaks and drains from our tank (as well as what we can do to plug those seeps and leaks or prevent the drain to begin with). If your only focus moving forward is preventing joy from seeping away, you still can have a joy-full business. But I suspect you're here to be joy-full *AF*. Putting joy first is not just about "not losing" joy, it's about filling up on as much of it as possible, and even expanding your capacity for it.

As we talked about in *But Joy Is*, joy is the key to long-term, sustainable business success. When we have delight, play, creativity, and/or connection to ourselves and something deeper, we are more likely to stay in for the long haul. But those positives are not the only reason we need to stay filled up on joy.

"Joy collected over time fuels resilience – ensuring we'll have reservoirs of strength when hard things do happen."

~ Brené Brown

Entrepreneurship requires incredible resilience. We don't have the same level of certainty that someone working a traditional 9-to-5 corporate job might have. (Though how certain is anything really when employers can lay off or fire people at a moment's notice?) We will inevitably go through long periods of time when nothing is working or our revenue dips. Depending on our business, we might be more susceptible to economic downturns or changing consumer preferences. Whether or not we have others to lead in our businesses, we must lead ourselves. That means getting cozy with our fears and doubts, learning what we struggle with and need outside help on, managing failure, and championing ourselves to move forward even when everything feels too hard and overwhelming. The more joy we have, the more able we are to weather any storm.

Joy is also an act of resistance.

Throughout this book, I've mentioned several societal influences on what we pursue and how (patriarchy, white supremacy, toxic capitalism, individualism). Being in our joy, and truly being in our fully authentic selves, is a way to break away from these oppressive systems. I believe that the more of us break away, the more we'll begin to break down systems and make room for positive social change.

Whether you purely want more joy for the joy of it, like the idea of creating fuel for resilience, or are ready to smash the patriarchy (and more), this section has something for you. Some conversations will help you find ways to infuse joy into everything you do (like … *AND it's Joy-full (Baking Joy into Every Goal)* and *Fill Up Your Joy Tank*). Others will give you specific suggestions (like *Fe-Fi-Fo-*

Fum … Plant Some Magic Beans and *It's All Fun and Games … No, Really!*) Feel free to pick and choose what works for you. (After all, if I haven't said it enough already, your way is always the most joy-full way.)

... AND IT'S JOY-FULL (BAKING JOY INTO EVERY GOAL)

When I say that creating and cultivating joy is an essential business strategy, I'm not saying that it should be your *only* strategy. I don't think it can be. But I do think it can inform all your other strategies in terms of what you pursue and how.

I also don't think being joy-full can be your only goal. In fact, it doesn't work well as a stand-alone. Goals are often specific, quantifiable targets that we move towards. We can measure our progress towards them, and assess where we might need to adjust or pivot in order to move forward. Once we hit our target, we often set a new one. Though we can always want more joy, there is no quantifiable target amount of joy-fullness to move towards. We can sort of measure progress, but it's more difficult to understand how far we need to go. That's because there is no "there" to get to — we can be "full" of joy, but there is infinite room for more. So once we start feeling joy-full, we can't just say "great, I checked that goal off the list. What's next?"

Joy-fullness is an ongoing pursuit.

So of course it's important to have other goals in your business. (And I'm guessing you already have plenty of them.) You might have a revenue target, or maybe a number of clients or customers that you'd like to serve. If you're building a community or an app, you might have a specific amount of people you'd like to see actively engaged daily, weekly, and/or monthly. Or you might have a goal around retaining members of that community or app. You may have a creative project that you want to get out in the world, like I did with this book.

Where does joy fit when we're setting goals?

Let's play with the example of setting a revenue target. It's a goal that nearly every business owner sets at some point in time. For imagination's sake, let's say you want to make $200K in your business this year. What immediately comes to mind for you as you begin to think about going towards that goal? Do you jump to working through how many clients or customers you'll need to serve to hit that target? Do you dive into creative brainstorming of marketing ideas or programs/products you might need to offer?

How does it *feel* to think about going after a $200K goal? How many of the ideas that popped into your head are exciting and challenging? How many are things that you believe *should* work, or even have worked in the past, but don't light you up? How many actively make you miserable just thinking about them?

If going after $200K in revenue feels the opposite of joy-full to go after, or has the potential to turn that way, why not infuse joy into the goal at the outset?

What I mean by that is adding an "AND" — look! my favorite word! — to your goal: "I'm going to make $200K in my business this year AND it will be joy-full."

By putting an AND in the goal, you've created some parameters or constraints that weren't there before. In this case, they are a good thing. Because now you have to get curious and creative. What are the joy-full paths to creating $200K? What aren't? How can you ensure that you stay on the joy-full path, especially when other paths feel more certain to help you reach your goal? You might also need to take courageous action, knowing that some of the joy-full paths involve taking risks and/or trying things you've never done before. And you might need to have the courage to let go of tried-and-true ways of creating revenue that have felt meh or miserable in the past.

Adding "… AND it's joy-full" to your goals completely shifts the emotional, mental, and physical energy of pursuing them. *This* is how joy as a strategy gets baked into everything you do.

Take stock of allw of your current goals. You may want to revisit ones you already explored in the "Goal Traps Check-in" in F*alling Into All Four Traps.*

Which ones are you already pursuing joy-fully? What, if anything, needs to happen to keep the joy flowing?

Which are actively stealing your joy and how?

Which are going fine, but could use an extra joy infusion? What would make them more joy-full?

WHEN DO YOU FEEL JOY-FULL?

When do you feel joy-full AF in your business? Stop for a second and think.

Have you ever asked yourself this question? If the answer is no, I would venture to guess that even though you started your business wanting more joy (whether you called it that or not), it's never been an explicit goal. (And as we've discussed in multiple conversations, you're not alone in that.) Up until reading this book, I'd bet you've never actively sought to create or cultivate it in your business. And you've likely never checked in on your joy the way you might with other metrics in your business.

And even if you *have* asked yourself this question, perhaps it's time to check in and re-evaluate.

So whether you've asked yourself before or not, take some time to check in right now. *Don't flip to the next conversation. Do not pass go. Do not collect $200. Really pause and sit with your answers here.*

When am I joy-full in my business?

What am I doing?

How am I doing it?

Who am I with?

I am joy-full when I'm coaching my clients. Even when we are dealing with heavy topics like unresolved trauma or systemic oppression. (Yes, these both show up in business and are important contexts to work with.) My whole body is on fire as I work with the human sitting in front of me (whether in person or on my Zoom screen). Who is this person? What are they all about? What lights them up? How does their brain work? Where do they want to go and who do they want to become in the process of getting there?

I am also joy-full when I'm teaching other coaches about coaching. There's coaching that helps on the surface, leading to temporary changes or incremental improvements, and there's deep coaching that changes people at a cellular level. I'm passionate about helping coaches master the art and science of deep coaching, and helping them become more trauma, nervous-system, neurodiversity, and systems-of-oppression informed. Anytime I am mentoring or teaching another coach, I feel tapped into my curiosity and creativity, and feel more connected to the "collective".

You will likely find that certain activities bring you joy, just like coaching, teaching, and mentoring do for me. You may also find that certain *ways* you approach activities bring you joy. For instance, I feel joy-full when I have a big goal in front of me and low attachment to whether I reach it. (We'll talk about this more in *Put on your HILA Hat.*) When I don't know if or when I'll get to a destination, I can be more curious and creative about my path along the way, and I tend to take more risks because I'm not taking failure too seriously. I also feel joy-full when I turn activities I that don't inherently love doing into games (We'll dive into this in *It's All Fun and Games … No, Really!*).

A less obvious, but important source of your joy might be in partnering with your brain. That is, working with its natural function. I am someone who cannot create a masterpiece from a blank canvas. I need ideas to react to. I need someone to say, "what if you painted the emotion you are feeling right now?" or "draw me your best representation of a farm." I don't consider myself an artist, but the metaphor works well for me. In business terms, I need something concrete to grasp onto. If I'm writing content — for this book, my newsletter, or social media — I am best if I'm responding to something that has come up in a coaching call, conversation with a friend, book, or someone else's social media post. Without something to react to, my brain spins. It's like I'm swimming in an ocean of possible things to write about but I can't seem to find a single coral reef to focus on. Having something to react to or that triggers a thought (or series of thoughts) creates ease, and when I feel ease, I also feel more joy.

Back to checking on when you feel joy-full. As you reflect, scan for activities, people, circumstances, thoughts, and ways you partner with your brain. If you'd like to get an even deeper pulse on your joy, ask yourself what about them makes them feel joy-full. Then, feel free to do the opposite and look at when you are least joy-full.

If you'd prefer to reflect through a more formal exercise. you could draw a line down a piece of paper and write joy-full at the top of the left column and joy-less at the top of the right. For a week, any time you notice something that brings or steals your joy, write it in the appropriate column. Or if you'd like something even more structured, you can go back and revisit *Joy Audit.*

WHAT MAKES YOU COME ALIVE?

So … maybe you read the last conversation about what makes you most joy-full and immediately had all the answers. Or maybe you read the earlier conversations about your Zone of Genius and knew immediately what activities have you operating joy-fully in that zone. But maybe the Zone of Genius concept threw everything you knew about yourself on its head. Maybe you've been so steeped in (and rewarded for) your Zone of Excellence that you're not even sure where to begin looking for your Zone of Genius. [If this is you, you're not alone. A few years ago, I discovered one of my geniuses is helping people find their Zone of Genius. I did several coaching sessions with colleagues who were at the top of their games and had done a lot of previous self-development work. They all were completely blind to their geniuses.]

One of the best ways to load up on more joy is through the activities that make you feel most alive. Are you creating or building something? Researching or experimenting? Leading other people? Teaching or mentoring? Creating order from chaos? Of course, in business, we wear multiple hats — especially if we're solopreneurs or lead a small team — so I'm not asking which hats you wear. I'm asking which ones are you wearing when you feel alive? When do you feel most driven or energized? Remember, your Zone of Genius is what you're good at and what you love to do. So, looking at what you're naturally driven towards can give you a clue, at least to the part of "what you love to do." Chances are, because it's a natural driver for you, you're also good at it.

If you're still not sure what makes you come alive, look back to your childhood for clues. What were you most drawn to then? Did you love to play with LEGO® or building blocks? Perhaps you're a builder. Did you have a science kit? Perhaps you're a researcher. Were you constantly gathering your friends for adventures in treehouses, on playgrounds, or through neighborhoods? Perhaps you're a leader. Or were you, like me, the confidant and advisor for all of your friends?

I'd be willing to bet that whatever you do in business taps into your natural drivers, though perhaps you've not been aware of them up until now. Or maybe you have been aware of these drivers but have told yourself they have no place in your business.

One of my clients, Sami, was a VP at a global consulting company when she first started working with me. She knew that eventually, she wanted to move onto another career, possibly in entrepreneurship, but she wasn't sure what made her come alive. We had talked extensively about her creative side. Growing up she'd been an artist and in her spare time outside of her VP role, she had created a calendar company as a side hustle. But it wasn't until we dug into what she was doing in her VP role that she connected the dots — she was a builder. She'd been building a digital product from the ground up and she loved it. Once she realized that, she knew she didn't want to leave the company until she saw that product all the way through to launch. Even if there were parts of her job burning her out, building the product made her come so alive that she couldn't imagine leaving quite yet. When she did leave the company, and we began to explore what was next for her, we kept the "Sami is a builder" idea in mind, knowing that her joy depended on her being able to create a product or service from scratch. (As of this writing she is still in exploration or I'd tell you what she landed on!)

Another client, Cody, had been a teacher when we first started working together. They were pondering moving into another career, and like Sami, were intrigued by entrepreneurship. When we dug into Cody's natural drivers, we found out that they come alive when teaching, coaching, and advocating for people. Learning that opened up a world of possibility to Cody. They went on to complete a yoga teacher training and have since explored various ways they can combine their love of yoga and mindfulness with their love of being around and teaching young kids.

The more you can align your work to what naturally makes you come alive, the more joy-full you will be. Though I'm generally not a fan of "personality tests", one that might be helpful in exploring your natural drivers is the Sparketype Assessment created by Jonathan Fields.[11] As a researcher, I'm pretty critical of tests, so I have to say that I can't tell from how the methodology is described whether it's scientifically valid. In truth, most tests like these (like the Myers Briggs Type Indicator) look scientific, but aren't. I also can't say whether it covers the full range of natural drivers in existence. However, I do know it can be a useful lens. The assessment asks questions about your past and present. You then get information on which of the ten Sparketypes is your primary driver, which is secondary and helps support you in your primary driver, and which is your anti-driver — the activity that sucks your joy the most and you should avoid or outsource at all costs. I highly recommend taking the test, but I also recommend reading about all ten Sparketypes. Sometimes you don't need an assessment to know what feels intuitively true for you.

Finally, if you're anti-test (like me), you can go back do the exercise from *What Makes You Joy-Full?* or you can simply start noticing in your day-to-day what lights you up and what drains you. See if you can find a pattern of activities on both the joy-full and joy-less side. That will provide a clue as to what kinds of activities to seek out or focus on over the long-run, and which you probably want to outsource or avoid at all costs.

FINDING THE *MOST* JOY-FULL PATH

Clients and colleagues ask me all the time ...

How do I know I'm on the most joy-full path?

How do I know that the actions I'm taking on my path are the most joy-full ones possible?

How do I know that my strategic plan is the most joy-full way forward?

How do I know that the service I provide / product I create is the most joy-full way to express or harness my passions and talents?

As a service provider, how do I know who my most joy-full clients are to work with?

Before we can answer any of these questions about what's *most* joy-full, you need to have a sense of what brings you joy in the first place. If you haven't answered the questions in *When Do You Feel Joy-Full?* or haven't done the *Joy Audit*, start there. If in doing those, you struggled to find joy in your current business activities, this is a great opportunity to get curious about what might create joy. You might even want to make a plan to actively explore and experiment.

Let's say that for now you have a pretty good grip on what makes you joy-full. You may want to know ...

How do I know I'm choosing the *most* joy-full option?

There are likely numerous ways for you to find the answer to this question. I'll talk about three paths here.

Listen to Your Body

One of the qualities that sets joy apart from other positive emotions is how we experience it in our body. It feels like it comes from somewhere deep within and fills us up completely. So naturally, our bodies are a great barometer of what is our most joy-full option. When you imagine yourself doing an activity (like attending an event or being interviewed on a podcast), following a path (like starting a podcast of your own or writing a book), or interacting with a person (like hiring an assistant or signing a client), do you feel a Full-Body-Hell-Yes!?

If you're reading this thinking, "Erin, I have no f*cking clue what my body would tell me. And even if it did tell me, I don't really trust it," you aren't alone. It's so common for us to be disconnected from our bodies. We are taught to listen to our rational minds when we make decisions. Many of us also have faced mental and physical health challenges that have left us distrusting and disliking our bodies. As someone who dealt with eating disorders in college and gender dysmorphia until I was in my mid-thirties, at times the last thing I've wanted to do is pay attention to my body.

So if listening to your body for a Full-Body-Hell-Yes isn't an option yet, here's how you can start to reconnect to joy as an embodied experience.

(*Note: if **connecting** to your body has the potential to trigger trauma or any other mental health issue, please feel free to skip this exercise and move onto the next option.*)

Close your eyes and recall a time you felt wildly joy-full. You don't need to find a moment in your business — any experience will do. Where were you? What were you doing? Who else was around? Were you indoors or outdoors? What was the temperature like? Try to recall as many details as possible, even the small ones. Now notice how your body feels as you recall. What sensations do you feel? Where do you feel them? What else can you notice about how joy shows up in your body? Really anchor into that feeling. It can now serve as a litmus test going forward. If, when you imagine, doing an activity or choosing to go down a path, your body feels similar to that moment, you've likely landed on quite a joy-full one!

If you do this activity and you don't get much of a connection with your body, that's okay. Just like you can build curiosity, creativity, and courage like a muscle, you can do the same with your connection to your body. (See the list at the end of this conversation for a variety of options.) With intentional focus on body connection, you might be surprised at how many decisions you make in your business from a place of, "Oh yeah, my body is lit up. That's a *Hell Yes!*" or just as importantly, "Nope, body's not feeling it. That's a *Hell No.*"

Is it a 10?

If you're a numbers nerd — or find listening to your body out of reach — you may love the idea of quantifying your joy. (This is a part of the book where I make a shameless plug for someone else's book … well, books. My friend, Mark Silverman, wrote two great books called *Only 10s* and *Only 10s 2.0*[13], from which I've borrowed this concept.) The idea is simple: for any clients, projects, activities, or business strategies that you are currently engaged in or are considering taking on, ask yourself if it feels like a 10 out of 10 on the joy-full scale for you. You may know something is a 10 based on direct experience. Such as, *I am giddy every time I sit down to write a newsletter, so that's a 10 I'm going to keep doing. Or, I've loved working with this client in the past, so I'll absolutely work with them again.* You may also sense that something will be a 10 based on what you know about yourself, like, *It energizes me to be on stage, so exploring speaking opportunities feels like a 10. Or, I adore Laurie, so creating an "Amateur Hour" group experience with her sounds positively joy-full.*

Asking, "Is it a 10?" requires you to get honest with yourself and others. (That's my favorite part of this whole concept! ☺) It means saying no to things that are a 7, 8, 9, or even a 9.9! They might feel pretty joy-full, but maybe not the *most* joy-full. It often means paring down what you're doing to focus on just a few things at a time. That can be uncomfortable if you're an ambitious person who tends to have a lot on your plate. When something isn't a 10, you might have to disappoint clients, collaborators, or friends. That can also be uncomfortable if you are someone with people-pleasing tendencies. As you seek joy-full 10s, you'll need to have faith that the more you say no to non-10s, the more space you'll have for true 10s to come into your purview.

Are neither of these concepts (tuning into your body or quantifying joy) your jam? How can you get curious and creative about what is? My book coach, Patti, shared while we were writing this that for her it's all about colors. If something comes up turquoise in her minds' eye, it's a go, but if it's purple, it's a hell no. What works for *you*?

Experiment with Joy

When listening to your body isn't an option and you don't have quite enough information to be certain something is a 10, you can explore and experiment instead.

Experimentation is one of the most trusty tools in my entrepreneur tool belt. It motivates the scientist in me because it's the best way, in my opinion, to find answers you can't "think" your way into. We'll talk more in-depth about the power of experimentation and putting on your proverbial lab coat in your business later. (Curious? Start with *It's All Research* and read the four conversations that follow.) For now, just know that you can experiment with your joy in the same way you can experiment with concrete elements of your business (like marketing messages, advertising, or services/products you provide).

Wondering if creating a podcast is the most joy-full way to build an audience? Commit to a six-month trial to feel it out. Or maybe you're wondering the same about LinkedIn. And because six months is a really long time in social media terms, perhaps instead you commit to posting every day for 100 days.

Sometimes you'll need to commit to a long-period of time to truly be able to assess. When I started my *Life in the And* podcast back in 2020, it took me at least three months to realize that though it was *a* joy-full path, it was not the *most* joy-full path in the context of my business at the time.

But you might reach clarity quickly. If it's joy-full AF — perhaps a 10! — keep going as long as it keeps being so. However, if it's not joy-full, you don't have to continue for the whole time period you initially committed to. My TikTok experiment worked that way for me. At one point, a mentor suggested that my personality and wisdom was perfect for TikTok. My body didn't give me much information on whether that was the most joy-full audience building activity I could be doing, so I committed to a 100-day experiment. About two weeks into the 100 days, I was clear: TikTok might be a smart business strategy, but it wasn't a joy-full one for me.

Let's finish here by circling back to the original question: How do I know what the *most* joy-full path is? You can check in with your body, ask if it is a 10, or design an experiment, and still wonder, "Is this the *most* joy-full? Are there 11s out there that I'm missing?" The truth is, you'll likely never be able to answer that question. There are so many options for how you can build and run your business that you won't be able to test and rank them all. The goal here is not optimization — though of course, we like to optimize things! And in fact, if you're constantly questioning whether something better is out there, you're likely not allowing yourself to feel the joy of what you're doing right now. Try to let it be enough that you've found a Full-Body-Hell-Yes, a 10, or simply that you're working towards that feeling. After all, if we have endless capacity for joy, we don't have to worry so much about finding the *best* thing — we can just keep adding to our tank.

Ideas For Connecting With Your Body

(A note of caution: please check in with your body before you do any of these. Find what feels good to you. And consider professional guidance for any activities that might be linked with trauma, mental health concerns, or simply feel too unsafe in your body to do them alone.)

- Do body scan meditation, focusing on all sensations big and small
- Practice yoga or stretch
- Do progressive muscle relaxation, tightening then releasing muscles from your head to toe
- Dance
- Deliberately engage your senses — stop and smell the roses, focus on what your food tastes like, feel your feet in the grass
- Exercise
- Spend time in nature
- Practice breath work
- Get a massage (or give one to yourself)
- Keep a journal of thoughts, emotions, and body sensations
- Create physical connection (hugs, cuddles) with loved ones and pets

CREATE METRICS
FOR ~~SUCCESS~~ JOY

How do you measure success? Depending on your business, you could have any or all of these on your radar:

- Revenue
- Profit
- # of clients, customers, users, or subscribers
- Customer retention rate
- Email open rate
- # of email subscribers
- # of followers on LinkedIn, TikTok, Instagram, or Facebook
- Average # of likes, comments, shares, and saves on your social posts
- Average # of podcast listens
- # of books sold
- Conversion rate
- Quantity of referrals
- Quality of referrals

These traditional metrics of success can be important to track. For instance, if your conversion rate is low, you might want to look at your sales process to see what can be improved. Are you reaching the right clients in your marketing and outreach? Are you providing a product or service that your ideal client needs? Are you clear about what you provide? On the flip side, if your conversion rate is high, or even outpacing what you can deliver, is it time to raise your prices? Would creating new products or services that can scale to more people help you keep up with demand? Is it time to hire a team (or more people for your existing team)?

In a sea of possible metrics, it's possible to choose poor ones. Likes, comments, shares, and saves are only the tip of the iceberg of who's paying attention on social media. Low engagement does not necessarily mean low impact of your content. A large following on social media, email, or a podcast matters very little if the people in your audience aren't right for you.

These types of metrics that don't paint a full or accurate picture are joy-sucks. They're also sneaky because they are easy for our brains to get attached to. We latch onto likes and comments on our content because we can't easily imagine the size of the iceberg under the surface of people lurking. (Couldn't they have the decency to soothe our anxieties with a simple 'like'!!!??? 😴) We also chase followers because we can't fathom why more isn't always better. (If it's not, why are people still in my DMs trying to sell me followers? And why do podcasts, speaking events, and book agents look at or ask for my follower counts to decide whether my pitch is worth considering?)

There are also metrics that are poor in a more inconspicuous way. These metrics get in the way of what's important to us. They may make logical sense on the surface. Or they might be great metrics for *other* people to track. They might even be great metrics for ourselves at different points in time. At several points while writing this book, if I had used revenue or a full client roster as metrics for success, I would have been miserable. (In fact, I did make myself miserable once or twice. Some metrics for success are hard for me to untangle from my sense of self-worth even when I logically know that they mean nothing about me and that I need to prioritize other things!)

Take a moment to do a brief check in with yourself on this. Are the things you're tracking giving you valuable information or are they joy-stealing distractions? Are they aligned with what's most important to you? What metrics do you want to keep and which do you need to get rid of or transform?

Beyond the traditional metrics, there are also metrics that you won't find in books, or downloadable pdfs on the internet. You likely won't hear about them from mentors and colleagues either. That's because they are individually suited to you. Chances are, these "personal metrics for success" are also your metrics for joy.

That was certainly true for my client, Kaya. She came to a coaching session feeling like a failure. Though she'd already been an entrepreneur and coach for years, she'd told herself a story that she wasn't successful because she didn't have a college degree and she wasn't yet at the revenue level or client load of some of her colleagues. It was immediately clear to me that based on her life history and the trajectory of her business, these were not the best markers for her. So I decided to do an exercise with Kaya to help create her own measures for success.

We first brainstormed a list of what would make her feel successful. Not surprisingly, her list of feel good metrics were wildly different from the commonly relied upon ones:

- I say yes to the things that matter
- I am in powerful service
- My work energizes me/lights me up
- I have and am part of epic support networks

- Life is deeply meaningful
- I am building my dream home
- I create what intuition and desire call for
- I am choosing life
- I am there for my children

To give her a way to track them over time, for each one I asked her, "On a scale of one to 10 where 10 is ideal, where do you feel you are on this measure right now?" Once she had her collective numbers in front of her, we chose two for her to focus on. We made a plan for how Kaya could move the needle on each of those by just one point.

This exercise was so powerful she decided to put her new list of metrics on a giant piece of paper so she could see it on her wall. For each measure, she drew a circle with 10 pie pieces. She then colored in the number of pieces that represented her starting place. As she started moving up in each of the measures, she could color in a new piece of the pie.

For Kaya, it didn't feel right to completely banish her previous measures of revenue and client load. So we made them secondary. She knew that being in powerful service, focusing on meaningful work that energizes her, and taking time for her children would naturally lead to more impact, and therefore more revenue and higher demand for her services.

What she had just made primary — though neither of us had the word in our vocabulary at the time — was her joy.

What metrics are stealing your joy? Do you *need* to track them? If so, could they be secondary to your metrics for joy?

What metrics for joy would you like to be tracking? You can use the same exercise that Kaya did to come up with hers.

MY METRICS FOR JOY

Make a list of what would (or already does) make you feel successful.

Go through each metric and assess where you are right now on a scale of 1-10, where 10 is ideal.

Then choose one or two to focus on for the next few weeks or months.

Make a specific plan on how you can move your number just one notch up towards 10.

WANT MORE JOY?
FEEL YOUR PAIN

In her famous TED talk on the power of vulnerability, Brené Brown said, "When we numb our pain, we numb our joy."[14]

She said this without a particular context in mind — I'm sure she believes it's true in ALL contexts. I agree, AND I think it's imperative that we put it in the context of entrepreneurship and business.

Your business needs your full humanity. Yes, conventional business wisdom tells us to take our humanity **out** of the business as much as possible:

"Work on your business, not in it!"

"Your business isn't personal."

And certainly, success requires us to keep our emotions at bay and focus on logic and rational decision-making:

"Show up as an experimenter and a scientist. Treat everything you do like data."

"Follow tried and true strategies and formulas, not your feelings."

I'll be the first to tell you some of this conventional wisdom has its place. We'll talk more about that later in *Data Hath No Meaning* and *Put on Your Lab Coat AND Feel Your Feelings Too*. But also, bringing a scientist's mind to your business does not require you to deny your feelings. It does not mean being a robot.

And because you are reading this book, it's safe to assume that you are not here to become a robot 😉.

Your business needs you to bring your full humanity to the table.

To truly create and cultivate a joy-full AF business, you need to be willing to sit with, hold space for, and fully experience all your emotions. Not just in your personal life, but also in your business.

Your sadness.

Anger.

Depression.

Anxiety.

Frustration.

Regret.

Hurt.

Fear.

Joy without those feelings isn't joy. It's emotional bypassing / toxic positivity. Now, let me be clear. I'm not saying that you have to seek out negative emotions just so you can experience joy. I'm also not saying that if you experience negative emotions in your business that you need to keep yourself feeling them in order to experience joy elsewhere or at some other time.

What I am saying is that in the pursuit of joy, we need to be careful to not demonize, or stuff down other emotions. Be careful not to criticize or lash yourself when you inevitably feel emotions that aren't joy.

Feeling joy-full 100% of the time is not the goal. It's not even humanly possible. But you can expand your capacity for joy in your business (and your life) by expanding your capacity for all emotions.

Also, if you're thinking, "Well, what if I let myself feel all the feelings in my personal life so I can keep my business *all* joy *all* the time," I hate to break it to you: We just can't compartmentalize our emotional life like that.

You will be joy-full AF in your business when you allow that all emotions are valid and necessary, and part of our human experience.

THERE IS NO JOY WITHOUT REST

When you're tired, and stressed out …

When you're burned to a crisp …

When your mind and body just can't …

There is no space for joy.

We cannot talk about joy without talking about rest.

If you're like me, rest feels awful. It's frustrating, depressing, and anxiety-producing. It can feel more miserable than the miserable we feel being on-the-go.

We've been programmed to avoid rest. Our toxic capitalist and white supremacist culture is about productivity and achievement. As if that's not enough to keep us in motion all the time, the business world reinforces it. The masculine, bro-y messaging that dominates business is about hustle and grind …

Get up at 4 a.m., so you can get in a workout, respond to emails, meditate, and write your book all by 6 a.m.!

If you're not working 14-hour days, you clearly don't want success. If you're not optimizing every minute of your day, you're sabotaging yourself.

If you could be doing more and you aren't, you're lazy.

My stomach is churning as I write this. We idealize so many unhealthy behaviors.

Even if we logically understand that rest is important — and that hustle and grind culture is damaging and toxic— we still avoid it. That's because, as I said above, rest can feel like shit. And taking the amount of rest that would *truly* recharge us feels like full-on *poopy shit* (to quote one of my favorite TV characters, Alice Pieszecki from *The L World*).

That's because our nervous systems react to us slowing down. For one, we are actively rebelling against internalized capitalism, patriarchy, and white supremacy. These systems of oppression fuel our hustle and grind culture, our over-focus on achievement, and our belief that work and output determine our value as people. We absorb the messages generated by these systems daily; sometimes in overt ways, but most of the time, more subtly. We've also been absorbing these messages since birth, and as a result, they have become embedded in our nervous systems. We're not even cognitively aware of how they impact us. So when we start to act out against them, our nervous systems flare up, as if we are doing something wrong.

On top of our nervous systems reacting to internalized oppression, they are also responding to physiological changes that happen when we slow down. When we go, go, go, we run on adrenaline and cortisol. Sometimes we ride on these hormones for years. The minute we begin to slow down, those hormones stop firing as much, and our bodies feel their withdrawal.

As if that's not enough for our systems to bear, we also start to feel things, emotionally and physically, that we've been ignoring. Society rewards intellectualism and living in our heads — so we actively stuff down emotions and ignore physical sensations. But if we slow down and rest, the emotions come bubbling to the top and so does the pain and exhaustion that our bodies have been holding at bay as we grit our teeth, grinding our way through what we've been schooled to believe is the way to success.

Instead of rest being a relief and a recharge, all these sensations added up feel like a bad hangover. Or as Simone Seol says in an Instagram post, "Rest […] is ACTIVE DETOX. Detox feels bad. Very bad. If detox felt pleasant, no one would ever struggle with addiction." EXACTLY, Simone! Who in their right mind would voluntarily go through that? It makes so much sense why we'd avoid that discomfort by continuing to hustle and grind, or by telling ourselves we're resting while still answering emails or diving into work-related books on the beach, or even why we'd cut our rest short.

But the more that we don't allow ourselves to truly rest, and the more we neglect our feelings, bodies, and nervous systems — the further away we get from joy.

We *have* to rest. We need courage to let go of the lies we've been told about our worth and laziness, to feel the feelings we've been stuffing down for so long, and to listen to what our bodies aches and pains are telling us. It requires immense self-compassion to face whatever comes up. When you have courage, self-compassion, and the willingness to meet what arises in the resting process, you will make space for joy. And in making space for joy, you will welcome the whole of your humanity — thoughts, feelings, and nervous system. Your whole humanity is worth resting for.

Imagine what might be possible for our society if we all allowed ourselves more rest.

WHAT IS THIS, AMATEUR HOUR? (THE JOY OF BEING A NEWBIE)

Yes, yes it is!

Call it what you will. Beginner. Newbie. Amateur.

I once thought these were insulting terms. When you're new to something, the assumption is that you're not that good at it. You might even be downright *bad* at it. I used to hate being bad at things. I especially hated being bad at things in front of other people. More so if that particular thing was really important to me.

When I first started coaching, I loathed the thought of someone experiencing or witnessing my coaching and concluding that I was bad at it. I was afraid of the judgments people would make about my competence, capabilities, and worthiness. At least that's what I told myself. In truth, I was more afraid that their assessments were true. (I've since learned that the only time other people's judgments affect us are when we believe there is a kernel of truth to them.) Thoughts like, "Who does Erin think they are? What a shitty coach!" and "They are foolish to think they can make it as a coach!" were what I imagined others saying, but really I was thinking them myself. The more I saw the gap between where I was skill-wise as a coach and where I wanted to be, the more my Inner Critic lashed me.

The only solution I saw was to try to be masterful and perfect as quickly as possible. I motivated myself using fear and shame, rather than using a growth mindset of **curiosity, courage**, and celebration of progress. Being a beginner, for me, completely sucked the joy out of learning and growing as a coach.

I know I'm not alone in having a joy-sucking relationship with being new or inexperienced at something. My clients bring this to me all the time. They are worried that if other people see them being weak at some skill, people will see them as stupid, incompetent, foolish, or silly. Of course, since judgment only matters if you believe there's truth to it, my clients are actually worried that they will see themselves as stupid, incompetent, foolish, and silly. Some clients also worry that people will spread rumors or gossip about them, which will, in their minds, inevitably lead to business failure. So, like me, they internally criticize themselves for not yet being at the level of mastery they expect of themselves. In some cases, clients have considered not starting a new endeavor at all — it's felt safer than experiencing the judgment they believe is inevitable. Others have decided to give being a beginner a whirl but have given up when they aren't immediately brilliant at their new skill.

Another reason we resist being new at something is that it's a lot of work. We have to put in more effort at the outset than when we've mastered it. Imagine learning to drive a car. At first, you have to think about each step:

"Okay, I have to push the pedal (A little more? What, maybe less?) and then I have to put two hands on the steering wheel (Crap, where do they go when I turn?!) and then eyes on the road (Where am I supposed to focus again? Am I seeing all the signs?), and wait, hold on — let me go back and check my rear-view mirrors (Can I see everything I'm supposed to?). Oh God, what I am forgetting!?"

Of course, as time goes on, all of that becomes automatic, and your focus is less on *how* you are driving and more on *where* you are heading.

When we start something new, we may convince ourselves we are starting off with a blank slate. So, we conclude in advance that we're going to be bad at it for some amount of time and it will demand an awful lot of effort to get good. No wonder we lose our joy! In reality, especially in business, we rarely come into something with absolutely no transferable experience or skills. Chances are, we are vastly underestimating ourselves.

I mentioned earlier that when I started coaching, I hated the idea of people judging my coaching. One of the reasons I hated it so much was that I assumed that I was at a much lower competency than I was. I hadn't considered that over the last decade, I'd built up a ton of skills that gave me the foundation of a good coach already. I wasn't as much of a beginner as I thought.

As a user experience researcher at Facebook and Microsoft, my job was to listen deeply to people, to hear not just what they were saying, but to consider what was going on for them underneath. If a research participant asked, "Can we move this button from here to here?" my job was to uncover what was behind that question. What need or want would moving that button fulfill for them? And could we even fulfill it in other (and better) ways? As a coach, I'm always looking for what's bubbling beneath the surface. That's where sustainable, long-term transformation happens. Another part of my job as a researcher was to pull together data points — from things people said in interviews or responses to surveys — and draw out connections and insights. I'm constantly doing the same thing with clients, except rather than gathering data across multiple people, I'm gathering data about a single person across time. I often notice things about people that they'd never considered until I highlight the patterns I see.

In my leadership roles at both companies, I helped people learn and grow as researchers and people. Part of that was helping them discover their superpowers. Another part was helping them understand their inner voices, especially the ones that were in the way of the impact they wanted to make or the goals they wanted to achieve. What I didn't realize until I started coaching-specific training was that I was just as much a coach as I was a manager. I just hadn't been called a coach.

Even if you are starting something that feels completely new to you, I want to invite you to dig a little deeper for where that might not be true. I tried visual art for a few months, explicitly to learn to cultivate joy in being bad at something. I couldn't imagine that I had any skills whatsoever, but I realized that I did have some art knowledge from growing up with parents who collected, and I had a decent understanding of color theory from working with visual designers in the tech world. (That being said, I was just as bad at art as I thought I was. Sometimes you won't be the blank slate you think you are and sometimes you'll find out that you're actually bad at something. Art for me as an exercise in learning to be okay with being bad at something, and realizing that being bad didn't mean diddly squat about me.)

So, sometimes you'll be less of a beginner than you think. And sometimes you'll actually be a beginner. When I was adamant that "beginner" was a dirty word, I didn't realize that there are plenty of upsides to being new at something. Those upsides are a great source of joy.

We'll dive into those upsides in a moment, but before we do, it's helpful to start by looking at the myths and downsides of being a master or expert. Here are some common beliefs we hold about masters:

- Mastery is a goal we should aspire to achieve.
- Once we have mastered something, it becomes easy.
- Masters don't fail as often as non-masters.
- People don't judge masters.
- Masters don't worry about judgment or other people's feedback.
- Masters have quiet or non-existent inner critics. They are confident in their capabilities and their worth.

Those beliefs all have some kernel of truth to them. But they're not completely true. Here are some things that can *also* be true about masters:

- Masters can have unreasonably high expectations of themselves. They put a lot of pressure on themselves to meet those expectations.
- Masters can believe they aren't supposed to fail. So they don't give themselves a lot of permission to — and they can beat themselves up when they do.

- Masters, in efforts not to fail, can sometimes take fewer risks than beginners.

- Masters can believe that others have high expectations for them, too. The fear of judgment doesn't magically go away as they become more masterful. In some ways, it can intensify. Being seen as bad at something as a master can feel way worse than as a beginner who is "supposed to be bad"!

- Masters can get stuck in rules, boxes, and how it's always been done before. They can even get stuck in a notion of what constitutes mastery (such as, master coaches do X, Y, and Z).

As I read these, many of them resonate for me. As I've become more masterful as a coach, at times, I've trapped myself in my own expectations, given myself less permission to take risks with my clients, and stayed more within a box of what I think good coaching is. Not only is none of that a recipe for joy, it's also not a recipe for powerfully serving my clients! When I notice myself falling into these traps, I know it's time to come back to a beginner's mind.

Let's come back to that, too. The downsides of mastery are precisely the upsides of being a beginner:

- Beginners have permission to screw up. In fact, it's more likely that people expect them to make mistakes than to be perfect. It comes with the territory of learning a new skill. (So already, being a beginner comes with a lot less pressure than you might have initially thought.)

- Beginners have much more freedom to take risks, because they have much more permission for those risks to not pan out.

- Beginners don't always have the knowledge or know-how that masters do. They don't know the rules, or the boxes they're supposed to fit in, or even what it means to be "masterful." Which means, beginners tend to break the rules. At times, beginners are more innovative than masters!

Beginners have a greater ability and more permission to tap into their curiosity, creativity, and courage than masters.

Early on in my coaching, I learned techniques that felt weird to me. They involved having people check in with where they felt thoughts and beliefs lived in their body. These techniques dealt with emotions on a much deeper level that I imagined I'd be going into as a coach. I wasn't quite convinced that they were as impactful as my teachers made them out to be. Most of my coaching clients at the time were people I'd known previously — colleagues from Facebook and Microsoft, and friends from other points in my life. They knew I was a beginner. They also trusted me. They were always game for me trying on some of these "weird" techniques with them. I still feel that those early sessions were some of my best. I took the pressure off of myself for what I was doing to "work" and got curious about what might happen.

With all this upside of being a beginner, am I saying that we should never become masters? Absolutely not. It's not possible if you continue to sharpen your knowledge and skills. Instead, I believe the recipe for joy is two-fold: finding joy in being a beginner when you actually are AND finding ways to keep a *beginner's mind* as you move toward mastery. What if masters had just as much allowance to screw up, take risks, and break rules!? We'd have to re-write the definition of a "master!"

If you're not convinced that being a beginner or keeping a beginner's mind can be a source of joy, take some comfort in knowing that neuroplasticity research supports this. Our brains are quite malleable throughout the course of our lifetimes. They will make new neuronal connections all the time. One of the best ways to create new connections is through learning. Dr. David Eagleman, a professor at Stanford and CEO of Neosensory, wrote *Livewired: The Inside Story of the Ever-Changing Brain*[15] and spoke about it on

Brené Brown's *Unlocking Us* podcast[16]. He shared that not only do our brains benefit from learning new things, they also benefit from us being *bad* at them. Say what!!?? Here I was hating being bad at new things, and I was taking care of my brain health! Eagleman also said that we need to put in the effort that we so dread to become good at things so that we can create and rewire neural pathways. It's not enough to simply be bad. We have to be bad for a while and keep up the effort to become better in order to maximize the benefits to our brains.

So perhaps you can now join me in the joy of being bad at something. If you're looking for ideas, make a list of, "It would be joy-full for me to be bad at _____," and tackle them one by one. I never became a visual artist, but I did enjoy the couple months that I made bad art. And perhaps along with the joy of being bad, you can also join me in the joy of having a beginner's mind no matter how good you are at the things you do!

YOU CAN'T IMAGINE YET
WHAT'S OVER THE HORIZON
(THE JOY OF PLAYING "THE LONG GAME")

*"There was always a large horizon. There is much to be done
... It's up to you to contribute some small part to a program of
human betterment for all time."*

~ Francis Perkins

Chances are, you haven't heard of Francis Perkins. It's even less likely you know her if you don't live in the United States. Even if you do, Perkins isn't a prominent figure in American history, despite contributing so much to our current reality. She was the Secretary of Labor in Franklin Delano Roosevelt's (FDR) cabinet in the 1930s and was the driving force behind the creation of some of America's basic social safety nets and labor laws, including social security, unemployment insurance, aid to the homeless, maternal and child welfare, the 40-Hour Workweek, minimum wage, and banning child labor.

Let me say this: I'm not writing about Francis Perkins in a book on joy in business for political reasons. Although her story is inspiring from a political perspective, I'm writing about her because of how she became the driving force behind so many monumental changes and what we can learn about joy from her story.

In 1911, twenty years before joining FDR's administration, she was visiting a friend in New York City when they heard sirens and came outside to see a clothing factory on fire. It was an event called the Triangle Shirtwaist Fire and it killed 147 people. She knew immediately that she wanted to get involved in a mission to end factory fires. Gradually, over many years, she became an influential figure in policy work within New York's city and state governments. To her surprise, as time went on, her mission and goals expanded.

By the time she was invited to serve as Secretary of Labor for the FDR administration, factory fires were just one small piece of a larger effort to protect workers and promote employment during the Great Depression.

When I read Perkins' story in a newsletter a few years ago, I took away two powerful messages that are relevant to joy-full AF business. One take away comes from the quote at the top of this conversation: "There's always a large horizon." She was committed to her mission for the long haul. Her biggest contribution didn't come until 20 years into her work. Had she been narrowly focused on the short term, she might have given up. Or she might have even seen her work as complete once city and state legislatures created better policies around factories. Who knows what the US would have looked like for the last 90 years had she not played a longer game.

Remembering that business is a long game is a challenge. We tend to plan and evaluate our progress in annual, quarterly, or even monthly chunks. We set annual revenue targets. We pay quarterly taxes. We look at month-over-month audience growth. When we overly zoom in on the short-term decisions and metrics, we can lose sight of the fact that we're really aiming to be in business over the long haul, whether that's for a few years or a few decades. We also lose sight of how our here-and-now decisions contribute (or not) to that future. If we find ourselves not meeting short-term goals, we may feel miserable, or even want to throw in the towel, forgetting that some of our biggest impact and achievements might be still years ahead of us.

The other powerful take-away from Perkins' story is that she could not have predicted where the long game would take her. She initially set out to fix a disastrous problem she saw in the present — factory fires. She had no way to predict in 1911 that following her passion would expand into a bigger mission, or that she would eventually become part of a presidential cabinet. I suspect that Francis Perkins knew something that many of us don't: the map you have of what's possible right now is based on what you know to be true ... *right now*. It represents all the knowledge and experience you have gathered from past experience and other people. But the future does not stay within the boundaries of the past. Otherwise, our lives would be very predictable and boring. Everything you do in your business has the potential to open new opportunities to explore — and to expand you into uncharted territory on the map. We'll talk in *Fe-Fi-Fo-Fum ... Plant Some Magic Beans* about ways you can keep your eyes on expanding that territory through intentionally planting seeds...err, Magic Beans ... of joy that may sprout into new opportunities and directions in the future.

Shortly before I started my business, I had a conversation with my financial advisor, who is also a dear family friend. She was fully in support of me starting a business under one condition: "Erin, you have to promise me that you'll stay in business for at least five years." When the COVID-19 pandemic hit, she told me to add another year onto that promise. And then as the pandemic dragged on, she continued to ask me to add more years. What JoAnna knows better than anyone is that it takes time to build a business and that the world operates in cycles. "You can't know until at least five years in whether you have a profitable or viable business. There are too many factors that contribute to success or lack thereof, including world politics and economics, to make sense of data on any shorter time scale."

We may not achieve our goals in the first six months, year, or two years that we're in business. No matter what business you are in, it takes time to develop things like your brand and customer base. It may also take time to master your craft. I know I become an exponentially better coach every year. My clients who are speakers, writers, and social media content creators tell me that the quality of their thoughts and the potency of their wisdom came from keeping at it for a really long time.

What's possible for your joy knowing that no matter where you are right now, there is much more to come and that you can't even imagine from where you are standing what it might look like? What might you do differently in the short-term (what activities would you do, or goals would you set) if your focus was also on the large horizon?

FE-FI-FO-FUM ...
PLANT SOME MAGIC BEANS

"Stop my boy! I'll swap your cow for magic beans.
They'll bring you lots of joy."

~ Jack and the Beanstalk

I have a quart-sized jar of jellybeans on my desk. These are my Magic Beans. Every time I "plant" a Magic Bean in my business, a jellybean goes into the jar.

As we talked about in *Focus on the Present ... But Not Too Much,* being overly focused on the present, and on what results we're creating *right now* can cost us joy. We limit ourselves by only doing activities that we believe will have immediate payoff. It's understandable that we fall into this trap. Because we can't predict the future, instant payoffs produce a sense of security. They can also give us validation that our efforts are not being wasted, or an indication that we're on the right path.

Businesses, like gardens, take time to grow. Not every planted seed will sprout. And of those that do, most won't sprout right away. If you planted a garden based on what would sprout quickly, you'd miss out on a whole variety of vegetables and plants.

If you've heard the idea of "planting seeds" before, it's probably because it's a popular one in business and personal development. Personally, I find that language and metaphor limiting. Which is why my seeds are Magic Beans. By the end of this conversation, I hope you will see yours that way too and be excited by the joy-fullness they can create in your business!

Unlike sowing a garden, you don't always know when you're planting a Magic Bean. In 2016, a Magic Bean proverbially fell out of my pocket when I flew to a weekend conference in New York City put on by Ramit Sethi called Forefront. The event was largely geared toward entrepreneurs, and though I was on the management path at Facebook at the time, something nudged me to go. I had no idea when I lingered a little longer than planned at a post-conference dinner that one of the people who joined us late, Caitlin Padgett, would become my first coach nearly a year later. Or that she'd introduce me to some of my closest friends, help me make life-changing decisions around my gender identity, and be the catalyst for me leaving corporate and becoming a coach myself. All I knew getting on the plane to the event was that flying across the country to hang out with 500 strangers was a growth edge for me, and I hoped it would bring me a few days of joy.

And unlike vegetables and flowers, when we plant a Magic Bean, it's not clear what could sprout. It's not like putting a zucchini seed in the ground and then, lo and behold, a zucchini pops up a little later. A virtual coffee date might sprout into a new client, collaborator, a referral months or years down the road. That doesn't mean all Beans are ambiguous. If we speak at a conference, we may sense that at least one new client could come our way. But I've found that more often than not, what sprouts is not necessarily what we expected.

Along with not always knowing *what* will sprout, we also can't predict *when* they will sprout. A zucchini takes six to eight weeks. A Magic Bean? Who knows! It could be immediate. But it could just as easily germinate months or years from now.

In early 2020, I attended a conference in Washington, D.C. Though a part of me secretly hoped I'd walk away from the conference with new clients, another part of me knew to go in with no agenda. This was a community I was unfamiliar with and a bit intimidated by. I had no idea if they were "my people" or if the topics on the conference agenda would light me up. At the end of the conference, I knew I had planted a Magic Bean or two, but I wasn't sure if any would sprout, or if they did, what they'd turn into. About a week later, one of the Beans sprouted when someone I had spent time with at the conference reached out about working with me. Another sprouted six months later (which in the early COVID-19 days felt like years) when a coach I'd spent quite a bit of time getting to know at the conference referred me to the daughter of one of his clients. She was an ideal fit and became one of my longest-term clients. If I'd been too wrapped up in finding new clients at the conference, I would have missed out on the joy of getting to know the coach, and he likely would have not referred me. I wouldn't be surprised at this point if there are still more Magic Beans yet to sprout from that conference!

I have a story that illustrates how long a Magic Bean can wait to sprout. In 2015, I was interviewed by the American Psychological Association about my non-traditional career path. In 2022, Stony Brook University's psychology department invited me to speak to their graduate students about non-traditional career paths. When I asked how they found me, it was that 2015 article — seven years that Bean was waiting to sprout! Thankfully, Stony Brook was open to me talking about any part of my path, so I spoke about coaching and entrepreneurship instead of Facebook. And who knows, if or what that Stony Brook speaking opportunity might sprout into later.

So, like me with Forefront in 2016, we don't always know that we're planting a Bean. And again, even when we do know, we don't always know if it will sprout. We also mostly don't know what it will sprout into or when. That, my friend, is not a run-of-the-mill garden; it's magic!

Imagine what might be possible in your garden (or the forests of your business wilderness, if that metaphor suits you better), if you pursued joy-full activities in the here and now, and then got curious about what might end up growing in the future as a result. It's a double dip of joy! You get it now planting it and again whenever that Bean magically sprouts in the future.

Magic Beans are one of my favorite ways to regularly create and cultivate joy. They not only fill a jar full of colorful jellybeans, they also help me keep my joy tank full. If you're not sure what counts as a Magic Bean, I want to reassure you that almost anything can.

The only "rule" is that you don't go in with an agenda about what, how, or when a Bean might sprout. That practically guarantees it to lose its magical properties. Here are a few ideas to get you started:

- Virtual coffee dates with old friends and colleagues
- Writing email newsletters
- Attending conferences, events or workshops on topics that interest you
- Going to networking events
- Giving talks or workshops
- Attending local meetups
- Putting out a podcast
- Guesting on a podcast
- Posting on social media
- Engaging with people on social media through DMs and comments

You may notice that all these ideas are business-relevant. But here's a sneaky secret — *some of the most magical of Beans come when you aren't even trying to plant them.* They'll come when you aren't necessarily thinking about your business. You can and *will* plant Magic Beans purely by pursuing joy in all areas of your life. I've met several clients at social meetups, parties, and through friends of friends. Some of my clients have met clients and collaborators on airplanes, golf courses, and tennis courts. You can plant a Magic Bean in any activity you do — you never know when you'll meet somebody who will open a door or show you a path that you hadn't yet seen.

I keep my joy tank full by planting one Magic Bean (or more) every day. As I watch my jellybean jar fill, I know that even when

I'm going through challenges or droughts in the business, things are always bubbling away beneath the surface.

MAGIC BEAN BRAINSTORM

Make a list of at least 100 activities you could do to plant a Magic Bean. Don't limit yourself to activities that you believe will create sprouts. Remember, any activity could turn into something magical in the future. Once you have a list, make a daily or weekly planting plan. And notice if your planting plan starts to suck away your joy. The magic is in following your joy, not a strict schedule.

If you like having something to look at, find a jar and fill it with anything that feels joy-full. I, for one, love the colorfulness of Jelly Belly beans, but I know many folks would not be able to keep themselves from eating them. (I know my wife often sneaks a few from the source bag when I'm "not looking"!) Thankfully, my sweet tooth craves other things!

PUT ON YOUR HILA HAT

We've covered several traps that we can fall into when setting goals (*Heading Toward Destinations on Other People's Maps, Going After Possible Goals, Chasing Happiness, Chasing Enoughness*). It's not just what goals we set, though, that can either cultivate or drain our joy — it's also about how we chase them.

Recall that we sometimes infer that achieving our goals says something about us — that we're competent, capable, and/or worthy (Trap #4). We also make failure mean something too — that we are none of those things. So if *success* = *worthy* and *failure* = *not worthy*, then reaching our goals becomes a high stakes, all-or-nothing endeavor. We then become needy, anxious, or clenching in our energy. We take fewer risks and put blinders on, focusing only on activities that move us toward the goal, rather than seeing opportunities along the path to try out new ideas or pivot completely.

The more we tie our self-worth or happiness to accomplishing the goal, the more hell bent we get on reaching it at all costs.

If we want to get out of the meaning-making trap, we can change which goals we go after. But that may not always be a solution. It's not necessarily the goal itself that is the problem. It's our attachment to reaching it. Often a better option is to change *how* we go after our goals. One of the most joy-full ways to change your "how" is to use HILA: high intention toward reaching the goal and low attachment to if, when, or how you get there. Back in the Introduction I mentioned that when I visualized HILA I saw it as a hat to wear while adventuring towards different destinations in the business wilderness.

Let's unpack HILA a bit, because it can be easily misunderstood. Being highly intentional means putting plans in place and taking steps toward reaching the goal. We'd LOVE to get there. But, having low attachment means that along the way we are open to shifts. Maybe we'll need to be creative about the steps we are taking toward the goal. We might need to take a right turn here, or a left turn there. Maybe we'll need to take longer to reach our goal than we originally hoped. Or maybe the goal itself will need to change. When we're open to shifts, we might even discover a better goal to go after.

Being in HILA also allows us to tap into three of the foundational ingredients of joy: curiosity, creativity, and courage.

Curiosity. We can ask ourselves questions like: I wonder how I can get to my goal? I wonder what I can do next? I wonder what's possible?

Creativity. When the path doesn't have to be set, we can lean into creative ways to get where we want to go. And when we hit inevitable roadblocks, creativity can help us change course or find a path forward.

Courage. We can take risks, stretch ourselves, do things we've never done before. And because we aren't attached to if or when we get to the finish line, we can fail, fail, fail, and fail again.

It might seem counterintuitive to set a goal that you aren't attached to achieving. It definitely felt this way for me when I first considered it. But, I've landed on a moon metaphor (pun intended) that soothes the parts of me that don't understand why I'd ever go after a goal that I'm not sure I'll reach. See, if we're too attached to reaching the moon, we may not allow ourselves to see all the opportunities for landing elsewhere. Maybe by tweaking our course, we could go even farther than planned, landing on Mars instead. Or maybe as we fly out of Earth's atmosphere, we'll hear a noise off to the left (yes, I know there's no sound in space, stick with me here!), and follow it to a wild party at the International Space Station. If we're truly unattached to if, when, or how we get to the moon, we may decide to hang out in Earth's orbit for a little while and take a little rest, before getting back on track to the moon. Or we might even decide to stay in Earth's orbit forever because that's pretty great. All of this to say that when you're overly attached to a particular destination, you miss all kinds of opportunities for joy.

Had I not put on my HILA Hat while writing a book, *Joy-Full AF* would not exist. When I first started (as I mentioned in *Why Did I Write a Book on Joy-full AF Business?*), I had a book idea about the word "And." Had I been overly attached to that idea, I would have written something that was maybe okay, but not what really lit my heart up. However, because I committed to HILA (I even publicly announced I was "HILA-ing" my book on Facebook!), when I realized the proverbial moon was no longer my destination, I gave myself permission to hang out in the Earth's orbit until I found a new direction. It took several iterations, and several more pauses along the way, to land at *Joy-Full AF*. The book in your hands is so much more powerful, and comes to you with so much more love in its words because of my willingness to stay unattached to what book I wrote.

HILA was not just about what book I wrote, though. It was also about if and when a book came out. This part of HILA was admittedly a bit more difficult for me to stick to. I was eager to get my words out in the world! But sure enough, every time I tried to set a deadline for myself, my energy clenched, I stressed, and I lost the joy. As soon as I put my HILA Hat back on around timelines, everything eased, creativity flowed, and I had more fun.

The last bit of HILA in writing this book came mid-process when I figured out that I needed to also be unattached to *how* I wrote the book. As I mentioned, the best way for me to write the first draft of this book ended up being by speaking it into Otter. AI. I also wrote it in conversations rather than traditional chapters. If I'd made my non-traditional writing process mean something about my capability or worth (or even whether or not I'm allowed to call myself a writer) it simply would not exist.

So how do you put on your HILA Hat? Take a look at the list of goals you have for your business right now. You may want to revisit the goals you listed in the exercise in *Falling Into Multiple Traps at Once.*

Are there any goals you already have naturally *high intention* and *low attachment* toward reaching? Great! You're already set up for joy in going after those.

How about goals where you have *low intention* and *low attachment toward* reaching them? You don't really want to go after them and you don't think it means anything about you if you don't reach them. I call these **Apathy Goals**. There's no joy in going after them. Throw them out completely.

Are there any goals you have *low intention* and *high attachment* to? You don't really want to go after them, but unlike Apathy Goals you think reaching those goals will mean something about you or bring you happiness. (If you're having a hard time wrapping your brain around a goal like this, I like the example of someone who doesn't want to be a manager in a corporate role, but goes after a promotion because they think it will signal they are good enough.) I call these **Should Goals**. As we've talked about in many conversations, *should* is a joy-suck! There are two options for these kinds of goals. Like Apathy Goals you can throw these out completely too. There's no sense in going after something you don't want. Or, you can ask yourself, what would turn this Should Goal into a **Want Goal** by shifting it from *low intention* to *high intention*? Once you have the want, or it's already clear what your want is, you may still have high attachment to getting there. We'll look at how to lower your attachment next.

Lastly, are there any goals (either from the original list or after changing some goals to Want Goals) where you have *high intention* and *high attachment*? You really want to get there and you believe it means something about you or your happiness if you do. Here are some questions you can ask yourself to lower your attachment:

- What's the *worst* that could happen if I don't achieve the goal?
- What's the *best* that could happen if I don't achieve the goal?

- What does it mean about me or my success if I don't achieve that goal?

- What will it mean about me or my success if I do achieve the goal?

- How can I move from clenching into curiosity? What specific steps can I take to do that?

- What do I need to let go of in order to lower my attachment?

You may notice that these questions are geared toward helping you shift away from outcomes as a metric of your success, worth, and emotional well-being. But once you have your HILA Hat on for a goal, you still may want to know, "How can I make the process even more joy-full?"

Here are some additional questions to ask yourself:

- What route would be the most fun to take towards my goal?

- What are some creative ways of getting there that I haven't thought of yet?

- What can I get curious about as I take each step?

- Where can I lean into fear, take risks, or stretch myself?

See what shifts in your business if you continuously wear your HILA Hat! If your experience is at all like mine, the twists and turns — even when frustrating — will be worth the unexpected directions you end up going!

[Before we move on, I should note that sometimes we resist putting on our HILA Hat because we're afraid of what others will think of us if we change our goal mid-progress. Unfortunately, it's true that people will judge. No matter what your reason, some people will see pivoting as flaky or uncommitted. But others will see it as inspiring and give them permission to do the same. I've found that when even one person tells me I've inspired them or given them permission to pivot or change, it immediately evaporates the weight of any judgment or criticism I may have received. You can't escape judgment no matter *what* you do. It's not only futile to try, it's a drain on your joy. If you can't please everyone, why not please yourself and follow your joy instead?]

IT'S ALL FUN AND GAMES ...
NO, REALLY!

I've said throughout that joy is about much more than fun and delight. But sometimes it IS about just that! Sometimes intentionally infusing fun and delight into your work gets your creative juices going. Sometimes you move faster towards your goals ... or even go further than you originally planned. And sometimes a little fun can move you through fear, challenge, and doubt in ways you can't when just tapping into your courage.

Gamification — the process of adding games or gamelike elements to an activity — has been popular for decades (McDonald's started their famous Monopoly game back in the late 80s), and has become even more widespread in the digital age. When I worked at Facebook on the content sharing team in 2017, we studied other apps that gamified content sharing (like Snapchat's "Streaks" of snapping with a friend at least once in a 24-hour period for more than 3 days) to see what we might incorporate into the Facebook experience. (Side note: nothing we considered made it past initial ideation. I'm personally grateful that neither Facebook or Instagram went down the gamification path, despite adopting several other successful features of Snapchat.) Gamification has become so popular that even some of my games have been gamified. Words with Friends allows me to collect coins by playing a certain number of words or taking certain actions in the app, and those coins can then be traded in for word hints and free tile swaps. My New York Times Crossword app tracks how many days I've completed a crossword without hints, and tracks my average completion times. Of course, I can't help but want to do even the hardest of puzzles as fast as possible, knowing that I might be able to beat my own record!

My examples may suggest that gamification is a dark psychology tactic for keeping people addicted to their phones — or in McDonald's case buying more Big Macs, chicken nuggies, and fries. It certainly can be. But it can also be a great way to stay motivated and consistent towards a goal. When you create games in your business, you can tap into at least three of the four ingredients of joy: curiosity, creativity, and courage.

So why might you create a game? I mentioned a few at the beginning of this conversation, but I'll repeat them and add a few more here:

- To have more fun! You don't need any justification to be playful!

- To take pressure off the work that you're doing. Some people thrive in pressure, but many don't. For me, there's a sweet spot, and games can help me alleviate just enough pressure that I can feel excited about my work again.

- To shift your focus away from outcomes/results so that you can be more present in the process of achieving your goals. As we talked about in several conversations (*Goal Traps, Put on Your HILA Hat*), we can lose joy when we are overly attached to and focused on the outcome.

- To move through a fear or challenge.

To give you a sense of what I mean by playing games, here are a couple I've played in my business. You can adopt them exactly how I describe them or adapt them any way that suits your needs. (And if creating your own game is more your jam, we'll talk about how you can do just that little later in this conversation.)

Collecting Nos

No matter what business you're in, you are going to experience people saying "No" to you or what you have to offer. Most of us hate the word "No." We don't like saying it to other people and we certainly don't like hearing it. It's a rejection and sometimes our brains can't differentiate between a rejection of an offer and a rejection of *us*. Even for the most confident and self-assured people, rejection can feel painful. Painful enough that it's worth actively avoiding. The fear of rejection can be so overwhelming at times that it leaves us paralyzed.

Collecting Nos is my favorite way to move through this fear or stuckness. The rules are simple: Set a target of how many Nos you want to collect either in a specific activity (like collect 20 Nos to guesting on a podcast) or across a period of time (like collect 20 Nos in a week). You can play the game in the context of something you've been afraid of or putting off in your business — like raising your fees — or purely to work on your fear of rejection. The latter is what my friend Candace did a few years ago.

Inspired by a TED talk called, "What I Learned from 100 Days of Rejection," Candace headed to a local mall and filmed herself *Collecting Nos*. Her goal was to collect 10 Nos in 100 minutes. She asked mall goers and shop employees for ridiculous things, including to work behind the counter at a pretzel shop, to give a stranger a haircut in the mall corridor, and to purchase just one shoe from a pair. She even asked if she could take home a $20 baby shark stuffed animal for free. To her surprise, the person said, "Yes!" In fact, she got more than one yes that day. On top of realizing that you can't always predict what people might say yes to, she also learned a profound lesson about No — even when people thought her request was preposterous, nothing bad happened. She was okay. She was safe. And the more she upped the ridiculousness of the request, the more fun she had. Candace probably could have convinced herself that rejection was safe through mindset work, but nothing could have come close to what her body knew thanks to experiencing it firsthand.

Networking Bingo

Are you one of those weirdos that actually likes networking? Do you find it naturally fun, easy, or dare I say, joy-full? If so, this game isn't for you and you can move onto the next one. (And would you mind teaching the rest of us the magic of your ways?)

Okay, if you're still here, this game is my secret weapon. Though I am quite social, I was very shy for the first few decades of my life, and that still shows up at times in networking situations. It happens most often when I'm in a room of strangers and I am unsure what we might have in common.

Most people don't like networking because it's socially awkward. We don't know what to say or ask. If the other person is also having trouble keeping the flow of conversation going, it becomes doubly awkward.

Before I tell you about the game, I want to shift your perspective on networking and meeting new people in general. Often we associate networking with selling ourselves or our business to other people. What if that's a backwards approach? What if the whole point is not to figure out what to say or how to sell yourself, but instead, to figure out what you can learn about other people?

From that perspective, networking can be a fantastic place to exercise your **curiosity**. Being **curious** about other people is all about asking great questions. But, what if you don't always know what questions to ask on the spot? That's where creating *Networking Bingo* before you head to the event comes in handy!

Spend some time thinking about what would be fun to know about others or fun to experience. It could be business-related, but it doesn't have to be. Maybe you want to see if you can have an entire conversation without the other person asking you a single question. That's a Bingo Square. Maybe you want to see if you can get the person to name a weird quirk about themselves. That's a Bingo Square. Be as **creative** and silly as you want. Tuck your "Bingo card" away on a note card in your pocket or make a note of things on your phone to score later. Even if you don't nail all your Bingo squares, I guarantee you'll have some joy-full, interesting conversations!

The 90 Day $ Game

Collecting Nos and *Networking Bingo* are both different ways of moving through fear, challenge, and discomfort. This next game can help take the pressure off your work and/or shift your focus from outcomes/results towards joy in the process. I learned the *90 Day $ Game* from Rich Litvin. He taught it in the context of revenue goals, but any quantifiable goal could be turned into a game. And of course, the 90-day timeframe is flexible too. For example, I once helped a leader at a small start-up design a Quarter 2 User Growth game (catchy title, I know). For explaining the game, though, let's stick to what Rich Litvin originally taught me.

As we've talked about in several of the *Goal Traps*, revenue goals can be joy-sucks. We can take on revenue goals that we've seen from others because we believe that's what we should aspire to. And we can get overly attached to reaching those goals, thinking that success or failure means something about our capability and worth. One of the additional challenges of revenue as a goal is that it's a lagging indicator — that is, revenue comes in only after a series of other things have happened. For instance, in my coaching practice, how much money I've brought in is a lagging indicator of how many clients I have enrolled, and how many clients I have enrolled is a lagging indicator of how many potential clients I've had introductory coaching sessions with. And of course, how many people I've had these sessions with depends on how many people I've invited to a coaching conversation, or how many people have reached out to me through social media, my website, or referrals. All those actions leading up to revenue are leading indicators. When we attach our feelings of success and worth to a lagging indicator like revenue, we lose focus on the leading indicators. The leading indicators are our opportunity to lean into joy. They are also rife for gamification.

In the *90 Day $ Game*, you set a money goal that feels like a courageous stretch, but not impossible. As we discussed in *Goal Trap #2 – Going After Possible Goals,* the sweet spot is a number that feels just on the other side of possible, but not so impossible that your nervous system flares up or shuts down. Then as, soon as you set the number for your $ goal, you put on your HILA Hat and unattach from if, when, or how you reach it. The game is not about whether you hit your target, it's about curiosity for how far you can get if you focus on leading indicators. And really, it helps you connect with and get creative and courageous about what those leading indicators are and how you go about them.

If your head is swirling a bit about leading and lagging indicators, let me make this more concrete with an example. The first time I played the *90 Day $ Game* was a few months into my business. I was attending Rich Litvin's in-person event for coaches called RLI, and he asked us all to write how much money we'd like to make in the next 90 days on a piece of paper. I wrote $100K. It felt ridiculous. I'd made something like $30K in my first three months in business, and now I was setting a goal to triple that in the following three months! Thankfully nobody needed to know my goal. Or so I thought. Rich asked one of the participants to share his goal. I don't remember what it was, but I know it was fairly low, and didn't satisfy Rich. He turned to me. Cue panic: *F*ck. Now I can't pretend I wrote something more reasonable down.* I took a deep breath and told him my number. Rich was intrigued. We could have done the math I demonstrated above, working backwards from how many one-on-one clients I'd need to enroll at my current prices (leading indicator), and then how many coaching conversations I'd need to have to enroll that many clients (leading indicator), and then how many people I need to invite to coaching conversations … but the math would have told me one thing: I needed to invite, coach, and enroll A LOT of people. Instead, Rich asked me, "What could you offer, and to whom, that a single client would pay you $100K for it?"

I knew that I likely wouldn't go down the route of offering a single client $100K, but the question got my creative juices flowing. What else could I offer besides 1:1 coaching? Who do I want to coach and what could I offer them? How might my coaching fees need to adjust? When I got home from the event, I brainstormed all kinds of ideas, including group programs, corporate workshops, and coaching packages that included transformational experiences and travel alongside coaching. Rich had encouraged me in another part of the event to triple my fees. I knew I wasn't ready for that, either in my level of coaching mastery or in my nervous system, but I did double them. Not only did I get creative about my offerings, but I also leaned into courage to offer free coaching to anyone who was interested. And *that* led me to lean into even more courage and speak about what I was doing in personal conversations and on social media. I wasn't going to create $100K in 90 days if people didn't know about what I was up to in the world!

I didn't hit the $100K goal. If you're thinking, "Oh no! The game didn't work," remember reaching $100K was not the point! I did make ~$66K though, more than double what I had made in my first three months, and for sure it was way more than I would have earned if I'd continued to go about my normal process without creatively and courageously stretching myself. I had more fun than I otherwise would have, too! In fact, one of the most fun parts was designing a "game board" on my whiteboard wall to track my progress. It was a rainbow road. Every thousand dollars, I colored in a brick on the road. And every thousand dollars in proposed fees (lead indicator) became a little pot of gold alongside the road!

I often suggest that my clients play the *90 Day $ Game* when they are first starting their business, but I also sometimes suggest it for clients who are in a rut and need a stretch to juice them up and bring them back into joy-full creation. No matter where you are in business, the *90 Day $ Game* can be a joy-infusion that has the bonus of potentially bringing you a cash-infusion too!

Create Your Own Game

If you'd like to create your own game, here are some ideas for getting started.

Design for the Journey Not the Destination.

This may seem counterintuitive. Yes, you want to have a destination in mind. But the whole idea is to make the journey more fun, creative, and/or courageous. Some questions you might ask yourself:

What would make each step along the journey more joy-full? It might be as simple as tracking them like in *Networking Bingo*. Or it might be tapping into your inner child and giving yourself gold star stickers as you reach particular milestones.

What would make the overall journey more creative? Are there alternate routes you can take to the same destination? As I mentioned, when I played the *90 Day $ Game* a few years ago, I expanded my offerings from solely one-on-one coaching to corporate workshops and a group program.

How can you stretch your courage muscle? Candace increased the boldness of her requests as she went along in her *Collecting Nos Game*. That helped her realize that no "NO" was as bad as she once thought it was.

Keep your HILA Hat on

Again, the game is all about the journey, so it's key to let go of attachment to the destination. The idea is not to win the game, and it means nothing about you if you don't. Remember, I made $66K of $100K in my first *90 Day $ Game*. What was important was the creativity and courage it evoked in me, not whether I hit the target.

Make it all up as you go!

Remember our earlier conversations about not needing a Why, What, or How (*Tell Me Why (Ain't Nothing but a Heartache)*, *We Don't Need No Destination!*, *How Do I ...*)? Those apply here too. You don't need a fully fleshed out structure or rules to get playing. Your game can be like a 5-year-old telling a story, full of unformed scenes, nonsensical tangents, and incongruous "and thens."

Pull out your arts and crafts supplies!

Part of the fun I have in playing games is creating a gameboard that delights and excites me. Sure, I could track progress in Excel or in a notebook, but where is the joy in that? We're here to MAXIMIZE our joy. So, pull out your drawing paper and colored pencils. Make a space on your white board. Heck, pull out a piece of wood to etch into or a canvas to paint on if that's your jam. Whatever your medium, make sure it can be put somewhere where you can see it.

A client who is a consultant for nonprofits and NGOs once said in a coaching session, "How can I *play* my way into signing my next client?" I love this question. It's a powerful and joy-full way to create success.

How can you play your way to whatever you want to achieve next?

"IT'S ALL RESEARCH"

I remember the moment my first coach, Caitlin Padgett (who you first met in *Fi Fi Fo Fum ... Plant Some Magic Beans*), said this on a group coaching call. A client was beating herself up for partying a little too hard the night before. The woman was mid-shame spiral when Caitlin stopped her and said something to the effect of, "Let's look at this differently. What if it's all research? What I mean by that is, last night happened. You can't change it. But you can learn something about it. What were the circumstances? Who was around? What were you thinking and feeling? What can you take going forward that will help you recognize your limits in the future?"

I watched as the shame and guilt rose out of Caitlin's client almost as if it was exorcised. With a sense of lightness and curiosity, she became a researcher on the previous night's experience. What had just moments ago been painful suddenly lost its charge. It was brilliant coaching AND a brilliant way to look at the world.

A light bulb went on for me in that moment. I am a scientist and researcher at heart. Between my academic history and my corporate roles, I spent nearly a decade eating, sleeping, and breathing all things data analysis, experimentation, surveys, and interviews. With "It's all research," Caitlin was speaking my language — but in a way I hadn't previously considered.

Since then, "It's all research" as a concept has expanded into much more for me than looking back on past actions to understand what led to them. Being a scientist and researcher is at the foundation of everything I do in my business. It's also a way I create and cultivate joy.

If you're wondering how something that sounds like hard science can relate to joy, let's start with some things that take us away from joy. After a night of partying, Caitlin's client was feeling the shame of her failure to moderate herself. Though she didn't share what her inner voices were saying to her, I can imagine that they were pretty nasty. In her mind, it meant something about her worth — that she'd "f*cked up and she was BAD."

Most of our fears, of failure, rejection, disappointing others, uncertainty, and even success, are about what we'll tell ourselves if they come true. If I fail, it means I'm not good enough. If I'm rejected, I'm unlovable. If I'm successful, I'll have to walk around hiding that I'm a fraud. Those voices in our head can be brutal. Often more so than what anyone outside of us might say.

To shut up those inner voices, we do everything possible to prevent our fears from coming true. That leads us to perfectionism and needing to "get it right" in our heads before we take action. We might sit on putting out a program, waiting for a sign that it's flawless and guaranteed to be a success. We might fret over an approach to something in our business, worried about what happens if we choose wrong.

Whether it's the pressure we put on ourselves prior to taking action or the ways we beat ourselves up for actions that don't work out as planned, we have no room for joy when everything feels high stakes for our self-esteem.

Over the next four conversations, we'll explore ways you can apply "It's all research" to keep out joy-stealing thoughts. We'll also talk about how it can *create* joy by helping you tap into your curiosity, creativity, and courage.

DATA HATH NO MEANING

"Data hath no meaning."

~ Michael Burgoon (my dad)

I'm not sure *I* ever heard my dad say this phrase, but I've been told by many of his former graduate students that he used it a lot as a professor and PhD advisor, especially when he was teaching. I have no idea where the saying comes from. For all I know, he invented it. Until recently I didn't even know what context he used it in. (I asked my mom, who was also a colleague of his, and learned there is a second part of the phrase ... it makes more sense for how he would have used it, but I prefer the sentence as I remember it).

I've personally adopted "Data Hath No Meaning" as a mantra in my business and life. Let me explain. Humans are meaning-making machines. I mean we are certifiable *experts* at telling ourselves stories about what our experiences mean. If we send a text to someone we have a crush on and they don't answer right away, we might tell ourselves that they aren't interested in us. Or that we're too forward. If we're at a party and we overhear a group of people laughing just after we walked by, we might tell ourselves that they were making fun of us.

Our meaning-making doesn't magically turn off when we're running our businesses. We tell ourselves all kinds of stories about what it means if we fill (or don't fill) a program, sell (or don't sell) a product, sign (or don't sign) a new client, hit (or don't hit) a revenue goal. When we succeed, we tell ourselves it means that we are smart, capable, valuable, creative, good enough. And on the flip side, when we fail, we aren't any of those things. Instead, we're incapable, incompetent, dumb as a box of rocks, unworthy, and certainly not good enough. We can be especially self-critical if we have a high "internal locus of control." That is, we believe that we are mostly responsible for, or in control of, our outcomes (as opposed to external forces like other people, luck, fate, or God being responsible for our situation). For instance, if I think it's 100% "on me" whether a client signs on to work with me, then I'm completely ignoring or discounting any other factors that might lead them to say yes or no. And that means their yes or no is about me — my capabilities as a coach and salesperson — and not anything else. Now my value or self-worth hinges on the decision they make, which ironically, gives all the control to my potential client!

The notion that we are in control of our destiny is baked into our individualistic society. In American this concept is particularly embedded, but it shows up in many other cultures as well. Individualism tells us, "Success is in your hands!" and "If you can't make it to the top, that's on you!" Now, this notion isn't *all* bad. In fact, people who believe they are in control of their outcomes do create more success, take more action, and are more confident in themselves than people who believe external factors are responsible for their outcomes. But, as I have already highlighted, when we completely shoulder the responsibility for our successes and failures, we can quickly make up false narratives about ourselves — and those stories can end up running the show. "I just signed a client. I'm a badass!" can quickly turn into, "I just got a no. I'm a shit coach. I'm a shit salesperson. I'm probably just shitty in general. I'm never going to make it … I might as well give up."

When our stories are in control, we cannot operate from **connection, curiosity, creativity,** or **courage.** In other words, our meaning-making crowds out our joy. This brings me back to my dad's phrase … *data hath no meaning.* A single data point can't tell us much. And depending on what question you are trying to answer with a quantitative approach, it can take hundreds of data points until a clear picture begins to emerge. The concept of collecting data in your business may not be new to you. After all, we live in a data-driven, quantification-obsessed world. But perhaps what will be new to you is what you can consider to be "data."

Everything you do is data.

Every action, nonaction, activity, project, or client. A single LinkedIn post. A single conversation at a conference. A single enrollment conversation with a client. A single unproductive day staring at the computer. Even a single thought or feeling! You might want to read that again because it's a game-changing concept. (At least it was for me.) And, again, a single piece of data carries no meaning. It says nothing about you, your process, or your strategy. Only after you have repeated something many times over can you start looking at the collection of data points for a story. After hundreds of LinkedIn posts, you might notice that certain types of content resonate with your audience. After multiple conversations at conferences and networking events, you may notice that how you talk about what you do isn't landing and could use some tweaks. After dozens of enrollment calls, you can start looking at what might be leading to a string of Nos. After weeks of unproductively staring at the computer, then you might be able to look deeper to make a connection about what is blocking you.

Attention: *Notice that making meaning about a collection of data doesn't mean making meaning about YOU.* Data is objective. It allows you to look at what you might keep doing and what may need a different approach. It doesn't allow you (or anyone for that matter) to judge you or your worth.

You might be wondering, well how much data do I need to collect before I can start looking for patterns? I don't have an answer for that. When it comes to seeing everything as data, it's more of an art than a science. I'm someone who likes to err on the side of making as little meaning as possible until it seems abundantly clear that there is a pattern and that no external circumstances could easily explain what is happening.

The more you put on your proverbial lab coat and operate your business like you're a scientist collecting data, the more you can follow your curiosity, creativity, and courage, and the less you'll internally lash yourself for a single mistake, misstep, or failure. And *also,* the more you'll come to realize that you are much less in control of your outcomes than our culture has taught you to believe. A post on social media can go viral or it can get crickets, and have nothing to do with the content of that post, but instead have everything to do with how the algorithm works or who just happened to share it with their networks. A group program might not fill because it's the middle of summer and people are prioritizing vacations. A revenue drought might be due to a pandemic, war, or economic recession that has people tightening their wallets or investing their money and time differently. We can do our best and the universe will still do what it does.

Data may hath no meaning, but it does "hath" 😉 the ability to create space for joy!

COLLECT SOME DATA

The best way to hone your ability to treat everything like a scientist is to track your actions and notice what feelings come up and what meaning you attach to outcomes. For each activity, note:

- the outcome as succinctly as possible like an experimenter would (success/fail)
- the emotion* that came up as a result of the outcome
- the meaning you made about the outcome (if any), and then, note the real meaning.

Don't skip the step of what you are/were making it mean if you've already reframed. It's important to track any patterns you have in meaning-making along with everything else.

*We'll talk about why tracking the emotion is important for your joy in *Put on Your Lab Coat AND Feel Your Feelings Too*.

Activity	Outcome (Success/Fail)	Emotion	What I'm Making It Mean	What It Really Means

JOY GUIDES;
EXPERIMENT DECIDES

There's a famous research adage that goes: "Theory guides. Experiment decides."[17] Well, that's all well and good for experiments in science, but we're talking business here! I like my version of the maxim (in the conversation title) a bit better 😌. But speaking of science, let's talk about my dad again ...

When I was a kid, I spent a lot of time at my parents' office at the University of Arizona. Behind my dad's door was a coat and hat rack. It held only one item — a lab coat. Just like I have no idea where his saying "data hath no meaning" came from, I don't have a clue where the lab coat came from. Maybe a Halloween costume or a practical joke by his grad students? It's possible I asked him at some point, but if I did, whatever he answered didn't stick. All I knew was that as a professor of communication, he wasn't the kind of doctor who needed a lab coat.

Nowadays I think about that lab coat almost every day in my business. In *Data Hath No Meaning,* I mentioned the idea of putting on your proverbial lab coat. Let me expand on that. One of my favorite ways to be in the joy of collecting data in my business is through designing experiments. And experiments always bring me back to that lab coat. But it wasn't my dad's coat that turned me on to a love of experimentation. It really started with my doctoral work where practically all my research involved running experiments. My love of it grew at Facebook where thousands of experiments were running at any given time to help decide what features ended up in the hands of end users and what exited the app stage right. Facebook tested (and still does!) almost everything you can imagine, from changing the location, text, or color of a button, to large new features like Facebook Stories.

Experimentation can be just as useful for solopreneurs and small businesses as it is for enterprise corporations. And in my opinion, even more joy-full. That's because our experiments don't have to be scientifically rigorous (and it's likely they can't be most of the time). They can, however, be rooted in **curiosity** about what might happen, **creativity** in what is being tested and how, and **courage** to take risks and try things that might fail.

Yet experimentation, as I've found with clients and peers, isn't always baked into business practice. I've seen entrepreneurs get trapped in their heads, trying to figure out the right next step or path, or trying to design the perfect product, service, or experience before taking any action. Life is full of trial and error, but somehow our brains are less forgiving of that in business contexts. Perhaps, as we talked about in *Tell Me Why (Ain't Nothing but a Heartache), We Don't Need No Destination!,* and *How Do I ...,* it's because we don't want to waste time, money, or effort going in the wrong direction. And — if we're not seeing our actions as objective data — we don't want to face our feelings (or our Inner Critic's lashings) about failure.

The truth is, it's damned hard to nail *anything* on the first try! And it's even harder to mentally predict what will and won't work. Sometimes we can make a guess, but there's no actual certainty. We can't know for sure what marketing copy is going to resonate with customers unless we put marketing in front of them. We can't know what social media content is going to change people's hearts and minds until we give them something to consume. We can't know what kind of course or program is going to be most useful to people before we run a course or program to try on some of our ideas for size. And that's all just about how other people will feel. What about *our* joy? We can't always know what's going to make us most joy-full to create or do until we try it!

If large enterprise companies can't figure out what will succeed unless they do thousands of experiments, why should we be expected to have all the answers before collecting data?

My client, Danika, was in the early stages of building her coaching practice when she started working with me. One session she came to me with a conundrum about enrolling clients. She was part of both Rich Litvin's and Stacey Boehman's coaching communities. Rich is known for his "Prosperous Coach" approach, which involves giving people deep coaching sessions that last anywhere from 90 minutes to 2 hours as part of enrolling clients. Stacey's approach is a more standard 30 minute "Discovery Call," where the coach gathers some information on the potential client and then talks the person through the different coaching options. In the Discovery Call approach, very little, if any, coaching is done. Danika felt torn. Which approach was right?

I reminded her that "Which approach is right?" was the wrong question. The better question was, "Which approach is right *for me*?" I encouraged her to explore which approach felt best and most aligned with her values, and which ultimately led to the types of clients and client relationships she wanted in her business.

So we designed an experiment: Over her next ten potential client conversations, half would take the Prosperous Coach approach and the other half would take the Discovery Call approach. At the end, she'd decide which *felt* best. Notice I didn't tell her to look at what *worked* best. Ten people, five in each "experimental group" was not enough data in my mind, to know which strategy would be more successful long-term with the types of clients she wanted to work with. What mattered more at this time was what felt the most aligned and joy-full for her. Sure enough, she found her answer. For the time being, the Prosperous Coach approach was going to be Danika's approach.

Doing any experiment requires some courage. Who knows how many of the five clients Danika tested Discovery calls with would have ended up as clients if she'd done all ten calls with the Prosperous Coach approach. Sometimes finding the most joy-full process for you over the long-term requires some short-term losses or costs. That can be hard to swallow if you're someone who wants to enroll every potential client or customer that comes through your door. But it's also better than staying stuck in decision paralysis or choosing a strategy without testing it first and only to find what you've chosen is joy-less.

Danika's experiment was numbers-based. That is, I suggested a certain number of potential clients she could have conversations with before determining her enrollment approach going forward. Another way to experiment is with using time.

My client, Jessica, did one of those with me. After leaving one of the biggest corporations in the world and then taking a maternity leave, Jessica had the opportunity to join the C-suite of a tiny start-up. On the table with the offer was the potential for Jessica to become a cofounder of the company several months down the line if she and the founder felt like they were good partners. On paper, it sounded like a dream next step. But as she came off maternity leave, she wasn't quite sure whether this start-up was the right next step *for her*. She'd been toying with the idea of her own start-up or even leaving tech altogether for a different entrepreneurial adventure.

Jessica had spent her entire career chasing promotions and titles, not because she wanted them, but because they told her something (in her mind) about her worth. She had worried constantly about how other people would judge her success. After working with me for several months, she knew that wasn't a healthy way to approach her career and had taken some meaningful steps towards separating her worth from her work. Now with this new role on the table, she worried that if she accepted it, she'd fall back onto old habits and chase the cofounder title as another way to prove herself, rather than truly evaluate whether the company and the title were right for her.

Like with Danika, I suggested an experiment. I hoped that if she was in the mindset of "testing whether it was a fit," she'd worry less about the cofounder possibility and avoid some of the behaviors around proving herself that were so familiar. I also imagined that it would help her try new leadership styles and develop skills (like focusing more on strategy than execution) with less pressure. The founder wanted to wait until Jessica was at the company for six months before evaluating the possibility of bringing her on as cofounder. That seemed like an excellent time frame to work with

— long enough to deeply immerse herself in the company, but not long enough that it felt like too large a commitment.

Framing Jessica's time at the start-up as an experiment was a huge success. It allowed her to show up with curiosity: "Which aspects of this role do I like? Which do I not? Which aspects of this company and this time do I like? Which do I not?" It allowed her to step into leadership and strategic thinking, and to discover that those were natural strengths. We checked in regularly about how the experiment was going. We'd make sure she wasn't being sucked into old stories and operating from fear. We'd look at what data supported her staying at the company long-term and what data suggested otherwise. On occasion I would ask her questions like, "What else would you need to find out in order for this experiment to give you a conclusive yes or no to continuing on?" and "At what point would the data be so conclusive, even in these initial six months, that continuing on could not possibly change the outcome?" At the six-month mark, she didn't have enough data, and neither did the founder. So she agreed to a three-month extension. Again, we looked at what data she needed to collect to have an answer. Ultimately, she came to a joy-full decision, one rooted in data and self-connection, that she wanted to head in a different direction.

The beauty of an experiment is that you set out a specific number of actions or a specific-time frame — nothing you are doing is forever. You can wait until the end of the experiment to draw conclusions, but you can also assess along the way whether the data is leaning so far one way or another that it makes sense not to continue.

Take a look at activities or projects that could benefit from you designing an experiment. You can let your joy (or pursuit of it) guide what experiments you try, and let the data decide what activities or projects you ultimately stick with.

IT'S AN 'EXPERIMENT'

In *Joy Guides; Experiment Decides* we talked about the joy of designing experiments to help us make decisions in business. We don't have to run actual experiments to take advantage of experimentation. We can view each action we take as an experiment, even if it's not part of a formal experiment (like Danika did to decide on her approach to enrolling clients and Jessica did to try on the idea of being a cofounder and strategic leader).

You might be thinking, "Wait, Erin, didn't you say everything we do is *data*? Now you're saying everything is an *experiment*. What's the difference?"

When I say everything is data (see *Data Hath No Meaning*), I mean that you can't draw any conclusions from a single action. You don't know why it was or wasn't successful. And data certainly makes no value judgments about who you are as a person. Seeing everything as data is a mindset shift around the *outcome*. When I say everything is an experiment, I mean that no action, activity, project, or program has to be polished or perfect. Ever. And certainly not on the first try.

Seeing everything you do as an experiment is more about the process than outcome.

Your biggest opportunity for joy, in my opinion, is when you see everything as an experiment AND as data. You can lean into curiosity, creativity, and courage in every stage of a process or action.

One of my favorite examples of leaning into the mindset of "It's an experiment" comes from my colleague, Abbey Gibb. Webinars and masterclasses were a bread-and-butter strategy for Abbey, an Emmy-winning journalist-turned-media and business mentor, as she quickly grew her business to 7-figures. Until she and I met, she'd never considered that she could run a masterclass *her way*.

She'd been taught strategies and tactics, and because they'd worked, she never questioned them. She'd also never asked herself whether her masterclasses brought her joy.

Abbey heard me talk about the Lab Coat concept enough times that she decided to try it for herself. She had an upcoming masterclass and instead of following the formulas and rules she normally adhered to, she let herself treat it as an experiment to see what would happen if she designed it based on questions like: "What would be fun for me?", "What would be most connective for me and for the people who attend?", and "What would feel like 'That's so Abbey?'" She ended up designing a masterclass that was altogether different from her usual. For one, instead of trying to pack as many people as possible into a Zoom room, she limited the number of participants so that she could make it much more intimate and interactive. She knew that by running it with fewer people she might make less money than she had in other masterclasses. That, for her, was a risk she was willing to take in exploring her joy.

Shortly after the masterclass, we were on a Zoom call together. She gushed. It was the most fun she'd ever had in her business. She wasn't sure what the financial outcome would be, or how it would compare to previous masterclasses, but that didn't matter to her. From now on, she was only going to run webinars and masterclasses *her way*, with her joy front and center. (And I suspect that was the start of her doing everything in her business that way.) She's now turning that masterclass content into a book. I am curious if the idea of a book would have come to her had she not leaned into her joy first …

After running an experiment with her masterclass, Abbey could have decided, "Yep, this is how I'll run masterclasses from now on." But I encouraged her to see every masterclass from now on as an experiment. There is no end point where you've perfected your craft and you never change anything ever again. You might as well give yourself permission, over and over again, to test new ideas and not have them all work out. The minute you tell yourself something is "final," you risk putting unnecessary pressure on yourself. There's no joy in that!

[If you're questioning whether *everything* can really be an experiment and that there are never any finished products, I'll use this book as an example. You may see it as a finished product because it's in your hands. I see it as an experiment. The format is unconventional. I know it brought me immense joy to write and format a book in the way my brain thinks, but will it be successful? Will it resonate with readers? Will it accomplish all the things I hope it does? I don't know. It's an experiment!]

PUT ON YOUR LAB COAT
AND FEEL YOUR FEELINGS TOO

Seeing our actions as both data collection and as experiments can create space for joy. We can sink into our curiosity and creativity, be more courageous in what we try, and pursue things that feel deeply connected to who we are and how we work. By stripping out some of the anxiety, fear, and pressure that we put on ourselves to be perfect (because after all, failure *means* something about us, right?) there is more room to tap into and cultivate joy. Taking on the mindset of a scientist can be a bit paradoxical, though. Collecting data asks us to be an impartial, emotionless observer. But there's also no joy in being emotionless. It's not possible for us to just get rid of our negative emotions and only keep the positive ones. Our capacity to experience joy is directly related to our capacity to experience pain. So if you want to expand your joy tank, you also need to expand every other emotional tank too!

What gives? How can we need to be objective scientists to feel joy AND at the same time, need to feel all our feelings in order to feel joy? Can they coexist? Yes, they can. That is the paradox. Or at least what appears to be a paradox.

It's best explained through an example, so let's talk about my friend, Inés Ruiz. Inés is the CEO and founder of ELEInternacional, an online school and certification program for Spanish Language teachers across the globe. She grew her business quickly, from low six-figures to seven-figures in the matter of a couple of years. One of her superpowers is putting on her proverbial lab coat and taking lots of action. A few years ago, she called me for a catch-up. I could tell immediately that she was feeling down. She explained that she had just run a webinar for a new product she was selling, and though she ran webinars often and usually had great attendance, this one had far fewer people show up than she hoped. On top of that, she hadn't made a single sale. She couldn't remember the last time this happened.

I could hear the disappointment and sadness in her voice, but I could also hear that she was trying to stuff down her emotions. She then said something to the effect of, "A good entrepreneur doesn't get caught in their feelings. I know I was trying something new and that doesn't always work. I should remember it's just one webinar. It's just a data point."

We were having this conversation long before joy was in my vocabulary, but what intuitively came out of me in that moment shaped my views on this lab coat paradox.

"Inés, it's okay. *And* … it sucks."

I went on to say, "You get to acknowledge and feel your feelings. Disappointment. Sadness. Frustration. Don't try to stuff it all down. Of course it's good to recognize that it's just a data point and you can't really know why there were fewer people and no sales today. Yes, you tried something different and that could have been why. But it absolutely could've been that it's a nice summer day and people didn't want to be on the computer. Or maybe it was a fluke and if you try again next week, you'll get a completely different result. But you don't stop being a person with feelings when this stuff happens."

Essentially, I was telling Inés to feel her feelings fully AND to not make any meaning out of the lower attendance and zero sales. When we collect data to remove emotionality from our actions, what we really want to do is remove the meaning-making thoughts and feelings (many of which are self-critical). There's a big difference between being disappointed in an outcome that didn't go your way and being disappointed in yourself (or even beating yourself up!). It was clear to me that Inés was experiencing the former — disappointment in the outcome — but she'd picked up a belief that all emotions were problematic and bad for business.

You might be thinking, "Well Erin, if she's caught up in her feelings, won't that stop her from moving forward?" Likely, not. Our emotional states are quite short-lived, lasting from a few minutes to a few hours. Rarely does an emotional state linger longer than a day. And if it does, that's certainly something to look at more deeply. But when we allow ourselves to feel our emotions fully, they dissipate, usually even more quickly than if we try to get rid of them by overriding them or stuffing them down. In fact, not feeling our emotions can lead to depression, lower self-esteem, stress, and physical illness. For Inés, feeling her feelings about the webinar was quite healthy … and great for filling up her joy tank!

You're allowed to have feelings about your successes and failures.

Back to our paradox. You can feel joy and celebration when something goes well. You can feel sadness, disappointment, frustration, anger, or any other emotion when something doesn't go as well as you'd hoped. The more you can feel your feelings, no matter the situation, the more you'll expand your joy tank. But you'll start to leak your joy when you buy into meaning-making thoughts and feelings about what those successes or failures say about you or your business.

In the exercise in *Data Hath No Meaning,* I included a column for emotion. Now that you've read this conversation, you know that it's important to make note of these emotions so that you can allow yourself to feel them independently of any mean-making your brain wants to create. And you may notice that once you remove the meaning from something, the emotion changes. For instance, if I catch myself lashing myself for a failure to enroll a client, the predominant emotion might be anger towards myself. Once I remove any stories I'm making up about myself, I might just feel a little bummed out that I won't get to work with that person. If given the choice between being a little bummed and trying to be a feelingless robot in my business, I'll choose being a little bummed every day of the week!

NEVER HIKE IN THE BUSINESS WILDERNESS ALONE

Entrepreneurship can be lonely as hell. And yet for some reason, we believe we have to do it (mostly) alone. This is a quick recipe for keeping our joy out. We are social creatures — we need connection and support for our well-being. We also can't see outside ourselves. We all have blind spots and limits to our perspective. Some of the best creativity can come out of other people seeing something that we can't.

Logically, we know we can't do this thing called business alone. But, it's easy to catch ourselves resisting support. Or being highly calculated about what we allow ourselves to seek and receive support on. Like when we don't allow ourselves to use our maps app anymore after a few days in a new city. Afterall, we should know where we are going by now, right?

Why do we do this to ourselves?

One of the hallmarks of our culture (especially for those of us in the United States) is a belief that's rooted in white supremacy, toxic capitalism, and rugged individualism: If we can't do it all by ourselves, there is something wrong with us. (We also glorify the folks who seem, at least to our eyes, to be able to.) We tell ourselves when we can't pull it off all on our own that we're not capable or competent, and ultimately, not good enough. We believe that we don't deserve to be an entrepreneur and that people will find out we're a fraud if we admit to needing help. Underneath this all is a fear that we'll have to face ourselves and our own self-loathing for the ways we've "failed." Ouch!

When we buy into these lies, we contribute to our own loneliness by denying ourselves access to full support. And really, it's a self-fulfilling prophecy ... we don't ask for the exact or full support we need, and then we don't get the help we need, and then we reinforce our belief that we aren't good enough. In what becomes a vicious cycle, we become even less likely to ask for help.

You can choose to continue going alone or being calculated about what support you get. You can even be quite successful. But is that the most joy-full path?

In these next two conversations, we'll explore various ways other people can help you fill your joy tank.

FRODO AND HIS MERRY BAND OF TRAVELERS

Raise your hand if you resonated with the last conversation: You know you can't do this thing called business alone, but you secretly believe you're supposed to. Or some part of you believes that a *true* solopreneur or small business CEO who is smart, capable, and creative enough doesn't really need personal help or support. Now, I'm not talking about flying solo to the degree that you don't hire anyone *in* your business. Depending on the size and nature of your business, you may not need much more than a virtual assistant, or you might need an entire team. The type of support I'm talking about is at the peer, coach, or mentorship level.

You can't see me right now, but I'm raising my hand. I used to believe that if I couldn't build and run a business on my own, I had no business being in business. Granted, it wasn't a completely black and white thought. Part of me saw the merit of coaches and peer circles — heck, I invested nearly six-figures in my first year of business in three coaches, two of whom also came with a community of fellow coaches. But despite having access to support, I couldn't entirely shake the belief that I was supposed to figure it all out on my own. I made sure my peers never saw what was really going on in my mind and heart. I felt ashamed showing weakness to my coaches. Anything I brought to coaching and peer circles was something safe enough that wouldn't conflict with my belief that good entrepreneurs are self-sufficient.

I was somewhat surprised when I realized that the "go alone" belief was secretly running the show. I grew up with two academic parents and was in academia as a PhD student myself. Almost nothing in academia is done alone. Whether it's coming up with research ideas, designing and executing experiments, or writing academic articles, everything is done in collaboration. There are occasionally single author papers, but they aren't necessarily held in higher regard than multi-author papers. As a student, I had the mentorship, guidance, and collaboration of my advisor, and I also collaborated with other grad students and professors at my school (University of Texas) and professors from other institutions. It would have never occurred to me that a successful academic career was a solo endeavor.

Another part of me, though, was not at all surprised to uncover the "go alone" belief. As I've talked about again and again, it's woven into the fabric of our individualistic, meritocratic society, particularly here in the United States. Doing something completely on your own carries a badge of honor. We praise people who have "pulled themselves up from their bootstraps" and we denigrate those who need assistance as weak, lazy, and stupid. In some business circles, any form of coaching or mentorship is stigmatized. A 2021 "Tech Crunch" article states, "Founders are resistant to hiring a coach themselves because they're worried about what their investors and board will think of them. They tell themselves: 'If I were normal, and good enough, I wouldn't need one.'"[18]

In my conscious mind, I recognized that I couldn't do it alone. I knew I needed guidance and education on being a coach and business owner. But operating below the surface was, "You're the CEO. You're the sole guide and director of your business." While *technically* true, that belief limited what I thought a coach, mentor, or peer could be useful for. The big vision for my business? Up to me. What I offered as services and programs? Up to me. Navigating some of the fears and challenges I faced as I built the business … most definitely up to me.

What did I get from these coaches, then? I absorbed a lot from their teachings and in watching them coach other people. With my one-on-one coach, I was cautious for a while, asking tactical rather than vulnerable questions about "How to do X," or getting feedback on things I'd already thought about and/or created. I wouldn't have dared come to her with, "Hey, I'd like some help brainstorming my next group program."

If I had reminded myself that the CEOs of some of the biggest corporations are almost never on their own — they almost always have advisors, coaches, *and* boards of directors — I might have had a different viewpoint. But I also heard that nagging inner voice reminding me, "If you can't do some of these things on your own, you shouldn't be in business." Thankfully I discovered early on (still in that first year of coaching while working with my three coaches) that a highly individualistic part of me was in the driver's seat.

When I started unpacking the belief that I shouldn't need help and instead leaned into support for all the things I felt I had to do alone, I realized it was a key to running a joy-full business. As I allowed myself to open up to coaches and peers in my community, I felt some of the same aliveness and fun that I used to experience when collaborating in the academic world. When I let my mentors fully help me, and when I leaned into peers for everything from brainstorming to emotional support, I noticed that they joy-fully engaged too. Who knew that me asking for help could be a source of joy for others!?

Nowadays, I always have one-on-one support from a coach or therapist (sometimes both) and I'm always part of a community. Who supports me and what community I participate in shifts with my needs, but one thing is constant: I'm never hiking in my business wilderness alone. I lean on my people for everything from strategy and tactics to deep emotional and nervous system support.

In a world that sees needing assistance as a sign of weakness, I've come to believe that the real weakness is flying solo. Not a personal weakness, but a weak position. There's a reason academia is a collaborative space. The biggest scientific breakthroughs have all come when people have pooled their resources — emotional, mental, and physical. I believe a similar thing can be true in our businesses: we create our greatest impact and most brilliant ideas when we allow ourselves to benefit from the wisdom, experience, and support of others.

"If you want to go fast, go alone;
if you want to go far, go together."

~ Origin unknown

I've seen and heard this quote many times in my circles. The quote as a whole doesn't exactly land for me since I don't think fast and far are mutually exclusive. But I do love the last part: "If you want to go far, go together." I'd even add, "If you want to go far *joy-fully*, go together."

Speaking of far, I've heard being in business likened to Joseph Campbell's hero's journey[19] in my circles. Almost all storytelling, from ancient myths to today's blockbusters, follow the hero's journey pattern where a main character sets out on a challenge, faces many obstacles along the way, and emerges victorious. One of the hallmarks of the hero's journey is that the hero never does it alone. He/she/they always have a mentor and a merry band of fellow travelers. When I think of the concept of "never hike alone," I think of *The Lord of the Rings*. After all, the journey from the Shire to Mordor *was* a hike! Frodo, in saving Middle Earth from Sauron, sets off with Gandalf (his mentor) and his cheery friends Pippin, Sam, and Merry. Along the way Aragorn, Legolas, Gimli, and Boromir join him. In the end, each character had a role to play in helping Frodo be successful.

Whether you see your business as a hike through the wilderness (like I do) or a hero's journey through Middle Earth, you will have more joy, and perhaps go farther than you thought possible, if you commit to never hiking alone. That could mean a one-on-one coach, a group program, a paid community, or simply gathering like-minded peers on a regular basis. (At times I've had all of them!) Investing time, money, and relational energy in your business and yourself is not only a source of joy in itself, but it's also a way to be supported in keeping joy front and center in everything you do.

RUNNING BUDDIES

Did you know there are apps for finding a running buddy? A simple Google search also brings up dozens of articles on where and how you can find the perfect running partner. And, if you're someone who is not yet convinced that you need a running buddy, there are dozens of articles on that too — all about the benefits of having someone running alongside you.

Why the hell am I talking about running in a book on joy-full AF business? I used to be a casual runner, and I see a lot of parallels between running and entrepreneurship. The most obvious is that it's a solo sport. Similarly, entrepreneurship can be or feel like a solo endeavor, whether you're a "company of one" or leader of a small operation. A less obvious, but perhaps more important, parallel is that entrepreneurship is something we need to take at our own pace. We have to learn to run our own race.

Still, even though runners need to learn their pace and run their own race, running buddies are quite common. That's why there are apps and Google articles dedicated to it. Regrettably, the same is not true for entrepreneurship. There are no apps for entrepreneurial "running buddies." I have not yet found any articles on how to find one or what the benefits are of having them. And in case you're wondering how this is different from the support we talked about in *Frodo and His Merry Band of Travelers*, let me draw the distinction. A coach in your business is akin to a running coach. Runners who are dedicated to racing often have coaches *and* running buddies. Your merry band of travelers — your peer community — most often is a place where you share with others *about* your business and get support. It's not always a place where people are actively working on their businesses in real-time together. There are many ways to "never hike alone" in my mind. Running buddies are just an additional option to the ones we've already talked about.

What exactly is a running buddy in the business context? We are all running our own race and at our own pace, but sometimes we are on the a similar course as some of our peers. For instance, you may be actively trying to grow your social media following and find that you have peers in the thick of that too. Or maybe you're writing a TEDx talk or book and have peers doing the same. You could certainly meet with your peers every week or two to talk *about* the process. Or if you're part of an online community, you might consider reaching out for support when you have a challenge. Both of those options follow the more traditional model I talked about in *Frodo and His Merry Band of Travelers*. Consider for a moment, if you had a running buddy or two, you'd be *in it* together, sharing your goals (like 'post once daily on social media' or 'write 100 words a day') and checking in with one another on progress. You could cheer each other on, support each other when things are challenging, or even simply have space to vent (one of my favorites parts of having running buddies).

My running buddies have been a huge help for me building a social media presence. When I tried to "run alone," holding myself accountable to posting and growing my network was difficult for me. I lost energy and motivation without someone in it with me. I'd make excuses not to post. I'd get lost in perfectionism or would talk myself out of posting certain things. It all makes sense, as I'm more able to accomplish my goals when I have external accountability. (According to Gretchen Rubin's in *The Four Tendencies*[20] — another not-so-scientific assessment that I still find to be a useful lens — I am an *Obliger*. Whereas some people need zero accountability to meet their goals, and others actively rebel against accountability, *Obligers* thrive with it. Turns out, I'm in good company: about 41% of people are *Obligers*.)

In late 2020, Varian Brandon, a colleague who had built an engaged and loyal following on Facebook, put out a program for people who wanted to unlock their authentic expression online. Initially, I wasn't going to join the program. At the time, I was sporadically posting on Facebook. I had done 90 days of Facebook lives (that I first mentioned in *Uncomfortable Versus Unsafe*) over a year earlier — I knew how to authentically express myself. I could even do it in a stream-of-conscious style live! I couldn't imagine paying Varian to help me with social media. (Of course, in true *Obliger* fashion, just because I knew how to do it didn't mean I could hold myself accountable to doing it!) Then I found out that two of my other colleagues, Matt and Andy, and my coach at the time, Christina, were joining. Now *that* was a compelling reason to jump in! I messaged Varian to sign me up.

The program had us posting multiple times a day. There was a Facebook group for everyone in the program, and alongside that, Andy, Matt, Christina, and I had a highly active text thread. It was so fun to share things, both on Facebook and over text, like "Wow, this post blew up!" and "Oh my gosh, that was vulnerable to share!" It was even nice to talk about the program itself: "Why do you think we're being asked to post this?" "What are you liking so far and what would you change?"

As soon as the program was over, we went our separate ways. Without my running buddies, my energy waned. I went back to sporadic posting, though it was probably slightly less sporadic than before the program. I even considered giving up social media. Until another opportunity for me to have some running buddies game along.

Just like the first program, I had no intention of joining a social media-based program. I'd been following the leader, Simone Seol, on Instagram for months, but never felt compelled to look into her Joyful Marketing Program. (You'd think I would have been all over something with 'Joyful' in the name, right?) Then I saw a colleague, David, post on his Instagram that he was in the program. Soon I found out two other colleagues, Allison and Christina (the same Christina who did Varian's program with me), had also just joined. I knew immediately that joining Joyful Marketing with these folks was the key to making my social media joy-full again. I proverbially ran (not walked 😊) to Simone's website and joined the program.

Like in Varian's program, Allison, Christina and I had a text thread where we shared our experience of going through the

"Garbage Post Challenge" — to create100 pieces of content in 30 days. My energy for social media returned in full force. So much was pouring out of me that I did 120 posts in the 30-day window. (In case you're thinking, holy moly that's a lot, anything with words counted as a post. If I posted a Story on Instagram about my dog with any caption at all, it qualified per the rules of the game.)

I don't need, or even want, running buddies for everything I do. But when I do, they help me do all sorts of things I might have struggled to complete on my own. That doesn't make me weak or wrong. Running buddies also take me *further* than I would have gone on my own — adding to my energy and joy (and therefore stamina) in whatever it is we're doing. It's fun to see where we each end up. And even without their motivation benefits, running buddies are simply joy-full to have with me on the journey — a solid reminder that we're never alone.

If the idea of having a running buddy as part of filling your joy tank is intriguing, I highly recommend first taking *The Four Tendencies* assessment. It will help you understand how you operate in regards to motivation and how running buddies (or which running buddies) might best work for you in the context of your business.

KEEP YOUR JOY TANK TOPPED OFF

Joy is vital fuel in your business. Having a full tank provides the resources and the resilience you need to endure the ebbs and flows that every business experiences. No business operates consistently. It's natural to go through times when nothing feels like it's working, or you're not totally sure where your next client is coming from. And it's just as normal to go through times when everything seems to work seamlessly, and clients and customers are abundant. As much as we'd like to be fully in control of the success of our businesses, and have clear predictability and consistency, all of these ideas are an illusion. COVID-19 was an extreme example of this, showing us that at any time, the entire world can come to an abrupt halt.

Joy can buffer us from the natural ebbs and flows in business, and those of the world. It's not just our businesses that are impacted by global pandemics, European wars, political upheaval, inflation, and stock market fluctuations. *We are affected as humans, too.* Our mental and emotional well-being depends on the context we live in, from running our businesses, to our personal lives, to national and world events.

Joy is the fuel and we need a full tank.

When I say joy is fuel and we need a full tank, it's not like gasoline in a car. You don't run the tank down, waiting until you're down to fumes and on the verge of crisis to fill back up again. Even if you're one of those highly conscientious folks who fills up before their tank reaches ¼ left, that just won't do for your joy tank.

Joy is more like water in our human body. We need lots of water in order to survive. But we're not supposed to just drink when we're thirsty. In fact, if we guzzle water after letting ourselves get parched (like after a day at the beach), we can feel ill afterwards. The more sustainable, healthy way to consume water is to drink it regularly and keep our hydration tank full. That's how I want you to think about your joy — it's a tank to keep as full as possible. That way you can draw on your joy tank without completely depleting yourself when things aren't going as well as you'd like or when the world seems like too much.

I hope that you've come to understand throughout these pages that it's not toxic positivity to seek joy. It's not burying your head in the sand either. Remember, we can experience joy alongside all kinds of other emotions. You can feel frustrated that nothing's working right now. You can feel anxious that your cash flow isn't as steady as you'd like it to be. You can feel downright angry and devastated by the impact of COVID-19, the Russian invasion of Ukraine, or the treatment of black people in America. *And* you can still find moments and pockets of joy to fill you up.

You can keep your joy tank topped off in multiple ways. I've given you several ideas in these pages — like creating games, planting Magic Beans, putting on your HILA hat, or wearing your lab coat — but there are an endless number of ways available to you. I make a regular practice of intentionally infusing joy into my work. Every Monday, I host a Zoom session called Joy-Full Biz Intentions Setting where I share journal prompts that help me and attendees plan more joy into their week. I also maintain a daily practice.

Every morning, I run through five questions:

First I ask, "Do I need rest?"

Did this question stop you in your tracks? Our first instinct when wanting more of something is to add more things to our to-do list. What if filling up on joy requires us to do less? And what would life be like if we asked ourselves, in any circumstance, what we can do less of before asking what we need to do more of?)

If the answer is yes ... I do not pass go. I do not collect $200. I figure out what I can cut out of my day to give myself time to re-energize. I also look at what personal joys might feel like rest that day, like going on a long walk or playing basketball in my driveway.

If the answer is no … I then turn to the four ingredients of joy:

What can I get curious about today?

What do I want to create today?

What act of courage can I take today?

How can I create a connection to myself or to someone else?

When I answer, I try to get as specific as possible. On days when joy feels difficult — when I want to throw in the towel on my business or I'm mad at the state of the world — I make sure all my answers are about the tiniest actions possible. What is a tiny curiosity? A tiny thing I can create? A tiny act of courage? A tiny moment of connection?

A tiny curiosity might be trying a new question or tool with a client. A tiny creation might be an Instagram Story. A tiny act of courage might be turning off my computer an hour early. A tiny act of connection might be sending a text to a colleague saying, "Hey, I'm thinking about you. I hope your day is going well!"

When I focus on these four ingredients — whether they are four separate activities, or one that includes all four ingredients — every day, my joy tank not only overflows, but it also expands its capacity.

Are you treating your joy like gas for the car or like water for your body? What could you do weekly or daily to cultivate more joy? Certainly, you could use the questions I ask myself, but perhaps it would be more joy-full to create your own!

Epilogue:
What Happens If We All Follow Our Joy?

"Everyone can dance;
they just have their own rhythm and style."

~ Patti Dizon

Growing up, I spent two weeks of every summer at Camp-Al-Gon-Quian in northern Michigan. (This was the camp I mentioned in ~~Love~~ *Joy and Basketball*.) It was a traditional YMCA camp with activities like sailing, canoeing, archery, and arts and crafts. To me, camp was the happiest place on earth. It was the only place, at the time, where I could be completely myself. I could play sports all day with the boys and nobody would bat an eye. I could be completely out of touch with current (feminine) fashion and actually fit in with many others who were equally out of touch. Though many campers knew each other from middle or high school, my schoolmates were thousands of miles away in Arizona. That meant I could experiment with and explore my identity (including thinking about whether I was gay). I could express myself in ways I would be shy about elsewhere. And I could make new friends away from social hierarchies.

I felt true belonging and acceptance at camp. From the moment I showed up there at 11 years old, I was shown unconditional love by campers and staff. As each year passed, that love grew stronger as I built relationships with people who came back year after year. Patti Dizon was one of those counselors. One evening when I was about 14, she and I were talking about the camp dance that was about to start. I was anxious. In my mind, I didn't know how to dance. Or if I did, I certainly wasn't very good at it. I was worried that I was about to embarrass myself in front of everyone. Without a beat she replied, "Oh Er-Bear (still her nickname for me), *everyone* can dance; they just have their own rhythm and style." To this day, it's one of the most profound things I've ever been told.

Patti was right. Everyone was so full of joy that night as they all danced their own dance. I didn't even think to look at whether they were "doing it right." (Okay maybe I did look a *little* bit. I was 14 after all!) She was also right about more than dance. At Camp Al-Gon-Quian, everyone was loved for exactly who they were, no matter what rhythm they were walking, running, or dancing to. They were even *encouraged* to bring out who they were in full force. Camp wasn't just a happy place — it was a joy-full place.

I've said for several years that I'm on a secret mission to make the world like summer camp. At least like Camp Al-Gon-Quian was in the late 90s. I've come to believe through writing *Joy-Full AF* that the key to achieving that mission is for all of us to follow our joy in everything we do, including business.

What does that look like in the business world? It starts with recognizing that Patti's advice holds true. We can all run successful businesses, and the most joy-full and sustainable way to do it is with our own rhythm and style. When we deeply connect with who we are, what lights us up, how we tick, and what our bodies are telling us … when we let our natural curiosity take over and allow ourselves to play, experiment, and wonder what might happen next … when we tap into our creative reservoirs to create inspired and innovative ideas … and when we courageously go after what our hearts and souls most deeply desire … we create success and fulfillment that keeps us going through the inevitable ebbs and flows. I believe that the more each of us follows our joy — and really the more we get to deeply know ourselves — the more we can create a new business culture that eschews the hustle and grind lifestyle, go-big-or-go-home mentality, and 10-step formulas for success, in favor of self-trust, authenticity, and individuality.

As I've written, following our joy can be uncomfortable. Often it requires that we question the advice and mentorship we've been soaking up as truth. It means confronting long-held beliefs and butting up against white supremacy culture, patriarchy, and internalized capitalism. And, as we look inward for answers in a society that has taught us to look outward, it means getting to know, like, and trust ourselves on levels more deeply than ever.

Choosing joy is an act of resistance

Even when we commit to our joy, we'll inevitably find ways to lose it. I'll be the first one to tell you that after all this exploration of joy, I *still* do too. The more aware we are of it happening, the sooner we can plug up the leaks. We also need to be intentional about choosing to infuse *more* joy into our work, especially when deadlines, priorities, and business challenges tempt us to put joy on the backburner. Putting joy first is not always easy. But I hope that after reading *Joy-Full AF*, you feel more equipped than before to do so.

May you chase joy and find that success chases you. May you seek joy and find *you* (and vice versa). And may we all find ourselves in business a world (and even broader world) that feels like summer camp.

Yours Joy-fully,

Erin

Resources

1 Robert A Emmons, "Joy: An introduction to this special issue," *The Journal of Positive Psychology* 15, no.1 (2020): 1-4. DOI: 10.1080/17439760.2019.1685580.

2 Samin Nostrat. *Salt, Fat, Acid, Heat: Mastering the Elements of Good Cooking* (New York, NY: Simon & Shuster, 2017).

3 Rob Bell, "An Introduction to Joy," July 18, 2020, YouTube video, 1:19:42, https://www.youtube.com/watch?v=sA7LmEn3xyc.

4 Simone Seol, "The Price of a Joyful Business with Caryn Gillen," *Joyful Marketing*, March 8, 2022, podcast audio, https://www.simonegraceseol.com/podcast/joyful-business-caryn-gillen.

5 Karen Walrond, *The Lightmaker's Manifesto: How to Work for Change Without Losing Your Joy* (Minneapolis, MN: Broadleaf Books, 2021).

6 Richard Schwartz, *No Bad Parts: Healing Trauma and Restoring Wholeness With the Internal Family Systems Model* (Boulder, CO: Sounds True, 2021)

7 Katherine Gustafson, "The Percentage of Businesses That Fail and How to Boost Your Chances of Success," Lending Tree, May 2, 2022, https://www.lendingtree.com/business/small/failure-rate/.

8 Gay Hendricks, *The Big Leap: Conquer Your Hidden Fear and Take Life to the Next Level* (New York, NY: Harper Collins, 2010).

9 Steve Chandler and Rich Litvin, *The Prosperous Coach: Increase Income and Impact for You and Your Clients* (Anna Maria, FL: Maurice Bassett, 2013).

10 "White Supremacy Culture Characteristics", https://www.whitesupremacyculture.info/characteristics.html.

11 Chip Heath and Dan Heath, *The Power of Moments* (London, UK: Random House, 2017).

12 Jonathan Fields, "Sparketypes Assessment: Discover What Makes You Come Alive", https://sparketype.com/.

13 Mark J. Silverman, *Only 10s 2.0: Confront Your To-Do List and Transform Your Life* (Mark J. Silverman, 2020).

14 Brené Brown, "The Power of Vulnerability", TEDxHouston, online video, 20:23, https://www.ted.com/talks/brene_brown_the_power_of_vulnerability?language=en.

15 David Eagleman, *Livewired: The Inside Story of the Ever-Changing Brain* (New York, NY: Vintage Books, 2020).

16 Brené Brown, "The Inside Story of the Ever-Changing Brain with David Eagleman," *Unlocking Us*, December 2, 2020, podcast audio, https://brenebrown.com/podcast/brene-with-david-eagleman-on-the-inside-story-of-the-ever-changing-brain/.

17 "Izaak Mauritis Kolthoff and Modern Analytical Chemistry," American Chemical Association, https://en.wikipedia.org/wiki/Izaak_Kolthoff.

18 Ariane de Bonvoison, "Investors and business leaders: It's time to take coaching mainstream," Tech Crunch, March 25, 2021, https://techcrunch.com/2021/03/25/investors-and-business-leaders-its-time-to-take-coaching-mainstream/.

19 "Hero's Journey", Wikipedia, https://en.wikipedia.org/wiki/Hero%27s_journey.

20 Gretchen Rubin, The Four Tendencies: The Indispensable Personality Profiles That Reveal How to Make Your Life Better (and Other People's Lives Better, Too) (New York, NY: Harmony Books, 2017). The Four Tendencies Quiz: https://quiz.gretchenrubin.com/.

Acknowledgments

I have been fortunate to not have to hike alone in writing this book. I've had some of the most incredible Gandalfs, merry bands of travelers, and running buddies that a human could ask for.

To Simone Seol: I have only experienced "take your breath away" joy a few times in my life, and one of those was reading your foreword. It beautifully captured the power of joy, the message of the book, and who I am, while also embodying who you BE as a leader and coach. I am honored that you agreed to be a part of this book and will be forever reminded that the best part of the "Collecting Nos" game is the feeling of surprise and excitement when someone says yes!

To my clients: I am profoundly grateful and honored to have walked alongside each of you on your journeys. You have trusted me with your hopes, dreams, desires, fears, vulnerabilities, and challenges. You have let me see, hold, and support all of you — the parts you love and the parts you don't. And you have generously allowed me to share your stories in the hope of helping others along the journey. You are the reason my work is joy-full AF.

To Patti M. Hall: You have been much more than a book coach and story builder for me over the last two years. From "a book about AND" to The Ten Essentials to *Joy-Full AF*, you were steadfast in helping me navigate the twists and turns, and ups and downs of the book-writing wilderness. You believed in me when I didn't. You refused to give up when I thought, "No, this time the joy really is gone. I'm quitting." Your heart, generosity, tenacity, and grit are unmatched. Words will never fully capture my gratitude.

To the Story House crew, Ken Bechtel and Tim Snell: You were my much-needed running buddies for the first several months of book writing. I am so grateful that Patti brought us together and that we could go through the early mess of "what am I writing a book on?" in good company. Book writing can be a lonely endeavor, but being "in it" with you made it so much more joy-full.

To Mark Silverman, Shelley Paxton, Mandy Lehto, Erin Hatzikostas, and Catherine Hammond: You are some of the most soulful, big-hearted, and brilliant humans I know. Thank you for sharing your wisdom and experience in writing and publishing your books. But even more so, thank you for being cheerleaders and champions of me and my work. I am grateful to not only call each of you colleagues but also soul friends.

To my coaches and business mentors over the last few years, Christina Berkley, Rich Litvin, Sean Smith, Caitlin Padgett, and Abbey Gibb: Each of you has had an indescribable impact on my life and business that can't be properly captured in an acknowledgments section. You have helped me become a more radically joy-full human who loves and trusts themself. You have also seen more in me than I did and believed in me when I didn't. I am honored to have *Joy-Full AF* contribute to your Ripples of Impact (ROI) in the world.

To my therapists, Sarah Rollins and Kayla LaJoie: I could not have asked for a better support team for managing my inner world and nervous system while writing a book, running a business, and having a personal life … all while living through a global pandemic. I am a more connected, curious, creative, courageous, compassionate, calm, clear, and confident person because of you.

To my 4PC and DFLA communities: What a merry band of travelers you have been for me over the last several years. My hero's journey would have been incomplete without you. Thank you for seeing, supporting, challenging, and inspiring me.

To the Wednesday Wonders, Jen Szad and Mahrukh Imtiaz: Thank goodness we decided all those years ago to ditch being a "goals mastermind" and become the tight-knit chosen family we are. Our friendships are some of my greatest joys. Thank you for the weekly deep conversations on all things personal development and business, but even more so, thank you for holding, cheerleading, and loving me.

To Laurie Shiers: There is no way this book would have seen the light of day without your unwavering belief in me and my writing. You epitomize joy and wonder. You inspire me to play, laugh, take life less seriously, and soak in being an amateur. And you remind me that taking time for a quick friend phone call during the middle of the workday is one of my not-so-secret pleasures.

To Allison Crow: My parts are grateful to have met and connected with such a kindred spirit during the pandemic and to have had you as a running buddy during the Garbage Post Challenge. Our mutual love of IFS, shared feelings about the coaching industry, and ability to hold space for one another's humanness has been lifeblood for me in this book process.

To my Kwan brothers, Matt Chavlovich and Andy Hite: You have kept my head on straight while also helping me keep the business running over the last two years. I'm deeply grateful for your support, love, and the occasional (okay, more than occasional) challenge of the stories I'm telling myself.

And finally, to my wife, Meryl Baker: I will forever be grateful for your mad editing skills. My book is more me thanks to you. But more so, I am thankful for your unflinching support and willingness to hold space when I needed to vent or melt down over these last two years. You always encourage me to follow my joy and help me to re-find it when I've lost it. I love you 6 ½.

About the Author

Dr. Erin Baker is a self-leadership coach, business strategist, social psychologist, Internal Family Systems practitioner, and official curator of joy. They hold a PhD from University of Texas at Austin and formerly held leadership roles at Facebook and Microsoft. Erin is known for their infectious energy, unapologetic authenticity, incisive wit, and unflinching commitment to helping their clients create joy-full AF businesses and lives that light them up.

The business world often recommends focusing on a singular audience, niche, or mission, but Erin realized early on that they have two equally important missions, and the most joy-full path has been to pursue both in their coaching, mentoring, teaching, and writing. First, they want to change the narrative in business about what truly creates impact and long-term success (putting joy front and center). Second, they want to create a more trauma-, neurodiversity-, mental health-, and systems-of-oppression-informed coaching industry.

Erin's clients are ambitious, values-driven, difference-makers who know the success and impact they crave hinges on them putting their joy first, but they're not quite sure how to get there on their own.

Beyond business, here are a few other things that fill Erin's joy tank:

- LGBTQIA+ and non-binary gender advocacy
- Collecting ties and bowties
- Rooting tirelessly for University of Michigan and University of Arizona sports — the size of their U of M gear collection rivals that of the tie collection
- Eccentric socks (especially ones with snarky phrases on them)
- Cuddling and playing with their beagle-mix, Harper, and their tabby cat, Lou
- Shooting hoops in their backyard
- Playing golf
- Relearning classic rock solos from Pink Floyd on their guitar
- Climbing mountains and getting lost in the wilderness
- Morning cribbage games and evening Jeopardy viewings with their wife, Meryl

To learn more about working with Erin, head over to https://erinmbaker.com or follow them on Instagram: @drerinbaker or LinkedIn: https://www.linkedin.com/in/erinmikaelabaker/.

Printed in Great Britain
by Amazon

35516448R00165

Be
Lib
This

30109 0 16429501

THE RACING WORLD
OF
DAMON RUNYON

The RACING
WORLD of
DAMON
RUNYON

CONSTABLE · LONDON

Published in Great Britain 1999
by Constable and Company Limited
3 The Lanchesters
162 Fulham Palace Road
London W6 9ER
Copyright © The Estate of Damon Runyon
Introduction © Robin Oakley 1999
ISBN 0 094 79510 X
Set in Monotype Caledonia 11pt by
Servis Filmsetting Ltd, Manchester
Printed in Great Britain by
St Edmundsbury Press Ltd
Bury St Edmunds, Suffolk

A CIP catalogue record for this book
is available from the British Library

BEXLEY LIBRARY SERVICES	CL
01642950 1	
H J	18/08/99
F	£14.99
ADF	

Publisher's Note

The stories included in this book have been taken
from the two omnibus volumes *Runyon on
Broadway* and *Runyon From First To Last*.
An appendix appears on page 171, in which are
listed all the stories contained in the two volumes.

Contents

Introduction

THE racing world of Damon Runyon bears no resemblance to the elegant lawns of Ascot, York and Goodwood. It is not populated by the characters you will see in tip-tilted trilbies and tweeds at Sandown or Cheltenham. Prepare to mingle instead in a world of small-time hustlers and impecunious trainers weaving around the line of strict legality, sometimes just inside it, more often just the other side, around the 1920s tracks in New York and Florida.

It is a world in which the virtuous God-fearing population rarely intrude, in which those with regular jobs rarely appear. It is a world of struggling, addicted, usually unsuccessful gamblers dreaming perpetually of accumulating what Runyon would call 'big potatoes' and spending most of their lives trying to 'make a scratch' to furnish the stake money to perpetuate the dream for another race or two. Above all it is the world of the old-fashioned tipster.

Older British readers may remember as I do from racecourse visits as a boy the car park circles around 'Prince' Monolulu with his frayed feather head-dress and throaty cries of 'I gotta horse'. They may recall the shifty-eyed fellows who alternated between running the three card trick on a couple of up-ended cardboard boxes and circulating in racecourse bars, offering to mark your card for a fiver. Some would even hand out envelopes with their 'good things' named on a slip inside. Since most slips named a different horse, the law of averages ensured that some customers were satisfied and grateful enough to pay for another tip.

Those kind of tipsters have virtually disappeared from British tracks and, I suspect, from American ones too. In our technological age they have been replaced by splashy newspaper advertisements for telephone tipping lines voiced over by retired jockeys. But in Runyon's stories the turf advisers, known to the authorities as touts, live on in the shape of such as the Seldom Seen Kid and Hot Horse Herbie. The Seldom Seen Kid, introduced in *Money From Home*, gets his name 'because he is seldom seen after anything comes off that anybody may wish to see him about, as he has a most retiring disposition, although he can talk a blue streak whenever talking becomes really necessary'. That is why, as a racing columnist, I rarely respond to requests for tips from my political friends. A journalist dependent on his contacts cannot afford to have to become the Seldom Seen Kid.

A Story Goes With It defines the role of Herbie and those like him. 'He is called Hot Horse Herbie because he nearly always has a very hot horse to tell you about. He nearly always has a horse that is so hot it is fairly smoking, a hot horse being a horse that cannot possibly lose a race unless it falls down dead, and while Herbie's hot horses often lose without falling down dead, this does not keep Herbie from coming up with others just as hot'.

Part of Runyon's appeal is that he manages to portray a band of petty swindlers living on their wits with enough charm to elicit your sympathy for their struggles to pay the bills for their seedy rooming houses (one character nails his empty, locked trunk to the floor so his landlord takes him for a man of possessions and therefore means). In the bitter-sweet tale of *The Lemon Drop*

Kid we are even induced to feel warm towards an incompetent tout who swindles an old man in a wheelchair, admittedly a cripple with plenty of potatoes, out of a hundred dollars.

He brings wry smiles with the eternal postponements as the cash promised for a wedding ring and a marriage licence for their long-suffering fiancées is raised, reinvested and lost again. These ladies, it has to be said, are not of a wide range. They tend to be well-endowed, squeaky-voiced blondes whose working hours are spent in frilly knickers toe-tapping on the chorus lines of vaudeville shows, although it is made clear that even those who earn their livings by 'dealing them off the arm' in nightclubs or artfully removing their underwear in burlesque joints are able to retain an air of untouchability.

In her intriguing study of racecourse behaviour for the British Horseracing Board *The Racing Tribe* in 1997 the sociologist Kate Fox offered a clue both to the invulnerability of the female on the racing scene and to the suspension of normal rules which enables us so to relish Runyon's demi-underworld: 'The racing tribe proved to be the kind of friendly, tolerant obliging "natives" that most anthropologists encounter only in their dreams. . . . Racing is far more than just an enjoyable spectator sport. It fulfils a fundamental need to escape from the restrictions of mundane existence. . . . For some racegoers the alternative world of racing is an opportunity to try on a different personality. At the racecourse, inhibited types may become the life and soul of their parties, cracking jokes in the bars and shouting "come on, my son" from the stands. Habitual worriers and penny-pinchers forget about their mortgages and their housekeeping budgets and spend their winnings – which everyone knows do not count as real money – on generous rounds of drinks. Respectable, bourgeois women dress up as seductive glamour-girls and act out their exhibitionist fantasies. . . . Behaviour towards women follows an unwritten code of rather old-fashioned chivalry. At the races all women are "ladies" and it is understood that they must be treated with due courtesy and respect. No woman walks around wearing such provocative clothing unless she feels completely secure and utterly invulnerable: female racegoers know that the code of chivalry will prevent male admirers from doing anything more than admire.'

As he introduces such apparent innocents as Eddie Yokum, the country boy hero who gets the girl in *Money From Home* and the recuperating Professor Woodhead, who triumphs against the odds in *Pick a Winner*, Damon Runyon would surely agree with Kate Fox's summary of the racing scene: 'This is not the real world: you can take a break from yourself and be someone else.'

Damon Runyon, born in 1884 in Manhattan, Kansas, and brought up in some poverty in Pueblo, Colorado, began writing for local newspapers while still at school. A war correspondent and then a columnist for the Hearst papers, a writer about baseball and boxing, he was a neglectful husband of his first wife Ellen Egan before marrying a second wife twenty-six years younger than himself. He was a nightbird who would stay up until the early hours in Lindy's all-night delicatessen, drinking forty cups of coffee a day and having a cigarette with most of them. Throughout his lifetime, before he died of throat cancer in 1946, he preferred the low-life, racy company of sportsmen, gangsters and gamblers. (Consorting with Runyon's friends would be enough to get most jockeys in Britain today banned under the 'inappropriate behaviour' rules.)

His biographer Jimmy Breslin says: 'Damon Runyon invented the Broadway of Guys and Dolls and the Roaring Twenties, neither of which existed but whose names and phrases became part of theatre history and the American language.' The characters around him, often only slightly varnished, (just as Lindy's became Mindy's in the stories) worked their way into his newspaper columns, then into his short stories, some thirty of which became films. Thus Unser Fritz, the scruffy horse-player, became the subject, you could hardly call him the hero, of the poignant tale *All Horse Players Die Broke*, both a story title and a Runyon line that is likely to go down through the ages.

The racing stories too, like *A Story Goes With It* contain that rich vein of Runyonesque sentimentality to be found in classics like Johnny One-Eye (about the relationship between a wounded gangster on the run and a kitten). But do not look to Runyon, brought up as a lonely child without a mother, for anything resembling political correctness. In *That Ever-Loving Wife of Hymie's* the lady known as 'Lasses (short for Molasses) is held to have jilted the bookmaker Brick McLoskey for Hymie Banjo Eyes 'because she is all sored up on Brick and she acts without thinking, as dolls often do, especially blonde dolls'. Runyon's female characters often exhibit what he likes to call 'restlessness' or 'nervousness', a restlessness which can normally be soothed with diamonds, emeralds, hotel suites or a few sawbucks. His women expect a constant round of entertainment and will go off with anyone who is likely to provide it. But there is a curious element of formality and respect all the same in the way they are addressed. It is Miss Cutie Singleton, Miss Beulah Beauregard, Miss Lola Ledare, Miss Florentine Fayette. According to Jimmy Breslin the dapper Runyon, who had what was probably the largest wardrobe in journalism and who would spend an hour most days choosing his tie, would never curse in front of a lady or allow others to do so, even if he might spit on the floor himself to emphasise a point.

Certainly do not look to Runyon for political correctness on the question of race. It is difficult to read some passages in *Money From Home*, the longest of these racing stories, without wincing over the crudity of the references to a black jockey and to a white rider who 'blacks up' to convince a characterful horse that he is to be mounted by a coloured jockey for a distinctly nerve-wracking ride. Nor should it be forgotten that Runyon, a man who worshipped money and who was happy to have anyone carve up his work for the cinema provided he was paid enough, consorted by choice with criminals and gangsters to collect his raw material. He sanitised and glamourised mayhem and thuggery.

Because his droll, deadpan style keeps the reader hovering on chuckle's edge and is served up with a whimsical sauce, author and reader slide together past the underlying violence. In *Johnny One-Eye* (not a racing story) the hit-man Rudolph uses his Betsy (which sounds so much less menacing than 'gun') to 'crocket his monogram' on the chest of a former associate, so leaving him 'exceptionally deceased'. Here, in *The Snatching of Bookie Bob* a wry tale about a kidnapping with not one but two twists in the tail, storyteller Runyon remarks of the victims, 'Sometimes the party is such a party as does not care to have matches run up and down the bottom of his feet, which often happens to parties who are snatched and who do not seem to wish to settle their bill promptly, because many parties are very ticklish on the bottom of their feet, especially if the matches are lit. . . .'

But then if you choose to enter Runyon's world, there is a different morality in play, a morality in which Harry The Horse, Spanish John and Little Isadore will happily go kidnapping to furnish their stake money but would regard it as a public disgrace to fail to pay their debts to a bookmaker.

Runyon's tales have endured for nearly seventy years already. They will continue to be read – although the world that he was writing about has passed – because of his sharp observation, his wittily laconic style and the richness of his field of characters. The argot in itself is a treat. He would have enjoyed a conversation with the jockey who rode a horse called Rhapsody in Blue, owned by the Eternal Optimists syndicate to which I belong, which has yet to score a place, let alone to grace the winner's enclosure. 'He's yet to find himself' said the little fellow with the big pay cheque. All we want is for Rhapsody occasionally to find the others in the race. But then there have to be a few still running for characters like Damon Runyon's to bet on. Rhapsody, I fear, is the sort of down-the-handicap performer who might well have finished up being trained by the ever-optimistic trainer Little Alfie in *It Comes Up Mud* or the ever-loyal Itchky Ironhat in *Old Em's Kentucky Home*.

Perhaps my favourite Runyon racing story is *A Story Goes With It*, the story of a race-fixing for a fine motive. At the end Hot Horse Herbie is about to make another pitch to the narrator, after a rare occasion when his first selection has come up, and neither of them have backed it. Narrator Runyon walks away. 'Now,' Herbie says, 'wait a minute. A story goes with it.' 'Well,' I say, coming back to him, 'let me hear the story.' Racing folk are sentimental folk. We will always cheer home the horse we haven't backed if there is a good story with it, a victory for a trainer going broke, a jockey riding a much needed winner after an injury lay-off. And with Runyon, there is always a story, and a twist.

ROBIN OAKLEY

The Snatching of Bookie Bob

NOW it comes on the spring of 1931, after a long hard winter, and times are very tough indeed, what with the stock market going all to pieces, and banks busting right and left, and the law getting very nasty about this and that, and one thing and another, and many citizens of this town are compelled to do the best they can.

There is very little scratch anywhere and along Broadway many citizens are wearing their last year's clothes and have practically nothing to bet on the races or anything else, and it is a condition that will touch anybody's heart.

So I am not surprised to hear rumours that the snatching of certain parties is going on in spots, because while snatching is by no means a high-class business, and is even considered somewhat illegal, it is something to tide over the hard times.

Furthermore, I am not surprised to hear that this snatching is being done by a character by the name of Harry the Horse, who comes from Brooklyn, and who is a character who does not care much what sort of business he is in, and who is mobbed up with other characters from Brooklyn such as Spanish John and Little Isadore, who do not care what sort of business they are in, either.

In fact, Harry the Horse and Spanish John and Little Isadore are very hard characters in every respect, and there is considerable indignation expressed around and about when they move over from Brooklyn into Manhattan and start snatching, because the citizens of Manhattan feel that if there is any snatching done in their territory, they are entitled to do it themselves.

But Harry the Horse and Spanish John and Little Isadore pay no attention whatever to local sentiment and go on the snatch on a pretty fair scale, and by and by I am hearing rumours of some very nice scores. These scores are not extra large scores, to be sure, but they are enough to keep the wolf from the door, and in fact from three different doors, and before long Harry the Horse and Spanish John and Little Isadore are around the race-tracks betting on the horses, because if there is one thing they are all very fond of, it is betting on the horses.

Now many citizens have the wrong idea entirely of the snatching business. Many citizens think that all there is to snatching is to round up the party who is to be snatched and then just snatch him, putting him away somewhere until his family or friends dig up enough scratch to pay whatever price the snatchers are asking. Very few citizens understand that the snatching business must be well organized and very systematic.

In the first place, if you are going to do any snatching, you cannot snatch just anybody. You must know who you are snatching, because naturally it is no good snatching somebody who does not have any scratch to settle with. And you cannot tell by the way a party looks or how he lives in this town if he has any scratch, because many a party who is around in automobiles, and wearing good clothes, and chucking quite a swell is nothing but the phonus bolonus and does not have any real scratch whatever.

So of course such a party is no good for snatching, and of course guys who are on the snatch cannot go around inquiring into bank accounts, or asking how much this and that party has in a safe-deposit vault, because such questions are apt to make citizens wonder why, and it is very dangerous to get citizens to wondering why about anything. So the only way guys who are on the snatch can find out about parties worth snatching is to make a connection with some guy who can put the finger on the right party.

The finger guy must know the party he fingers has plenty of ready scratch to begin with, and he must also know that this party is such a party as is not apt to make too much disturbance about being snatched, such as telling the gendarmes. The party may be a legitimate party, such as a business guy, but he will have reasons why he does not wish it to get out that he is snatched, and the finger must know these reasons. Maybe the party is not leading the right sort of life, such as running around with blondes when he has an ever-loving wife and seven children in Mamaroneck, but does not care to have his habits known, as is apt to happen if he is snatched, especially if he is snatched when he is with a blonde.

And sometimes the party is such a party as does not care to have matches run up and down the bottom of his feet, which often happens to parties who are snatched and who do not seem to wish to settle their bill promptly, because many parties are very ticklish on the bottom of the feet, especially if the matches are lit. On the other hand, maybe the party is not a legitimate guy, such as a party who is running a crap game or a swell speakeasy, or who has some other dodge he does not care to have come out, and who also does not care about having his feet tickled.

Such a party is very good indeed for the snatching business, because he is pretty apt to settle without any argument. And after a party settles one snatching, it will be considered very unethical for anybody else to snatch him again very soon, so he is not likely to make any fuss about the matter. The finger guy gets a commission of twenty-five per cent. of the settlement, and one and all are satisfied and much fresh scratch comes into circulation, which is very good for the merchants. And while the party who is snatched may know who snatches him, one thing he never knows is who puts the finger on him, this being considered a trade secret.

I am talking to Waldo Winchester, the newspaper scribe, one night and something about the snatching business comes up, and Waldo Winchester is trying to tell me that it is one of the oldest dodges in the world, only Waldo calls it kidnapping, which is a title that will be very repulsive to guys who are on the snatch nowadays. Waldo Winchester claims that hundreds of years ago guys are around snatching parties, male and female, and holding them for ransom, and furthermore Waldo Winchester says they even snatch very little children and Waldo states that it is all a very, very wicked proposition.

Well, I can see where Waldo is right about it being wicked to snatch dolls and little children, but of course no guys who are on the snatch nowadays will ever think of such a thing, because who is going to settle for a doll in these times when you can scarcely even give them away? As for little children, they are apt to be a great nuisance, because their mammas are sure to go running around hollering bloody murder about them, and furthermore little children are very dangerous, indeed, what with being apt to break out with measles and mumps and one thing and another any minute and give it to everybody in the neighbourhood.

Well, anyway, knowing that Harry the Horse and Spanish John and Little Isadore are now on the snatch, I am by no means pleased to see them come along one Tuesday evening when I am standing at the corner of Fiftieth and Broadway, although of course I give them a very jolly hello, and say I hope and trust they are feeling nicely.

They stand there talking to me a few minutes, and I am very glad indeed that Johnny Brannigan, the strong-arm cop, does not happen along and see us, because it will give Johnny a very bad impression of me to see me in such company, even though I am not responsible for the company. But naturally I cannot haul off and walk away from this company at once, because Harry the Horse and Spanish John and Little Isadore may get the idea that I am playing the chill for them, and will feel hurt.

[4]

'Well,' I say to Harry the Horse, 'how are things going, Harry?'

'They are going no good,' Harry says. 'We do not beat a race in four days. In fact,' he says, 'we go overboard to-day. We are washed out. We owe every bookmaker at the track that will trust us, and now we are out trying to raise some scratch to pay off. A guy must pay his bookmaker no matter what.'

Well, of course this is very true, indeed, because if a guy does not pay his bookmaker it will lower his business standing quite some, as the bookmaker is sure to go around putting the blast on him, so I am pleased to hear Harry the Horse mention such honourable principles.

'By the way,' Harry says, 'do you know a guy by the name of Bookie Bob?'

Now I do not know Bookie Bob personally, but of course I know who Bookie Bob is, and so does everybody else in this town that ever goes to a race-track, because Bookie Bob is the biggest bookmaker around and about, and has plenty of scratch. Furthermore, it is the opinion of one and all that Bookie Bob will die with this scratch, because he is considered a very close guy with his scratch. In fact, Bookie Bob is considered closer than a dead heat.

He is a short fat guy with a bald head, and his head is always shaking a little from side to side, which some say is a touch of palsy, but which most citizens believe comes of Bookie Bob shaking his head 'No' to guys asking for credit in betting on the races. He has an ever-loving wife, who is a very quiet little old doll with grey hair and a very sad look in her eyes, but nobody can blame her for this when they figure that she lives with Bookie Bob for many years.

I often see Bookie Bob and his ever-loving wife eating in different joints along in the Forties, because they seem to have no home except an hotel, and many a time I hear Bookie Bob giving her a going-over about something or other, and generally it is about the price of something she orders to eat, so I judge Bookie Bob is as tough with his ever-loving wife about scratch as he is with everybody else. In fact, I hear him bawling her out one night because she has on a new hat which she says costs her six bucks, and Bookie Bob wishes to know if she is trying to ruin him with her extravagances.

But of course I am not criticizing Bookie Bob for squawking about the hat, because for all I know six bucks may be too much for a doll to pay for a hat, at that. And furthermore, maybe Bookie Bob has the right idea about keeping down his ever-loving wife's appetite, because I know many a guy in this town who is practically ruined by dolls eating too much on him.

'Well,' I say to Harry the Horse, 'if Bookie Bob is one of the bookmakers you owe, I am greatly surprised to see that you seem to have both eyes in your head, because I never before hear of Bookie Bob letting anybody owe him without giving him at least one of their eyes for security. In fact,' I say, 'Bookie Bob is such a guy as will not give you the right time if he has two watches.'

'No,' Harry the Horse says, 'we do not owe Bookie Bob. But,' he says, 'he will be owing us before long. We are going to put the snatch on Bookie Bob.'

Well, this is most disquieting news to me, not because I care if they snatch Bookie Bob or not, but because somebody may see me talking to them who will remember about it when Bookie Bob is snatched. But of course it will not be good policy for me to show Harry the Horse and Spanish John and Little Isadore that I am nervous, so I only speak as follows:

'Harry,' I say, 'every man knows his own business best, and I judge you know what you are doing. But,' I say, 'you are snatching a hard guy when you snatch Bookie Bob. A very hard guy, indeed. In fact,' I say, 'I hear the softest thing about him is his front teeth, so it may be very difficult for you to get him to settle after you snatch him.'

'No,' Harry the Horse says, 'we will have no trouble about it. Our finger gives us Bookie Bob's hole card, and it is a most surprising thing, indeed. But,' Harry the Horse says, 'you come upon many surprising things in human nature when you are on the snatch. Bookie Bob's hole card is his ever-loving wife's opinion of him.

'You see,' Harry the Horse says, 'Bookie Bob has been putting himself away with his ever-loving wife for years as a very important guy in this town, with much power and influence, although of course Bookie Bob knows very well he stands about as good as a broken leg. In fact,' Harry the Horse says, 'Bookie Bob figures that his ever-loving wife is the only one in the world who looks on him as a big guy, and he will sacrifice even his scratch, or anyway some of it, rather than let her know that guys have such little respect for him as to put the snatch on him. It is what you call psychology,' Harry the Horse says.

Well, this does not make good sense to me, and I am thinking to myself that the psychology that Harry the Horse really figures to work out nice on Bookie Bob is tickling his feet with matches, but I am not anxious to stand there arguing about it, and pretty soon I bid them all good evening, very polite, and take the wind, and I do not see Harry the Horse or Spanish John or Little Isadore again for a month.

In the meantime, I hear gossip here and there that Bookie Bob is missing for several days, and when he finally shows up again he gives it out that he is very sick during his absence, but I can put two and two together as well as anybody in this town and I figure that Bookie Bob is snatched by Harry the Horse and Spanish John and Little Isadore, and the chances are it costs him plenty.

So I am looking for Harry the Horse and Spanish John and Little Isadore to be around the race-track with plenty of scratch and betting them higher than a cat's back, but they never show up, and what is more I hear they leave Manhattan, and are back in Brooklyn working every day handling beer. Naturally this is very surprising to me, because the way things are running beer is a tough dodge just now, and there is very little profit in same, and I figure that with the scratch they must make off Bookie Bob, Harry the Horse and Spanish John and Little Isadore have a right to be taking things easy.

Now one night I am in Good Time Charley Bernstein's little speak in Forty-eighth Street, talking of this and that with Charley, when in comes Harry the Horse, looking very weary and by no means prosperous. Naturally I gave him a large hello, and by and by we get to gabbing together and I ask him whatever becomes of the Bookie Bob matter, and Harry the Horse tells me as follows:

Yes [Harry the Horse says], we snatch Bookie Bob all right. In fact, we snatch him the very next night after we are talking to you, or on a Wednesday night. Our finger tells us Bookie Bob is going to a wake over in his old neighbourhood on Tenth Avenue, near Thirty-eighth Street, and this is where we pick him up.

He is leaving the place in his car along about midnight, and of course Bookie Bob is alone as he seldom lets anybody ride with him because of the wear and tear on his car cushions, and Little Isadore swings our flivver in front of him and makes him stop. Naturally Bookie Bob is greatly surprised when I poke my head into his car and tell him I wish the pleasure of his company for a short time, and at first he is inclined to argue the matter, saying I must make a mistake, but I put the old convincer on him by letting him peek down the snozzle of my John Roscoe.

We lock his car and throw the keys away, and then we take Bookie Bob in our car and go to a certain spot on Eighth Avenue where we have a nice little apartment all ready. When we get there I tell Bookie Bob that he can call up anybody he wishes and state that the snatch is on him and that it will require twenty-five G's, cash money, to take it off, but of course I also tell Bookie Bob that he is not to mention where he is or something may happen to him.

Well, I will say one thing for Bookie Bob, although everybody is always weighing in the sacks on him and saying he is no good – he takes it like a gentleman, and very calm and businesslike.

Furthermore, he does not seem alarmed, as many citizens are when they find themselves in such a situation. He recognizes the justice of our claim at once, saying as follows:

'I will telephone my partner, Sam Salt,' he says. 'He is the only one I can think of who is apt to have such a sum as twenty-five G's cash money. But,' he says, 'if you gentlemen will pardon the question, because this is a new experience to me, how do I know everything will be okay for me after you get the scratch?'

'Why,' I say to Bookie Bob, somewhat indignant, 'it is well known to one and all in this town that my word is my bond. There are two things I am bound to do,' I say, 'and one is to keep my word in such a situation as this, and the other is to pay anything I owe a bookmaker, no matter what, for these are obligations of honour with me.'

'Well,' Bookie Bob says, 'of course I do not know you gentlemen, and, in fact, I do not remember ever seeing any of you, although your face is somewhat familiar, but if you pay your book-maker you are an honest guy, and one in a million. In fact,' Bookie Bob says, 'if I have all the scratch that is owing to me around this town, I will not be telephoning anybody for such a sum as twenty-five G's. I will have such a sum in my pants pocket for change.'

Now Bookie Bob calls a certain number and talks to somebody there but he does not get Sam Salt, and he seems much disappointed when he hangs up the receiver again.

'This is a very tough break for me,' he says. 'Sam Salt goes to Atlantic City an hour ago on very important business and will not be back until to-morrow evening, and they do not know where he is to stay in Atlantic City. And,' Bookie Bob says, 'I cannot think of anybody else to call up to get this scratch, especially anybody I will care to have know I am in this situation.'

'Why not call your ever-loving wife?' I say. 'Maybe she can dig up this kind of scratch.'

'Say,' Bookie Bob says, 'you do not suppose I am chump enough to give my ever-loving wife twenty-five G's, or even let her know where she can get her dukes on twenty-five G's belonging to me, do you? I give my ever-loving wife ten bucks per week for spending money,' Bookie Bob says, 'and this is enough scratch for any doll, especially when you figure I pay for her meals.'

[9]

Well, there seems to be nothing we can do except wait until Sam Salt gets back, but we let Bookie Bob call his ever-loving wife, as Bookie Bob says he does not wish to have her worrying about his absence, and tells her a big lie about having to go to Jersey City to sit up with a sick Brother Elk.

Well, it is now nearly four o'clock in the morning, so we put Bookie Bob in a room with Little Isadore to sleep, although, personally, I consider making a guy sleep with Little Isadore very cruel treatment, and Spanish John and I take turns keeping awake and watching out that Bookie Bob does not take the air on us before paying us off. To tell the truth, Little Isadore and Spanish John are somewhat disappointed that Bookie Bob agrees to settle so promptly, because they are looking forward to tickling his feet with great relish.

Now Bookie Bob turns out to be very good company when he wakes up the next morning, because he knows a lot of race-track stories and plenty of scandal, and he keeps us much interested at breakfast. He talks along with us as if he knows us all his life, and he seems very nonchalant indeed, but the chances are he will not be so nonchalant if I tell him about Spanish John's thought.

Well, about noon Spanish John goes out of the apartment and comes back with a racing sheet, because he knows Little Isadore and I will be wishing to know what is running in different spots although we do not have anything to bet on these races, or any way of betting on them, because we are overboard with every bookmaker we know.

Now Bookie Bob is also much interested in the matter of what is running, especially at Belmont, and he is bending over the table with me and Spanish John and Little Isadore, looking at the sheet, when Spanish John speaks as follows:

'My goodness,' Spanish John says, 'a spot such as this fifth race with Questionnaire at four to five is like finding money in the street. I only wish I have a few bobs to bet on him at such a price,' Spanish John says.

'Why,' Bookie Bob says, very polite, 'if you gentlemen wish to bet on these races I will gladly book to you. It is a good way to pass away the time while we are waiting for Sam Salt, unless you will rather play pinochle?'

'But,' I say, 'we have no scratch to play the races, at least not much.'

'Well,' Bookie Bob says, 'I will take your markers, because I hear what you say about always paying your bookmaker, and you put yourself away with me as an honest guy, and these other gentlemen also impress me as honest guys.'

Now what happens but we begin betting Bookie Bob on the different races, not only at Belmont, but at all the other tracks in the country, for Little Isadore and Spanish John and I are guys who like plenty of action when we start betting on the horses. We write out markers for whatever we wish to bet and hand them to Bookie Bob, and Bookie Bob sticks these markers in an inside pocket, and along in the late afternoon it looks as if he has a tumour on his chest.

We get the race results by 'phone off a poolroom down-town as fast as they come off, and also the prices, and it is a lot of fun, and Little Isadore and Spanish John and Bookie Bob and I are all little pals together until all the races are over and Bookie Bob takes out the markers and starts counting himself up.

It comes out then that I owe Bookie Bob ten G's, and Spanish John owes him six G's, and Little Isadore owes him four G's, as Little Isadore beats him a couple of races out west.

Well, about this·time, Bookie Bob manages to get Sam Salt on the 'phone, and explains to Sam that he is to go to a certain safe-deposit box and get out twenty-five G's, and then wait until midnight and hire himself a taxicab and start riding around the block between Fifty-first and Fifty-second, from Eighth to Ninth avenues, and to keep riding until somebody flags the cab and takes the scratch off him.

Naturally Sam Salt understands right away that the snatch is on Bookie Bob, and he agrees to do as he is told, but he says he cannot do it until the following night because he knows there is not twenty-five G's in the box, and he will have to get the difference at the track the next day. So there we are with another day in the apartment and Spanish John and Little Isadore and I are just as well pleased because Bookie Bob has us hooked and we naturally wish to wiggle off.

But the next day is worse than ever. In all the years I am playing the horses I never have such a tough day, and Spanish John and Little Isadore are just as bad. In fact, we are all going so bad that Bookie Bob seems to feel sorry for us and often lays us a couple of points above the track prices, but it does no good. At the end of the day, I am in a total of twenty G's, while Spanish John owes fifteen, and Little Isadore fifteen, a total of fifty G's among the three of us. But we are never any hands to hold post-mortems on bad days, so Little Isadore goes out to a delicatessen store and lugs in a lot of nice things to eat, and we have a fine dinner, and then we sit around with Bookie Bob telling stories, and even singing a few songs together until time to meet Sam Salt.

When it comes on midnight Spanish John goes out and lays for Sam, and gets a little valise off of Sam Salt. Then Spanish John comes back to the apartment and we open the valise and the twenty-five G's are there okay, and we cut this scratch three ways.

Then I tell Bookie Bob he is free to go on about his business, and good luck to him, at that, but Bookie Bob looks at me as if he is very much surprised, and hurt, and says to me like this:

'Well, gentlemen, thank you for your courtesy, but what about the scratch you owe me? What about these markers? Surely, gentlemen, you will pay your bookmaker?'

Well, of course we owe Bookie Bob these markers, all right, and of course a man must pay his bookmaker, no matter what, so I hand over my bit and Bookie Bob puts down something in a little note-book that he takes out of his kick.

Then Spanish John and Little Isadore hand over their dough, too, and Bookie Bob puts down something more in the little note-book.

'Now,' Bookie Bob says, 'I credit each of your accounts with these payments, but you gentlemen still owe me a matter of twenty-five G's over and above the twenty-five I credit you with, and I hope and trust you will make arrangements to settle this at once because,' he says, 'I do not care to extend such accommodations over any considerable period.'

'But,' I say, 'we do not have any more scratch after paying you the twenty-five G's on account.'

'Listen,' Bookie Bob says, dropping his voice down to a whisper, 'what about putting the snatch on my partner, Sam Salt, and I will wait over a couple of days with you and keep booking to you, and maybe you can pull yourselves out. But of course,' Bookie Bob whispers, 'I will be entitled to twenty-five per cent. of the snatch for putting the finger on Sam for you.'

But Spanish John and Little Isadore are sick and tired of Bookie Bob and will not listen to staying in the apartment any longer, because they say he is a jinx to them and they cannot beat him in any manner, shape or form. Furthermore, I am personally anxious to get away because something Bookie Bob says reminds me of something.

It reminds me that besides the scratch we owe him, we forget to take out six G's two-fifty for the party who puts the finger on Bookie Bob for us, and this is a very serious matter indeed, because anybody will tell you that failing to pay a finger is considered a very dirty trick. Furthermore, if it gets around that you fail to pay a finger, nobody else will ever finger for you.

So [Harry the Horse says] we quit the snatching business because there is no use continuing while this obligation is outstanding against us, and we go back to Brooklyn to earn enough scratch to pay our just debts.

We are paying off Bookie Bob's IOU a little at a time, because we do not wish to ever have anybody say we welsh on a bookmaker, and furthermore we are paying off the six G's two-fifty commission we owe our finger.

And while it is tough going, I am glad to say our honest effort is doing somebody a little good, because I see Bookie Bob's ever-loving wife the other night all dressed up in new clothes and looking very happy, indeed.

And while a guy is telling me she is looking so happy because she gets a large legacy from an uncle who dies in Switzerland, and is now independent of Bookie Bob, I only hope and trust [Harry the Horse says] that it never gets out that our finger in this case is nobody but Bookie Bob's ever-loving wife.

Pick the Winner

WHAT I am doing in Miami associating with such a character as Hot Horse Herbie is really quite a long story, and it goes back to one cold night when I am sitting in Mindy's restaurant on Broadway thinking what a cruel world it is, to be sure, when in comes Hot Horse Herbie and his ever-loving fiancée, Miss Cutie Singleton.

This Hot Horse Herbie is a tall, skinny guy with a most depressing kisser, and he is called Hot Horse Herbie because he can always tell you about a horse that is so hot it is practically on fire, a hot horse being a horse that is all readied up to win a race, although sometimes Herbie's hot horses turn out to be so cold they freeze everybody within fifty miles of them.

He is following the races almost since infancy, to hear him tell it. In fact, old Captain Duhaine, who has charge of the Pinkertons around the race tracks, says he remembers Hot Horse Herbie as a little child, and that even then Herbie is a hustler, but of course Captain Duhaine does not care for Hot Horse Herbie, because he claims Herbie is nothing but a tout, and a tout is something that is most repulsive to Captain Duhaine and all other Pinkertons.

A tout is a guy who goes around a race track giving out tips on the races, if he can find anybody who will listen to his tips, especially suckers, and a tout is nearly always broke. If he is not broke, he is by no means a tout, but a handicapper, and is respected by one and all, including the Pinkertons, for knowing so much about the races.

Well, personally, I have nothing much against Hot Horse Herbie, no matter what Captain Duhaine says he is, and I certainly have nothing against Herbie's ever-loving fiancée, Miss Cutie Singleton. In fact, I am rather in favour of Miss Cutie Singleton, because in all the years I know her, I wish to say I never catch Miss Cutie Singleton out of line, which is more than I can say of many other dolls I know.

She is a little, good-natured blonde doll, and by no means a crow, if you care for blondes, and some people say that Miss Cutie Singleton is pretty smart, although I never can see how this can be, as I figure a smart doll will never have any truck with a guy like Hot Horse Herbie, for Herbie is by no means a provider.

But for going on ten years, Miss Cutie Singleton and Hot Horse Herbie are engaged, and it is well known to one and all that they are to be married as soon as Herbie makes a scratch. In fact, they are almost married in New Orleans in 1928, when Hot Horse Herbie beats a good thing for eleven C's, but the tough part of it is the good thing is in the first race, and naturally Herbie bets the eleven C's right back on another good thing in the next race, and this good thing blows, so Herbie winds up with nothing but the morning line and is unable to marry Miss Cutie Singleton at this time.

Then again in 1929 at Churchill Downs, Hot Horse Herbie has a nice bet on Naishapur to win the Kentucky Derby, and he is so sure Naishapur cannot miss that the morning of the race he sends Miss Cutie Singleton out to pick a wedding ring. But Naishapur finishes second, so naturally Hot Horse Herbie is unable to buy the ring, and of course Miss Cutie Singleton does not wish to be married without a wedding ring.

They have another close call in 1931 at Baltimore when Hot Horse Herbie figures Twenty Grand a standout in the Preakness, and in fact is so sure of his figures that he has Miss Cutie Singleton go down to the city hall to find out what a marriage licence costs. But of course Twenty Grand does not win the Preakness, so the information Miss Cutie Singleton obtains is of no use to them, and anyway Hot Horse Herbie says he can beat the price on marriage licences in New York.

However, there is no doubt but what Hot Horse Herbie and Miss Cutie Singleton are greatly in love, although I hear rumours that for a couple of years past Miss Cutie Singleton is getting somewhat impatient about Hot Horse Herbie not making a scratch as soon as he claims he is going to when he first meets up with her in Hot Springs in 1923.

In fact, Miss Cutie Singleton says if she knows Hot Horse Herbie is going to be so long delayed in making his scratch she will never consider becoming engaged to him, but will keep her job as a manicurist at the Arlington Hotel, where she is not doing bad, at that.

It seems that the past couple of years Miss Cutie Singleton is taking to looking longingly at the little houses in the towns they pass through going from one race track to another, and especially at little white houses with green shutters and yards and vines all around and about, and saying it must be nice to be able to live in such places instead of in a suitcase.

But of course Hot Horse Herbie does not put in with her on these ideas, because Herbie knows very well if he is placed in a little white house for more than fifteen minutes the chances are he will lose his mind, even if the house has green shutters.

Personally, I consider Miss Cutie Singleton somewhat ungrateful for thinking of such matters after all the scenery Hot Horse Herbie lets her see in the past ten years. In fact, Herbie lets her see practically all the scenery there is in this country, and some in Canada, and all she has to do in return for all this courtesy is to occasionally get out a little crystal ball and deck of cards and let on she is a fortune teller when things are going especially tough for Herbie.

Of course Miss Cutie Singleton cannot really tell fortunes, or she will be telling Hot Horse Herbie's fortune, and maybe her own, too, but I hear she is better than a raw hand at making people believe she is telling their fortunes, especially old maids who think they are in love, or widows who are looking to snare another husband and other such characters.

Well, anyway, when Hot Horse Herbie and his ever-loving fiancée come into Mindy's, he gives me a large hello, and so does Miss Cutie Singleton, so I hello them right back, and Hot Horse Herbie speaks to me as follows:

'Well,' Herbie says, 'we have some wonderful news for you. We are going to Miami,' he says, 'and soon we will be among the waving palms, and revelling in the warm waters of the Gulf Stream.'

Now of course this is a lie, because while Hot Horse Herbie is in Miami many times, he never revels in the warm waters of the Gulf Stream, because he never has time for such a thing, what with hustling around the race tracks in the daytime, and around the dog tracks and the gambling joints at night, and in fact I will lay plenty of six to five Hot Horse Herbie cannot even point in the direction of the Gulf Stream when he is in Miami, and I will give him three points, at that.

But naturally what he says gets me to thinking how pleasant it is in Miami in the winter, especially when it is snowing up north, and a guy does not have a flogger to keep himself warm, and I am commencing to feel very envious of Hot Horse Herbie and his ever-loving fiancée when he says like this:

'But,' Herbie says, 'our wonderful news for you is not about us going. It is about you going,' he says. 'We already have our rail-road tickets,' he says, 'as Miss Cutie Singleton, my ever-loving fiancée here, saves up three C's for her hope chest the past summer, but when it comes to deciding between a hope chest and Miami, naturally she chooses Miami, because,' Herbie says, 'she claims she does not have enough hope left to fill a chest. Miss Cutie Singleton is always kidding,' he says.

'Well now,' Herbie goes on, 'I just run into Mr. Edward Donlin, the undertaker, and it seems that he is sending a citizen of Miami back home to-morrow night, and of course you know,' he says, 'that Mr. Donlin must purchase two railroad tickets for this journey, and as the citizen has no one else to accompany him, I got to thinking of you. He is a very old and respected citizen of Miami,' Herbie says, 'although of course,' he says, 'he is no longer with us, except maybe in spirit.'

Of course such an idea is most obnoxious to me, and I am very indignant that Hot Horse Herbie can even think I will travel in this manner, but he gets to telling me that the old and respected citizen of Miami that Mr. Donlin is sending back home is a great old guy in his day, and that for all anybody knows he will appreciate having company on the trip, and about this time Big Nig, the crap shooter, comes into Mindy's leaving the door open behind him so that a blast of cold air hits me, and makes me think more than somewhat of the waving palms and the warm waters of the Gulf Stream.

So the next thing I know, there I am in Miami with Hot Horse Herbie, and it is the winter of 1931, and everybody now knows that this is the winter when the suffering among the horse players in Miami is practically horrible. In fact, it is worse than it is in the winter of 1930. In fact, the suffering is so intense that many citizens are wondering if it will do any good to appeal to Congress for relief for the horse players, but The Dancer says he hears Congress needs a little relief itself.

Hot Horse Herbie and his ever-loving fiancée, Miss Cutie Singleton, and me have rooms in a little hotel on Flagler Street, and while it is nothing but a fleabag, and we are doing the landlord a favour by living there, it is surprising how much fuss he makes any time anybody happens to be a little short of the rent. In fact, the landlord hollers and yells so much any time anybody is a little short of the rent that he becomes a very great nuisance

[19]

to me, and I have half a notion to move, only I cannot think of any place to move to. Furthermore, the landlord will not let me move unless I pay him all I owe him, and I am not in a position to take care of this matter at the moment.

Of course I am not very dirty when I first come in as far as having any potatoes is concerned, and I start off at once having a little bad luck. It goes this way a while, and then it gets worse, and sometimes I wonder if I will not be better off if I buy myself a rope and end it all on a palm tree in the park on Biscayne Boulevard. But the only trouble with the idea is I do not have the price of a rope, and anyway I hear most of the palm trees in the park are already spoken for by guys who have the same notion.

And bad off as I am, I am not half as bad off as Hot Horse Herbie, because he has his ever-loving fiancée, Miss Cutie Singleton, to think of, especially as Miss Cutie Singleton is putting up quite a beef about not having any recreation, and saying if she only has the brains God gives geese she will break off their engagement at once and find some guy who can show her a little speed, and she seems to have no sympathy whatever for Hot Horse Herbie when he tells her how many tough snoots he gets beat at the track.

But Herbie is very patient with her, and tells her it will not be long now, because the law of averages is such that his luck is bound to change, and he suggests to Miss Cutie Singleton that she get the addresses of a few preachers in case they wish to locate one in a hurry. Furthermore, Hot Horse Herbie suggests to Miss Cutie Singleton that she get out the old crystal ball and her deck of cards, and hang out her sign as a fortune teller while they are waiting for the law of averages to start working for him, although personally I doubt if she will be able to get any business telling fortunes in Miami at this time because everybody in Miami seems to know what their fortune is already.

Now I wish to say that after we arrive in Miami I have very little truck with Hot Horse Herbie, because I do not approve of some of his business methods, and furthermore I do not wish

Captain Duhaine and his Pinkertons at my hip all the time, as I never permit myself to get out of line in any respect, or anyway not much. But of course I see Hot Horse Herbie at the track every day, and one day I see him talking to the most innocent-looking guy I ever see in all my life.

He is a tall, spindling guy with a soft brown Vandyke beard, and soft brown hair, and no hat, and he is maybe forty-odd, and wears rumpled white flannel pants, and a rumpled sports coat, and big horn cheaters, and he is smoking a pipe that you can smell a block away. He is such a guy as looks as if he does not know what time it is, and furthermore he does not look as if he has a quarter, but I can see by the way Hot Horse Herbie is warming his ear that Herbie figures him to have a few potatoes.

Furthermore, I never know Hot Horse Herbie to make many bad guesses in this respect, so I am not surprised when I see the guy pull out a long flat leather from the inside pocket of his coat and weed Herbie a bank-note. Then I see Herbie start for the mutuels windows, but I am quite astonished when I see that he makes for a two-dollar window. So I follow Hot Horse Herbie to see what this is all about, because it is certainly not like Herbie to dig up a guy with a bank roll and then only promote him for a deuce.

When I get hold of Herbie and ask him what this means, he laughs, and says to me like this:

'Well,' he says, 'I am just taking a chance with the guy. He may be a prospect, at that,' Herbie says. 'You never can tell about people. This is the first bet he ever makes in his life, and furthermore,' Herbie says, 'he does not wish to bet. He says he knows one horse can beat another, and what of it? But,' Herbie says, 'I give him a good story, so he finally goes for the deuce. I think he is a college professor somewhere,' Herbie says, 'and he is only wandering around the track out of curiosity. He does not know a soul here. Well,' Herbie says, 'I put him on a real hot horse, and if he wins maybe he can be developed into something. You know,' Herbie says, 'they can never rule you off for trying.'

Well, it seems that the horse Herbie gives the guy wins all right and at a fair price, and Herbie lets it go at that for the time being, because he gets hold of a real good guy, and cannot be bothering with guys who only bet deuces. But every day the professor is at the track and I often see him wandering through the crowds, puffing at his old stinkaroo and looking somewhat bewildered.

I get somewhat interested in the guy myself, because he seems so much out of place, but I wish to say I never think of promoting him in any respect, because this is by no means my dodge, and finally one day I get to talking to him and he seems just as innocent as he looks. He is a professor at Princeton, which is a college in New Jersey, and his name is Woodhead, and he has been very sick, and is in Florida to get well, and he thinks the track mob is the greatest show he ever sees, and is sorry he does not study this business a little earlier in life.

Well, personally, I think he is a very nice guy, and he seems to have quite some knowledge of this and that and one thing and another, although he is so ignorant about racing that it is hard to believe he is a college guy.

Even if I am a hustler, I will just as soon try to hustle Santa Claus as Professor Woodhead, but by and by Hot Horse Herbie finds things getting very desperate indeed, so he picks up the professor again and starts working on him, and one day he gets him to go for another deuce, and then for a fin, and both times the horses Herbie gives him are winners, which Herbie says just goes to show you the luck he is playing in, because when he has a guy who is willing to make a bet for him, he cannot pick one to finish fifth.

You see, the idea is when Hot Horse Herbie gives a guy a horse he expects the guy to bet for him, too, or maybe give him a piece of what he wins, but of course Herbie does not mention this to Professor Woodhead as yet, because the professor does not bet enough to bother with, and anyway Herbie is building him up by degrees, although if you ask me, it is going to be slow work, and finally Herbie himself admits as much, and says to me like this:

'It looks as if I will have to blast,' Herbie says. 'The professor is a nice guy, but,' he says, 'he does not loosen so easy. Furthermore,' Herbie says, 'he is very dumb about horses. In fact,' he says, 'I never see a guy so hard to educate, and if I do not like him personally, I will have no part of him whatever. And besides liking him personally,' Herbie says, 'I get a gander into that leather he carries the other day, and what do I see,' he says, 'but some large, coarse notes in there back to back.'

Well, of course this is very interesting news, even to me, because large, coarse notes are so scarce in Miami at this time that if a guy runs into one he takes it to a bank to see if it is counterfeit before he changes it, and even then he will scarcely believe it.

I get to thinking that if a guy such as Professor Woodhead can be going around with large, coarse notes in his possession, I make a serious mistake in not becoming a college professor myself, and naturally after this I treat Professor Woodhead with great respect.

Now what happens one evening, but Hot Horse Herbie and his ever-loving fiancée, Miss Cutie Singleton, and me are in a little grease joint on Second Street putting on the old hot tripe à la Creole, which is a very pleasant dish, and by no means expensive, when who wanders in but Professor Woodhead.

Naturally Herbie calls him over to our table and introduces Professor Woodhead to Miss Cutie Singleton, and Professor Woodhead sits there with us looking at Miss Cutie Singleton with great interest, although Miss Cutie Singleton is at this time feeling somewhat peevish because it is the fourth evening hand running she has to eat tripe à la Creole, and Miss Cutie Singleton does not care for tripe under any circumstances.

She does not pay any attention whatever to Professor Woodhead, but finally Hot Horse Herbie happens to mention that the professor is from Princeton, and then Miss Cutie Singleton looks at the professor, and says to him like this:

'Where is this Princeton?' she says. 'Is it a little town?'

'Well,' Professor Woodhead says, 'Princeton is in New Jersey, and it is by no means a large town, but,' he says, 'it is thriving.'

'Are there any little white houses in this town?' Miss Cutie Singleton asks. 'Are there any little white houses with green shutters and vines all around and about?'

'Why,' Professor Woodhead says, looking at her with more interest than somewhat, 'you are speaking of my own house,' he says. 'I live in a little white house with green shutters and vines all around and about, and,' he says, 'it is a nice place to live in, at that, although it is sometimes a little lonesome, as I live there all by myself, unless,' he says, 'you wish to count old Mrs. Bixby, who keeps house for me. I am a bachelor,' he says.

Well, Miss Cutie Singleton does not have much to say after this, although it is only fair to Miss Cutie Singleton to state that for a doll, and especially a blonde doll, she is never so very gabby, at that, but she watches Professor Woodhead rather closely, as Miss Cutie Singleton never before comes in contact with anybody who lives in a little white house with green shutters.

Finally we get through with the hot tripe à la Creole and walk around to the fleabag where Hot Horse Herbie and Miss Cutie Singleton and me are residing, and Professor Woodhead walks around with us. In fact, Professor Woodhead walks with Miss Cutie Singleton, while Hot Horse Herbie walks with me, and Hot Horse Herbie is telling me that he has the very best thing of his entire life in the final race at Hialeah the next day, and he is expressing great regret that he does not have any potatoes to bet on this thing, and does not know where he can get any potatoes.

It seems that he is speaking of a horse by the name of Breezing Along, which is owned by a guy by the name of Moose Tassell, who is a citizen of Chicago, and who tells Hot Horse Herbie that the only way Breezing Along can lose the race is to have somebody shoot him at the quarter pole, and of course nobody is shooting horses at the quarter pole at Hialeah, though many citizens often feel like shooting horses at the half.

Well, by this time we get to our fleabag, and we all stand there talking when Professor Woodhead speaks as follows:

'Miss Cutie Singleton informs me,' he says, 'that she dabbles somewhat in fortune telling. Well,' Professor Woodhead says, 'this is most interesting to me, because I am by no means sceptical of fortune telling. In fact,' he says, 'I make something of a study of the matter, and there is no doubt in my mind that certain human beings *do* have the faculty of foretelling future events with remarkable accuracy.'

Now I wish to say one thing for Hot Horse Herbie, and this is that he is a quick-thinking guy when you put him up against a situation that calls for quick thinking, for right away he speaks up and says like this:

'Why, Professor,' he says, 'I am certainly glad to hear you make this statement, because,' he says, 'I am a believer in fortune telling myself. As a matter of fact, I am just figuring on having Miss Cutie Singleton look into her crystal ball and see if she can make out anything on a race that is coming up to-morrow, and which has me greatly puzzled, what with being undecided between a couple of horses.'

Well, of course, up to this time Miss Cutie Singleton does not have any idea she is to look into any crystal ball for a horse, and furthermore, it is the first time in his life Hot Horse Herbie ever asks her to look into the crystal ball for anything whatever, except to make a few bobs for them to eat on, because Herbie by no means believes in matters of this nature.

But naturally Miss Cutie Singleton is not going to display any astonishment, and when she says she will very glad to oblige, Professor Woodhead speaks up and says he will be glad to see this crystal gazing come off, which makes it perfect for Hot Horse Herbie.

So we all go upstairs to Miss Cutie Singleton's room, and the next thing anybody knows there she is with her crystal ball, gazing into it with both eyes.

Now Professor Woodhead is taking a deep interest in the

proceedings, but of course Professor Woodhead does not hear what Hot Horse Herbie tells Miss Cutie Singleton in private, and as far as this is concerned neither do I, but Herbie tells me afterwards that he tells her to be sure and see a breeze blowing in the crystal ball. So by and by, after gazing into the ball a long time, Miss Cutie Singleton speaks in a low voice as follows:

'I seem to see trees bending to the ground under the force of a great wind,' Miss Cutie Singleton says. 'I see houses blown about by the wind,' she says. 'Yes,' Miss Cutie Singleton says, 'I see pedestrians struggling along and shivering in the face of this wind, and I see waves driven high on a beach and boats tossed about like paper cups. In fact,' Miss Singleton says, 'I seem to see quite a blow.'

Well, then, it seems that Miss Cutie Singleton can see no more, but Hot Horse Herbie is greatly excited by what she sees already, and he says like this:

'It means this horse Breezing Along,' he says. 'There can be no doubt about it. Professor,' he says, 'here is the chance of your lifetime. The horse will be not less than six to one,' he says. 'This is the spot to bet a gob, and,' he says, 'the place to bet it is downtown with a bookmaker at the opening price, because there will be a ton of money for the horse in the machines. Give me five C's,' Hot Horse Herbie says, 'and I will bet four for you, and one for me.'

Well, Professor Woodhead seems greatly impressed by what Miss Cutie Singleton sees in the crystal ball, but of course taking a guy from a finnif to five C's is carrying him along too fast, especially when Herbie explains that five C's is five hundred dollars, and naturally the professor does not care to bet any such money as this. In fact, the professor does not seem anxious to bet more than a sawbuck, tops, but Herbie finally moves him up to bet a yard, and of this yard twenty-five bobs is running for Hot Horse Herbie, as Herbie explains to the professor that a remittance he is expecting from his New York bankers fails him.

The next day Herbie takes the hundred bucks and bets it with

Gloomy Gus downtown, for Herbie really has great confidence in the horse.

We are out to the track early in the afternoon and the first guy we run into is Professor Woodhead, who is very much excited. We speak to him, and then we do not see him again all day.

Well, I am not going to bother telling you the details of the race, but this horse Breezing Along is nowhere. In fact, he is so far back that I do not recollect seeing him finish, because by the time the third horse in the field crosses the line, Hot Horse Herbie and me are on our way back to town, as Herbie does not feel that he can face Professor Woodhead at such a time as this. In fact, Herbie does not feel that he can face anybody, so we go to a certain spot over on Miami Beach and remain there drinking beer until a late hour, when Herbie happens to think of his ever-loving fiancée, Miss Cutie Singleton, and how she must be suffering from lack of food, so we return to our fleabag so Herbie can take Miss Cutie Singleton to dinner.

But he does not find Miss Cutie Singleton. All he finds from her is a note, and in this note Miss Cutie Singleton says like this: 'Dear Herbie,' she says, 'I do not believe in long engagements any more, so Professor Woodhead and I are going to Palm Beach to be married to-night, and are leaving for Princeton, New Jersey, at once, where I am going to live in a little white house with green shutters and vines all around and about. Good-bye, Herbie,' the note says. 'Do not eat any bad fish. Respectfully, Mrs. Professor Woodhead.'

Well, naturally this is most surprising to Hot Horse Herbie, but I never hear him mention Miss Cutie Singleton or Professor Woodhead again until a couple of weeks later when he shows me a letter from the professor.

It is quite a long letter, and it seems that Professor Woodhead wishes to apologize, and naturally Herbie has a right to think that the professor is going to apologize for marrying his ever-loving fiancée, Miss Cutie Singleton, as Herbie feels he has an apology coming on this account.

But what the professor seems to be apologizing about is not being able to find Hot Horse Herbie just before the Breezing Along race to explain a certain matter that is on his mind.

'It does not seem to me,' the professor says, as near as I can remember the letter, 'that the name of your selection is wholly adequate as a description of the present Mrs. Professor Woodhead's wonderful vision in the crystal ball, so,' he says, 'I examine the programme further, and finally discover what I believe to be the name of the horse meant by the vision, and I wager two hundred dollars on this horse, which turns out to be the winner at ten to one, as you may recall. It is in my mind,' the professor says, 'to send you some share of the proceeds, inasmuch as we are partners in the original arrangement, but the present Mrs. Woodhead disagrees with my view, so all I can send you is an apology, and best wishes.'

Well, Hot Horse Herbie cannot possibly remember the name of the winner of any race as far back as this, and neither can I, but we go over to the Herald office and look at the files, and what is the name of the winner of the Breezing Along race but Mistral, and when I look in the dictionary to see what this word means, what does it mean but a violent, cold and dry northerly wind.

And of course I never mention to Hot Horse Herbie or anybody else that I am betting on another horse in this race myself, and the name of the horse I am betting on is Leg Show, for how do I know for certain that Miss Cutie Singleton is not really seeing in the crystal ball just such a blow as she describes?

The Lemon Drop Kid

I AM going to take you back a matter of four or five years ago
to an August afternoon and the race track at Saratoga, which
is a spot in New York state very pleasant to behold, and also
to a young guy by the name of The Lemon Drop Kid, who is
called The Lemon Drop Kid because he always has a little sack
of lemon drops in the side pocket of his coat, and is always
munching at same, a lemon drop being a breed of candy that is
relished by many, although personally I prefer peppermints.

On this day I am talking about, The Lemon Drop Kid is
looking about for business, and not doing so good for himself, at
that, as The Lemon Drop Kid's business is telling the tale, and he
is finding it very difficult indeed to discover citizens who are
willing to listen to him tell the tale.

And of course if a guy whose business is telling the tale cannot
find anybody to listen to him, he is greatly handicapped, for the
tale such a guy tells is always about how he knows something is
doing in a certain race, the idea of the tale being that it may
cause the citizen who is listening to it to make a wager on this
certain race, and if the race comes out the way the guy who is
telling the tale says it will come out, naturally the citizen is

[29]

bound to be very grateful to the guy, and maybe reward him liberally.

Furthermore, the citizen is bound to listen to more tales, and a guy whose business is telling the tale, such as The Lemon Drop Kid, always has tales to tell until the cows come home, and generally they are long tales, and sometimes they are very interesting and entertaining, according to who is telling them, and it is well known to one and all that nobody can tell the tale any better than The Lemon Drop Kid.

But old Cap Duhaine and his sleuths at the Saratoga track are greatly opposed to guys going around telling the tale, and claim that such guys are nothing but touts, and they are especially opposed to The Lemon Drop Kid, because they say he tells the tale so well that he weakens public confidence in horse racing. So they are casing The Lemon Drop Kid pretty close to see that he does not get some citizen's ear and start telling him the tale, and finally The Lemon Drop Kid is greatly disgusted and walks up the lawn towards the head of the stretch.

And while he is walking, he is eating lemon drops out of his pocket, and thinking about how much better off he will be if he puts in the last ten years of his life at some legitimate dodge, instead of hop-scotching from one end of the country to the other telling the tale, although just off-hand The Lemon Drop Kid cannot think of any legitimate dodge at which he will see as much of life as he sees around the race tracks since he gets out of the orphan asylum in Jersey City where he is raised.

At the time this story starts out, The Lemon Drop Kid is maybe twenty-four years old, and he is a quiet little guy with a low voice, which comes of keeping it confidential when he is telling the tale, and he is nearly always alone. In fact, The Lemon Drop Kid is never known to have a pal as long as he is around telling the tale, although he is by no means an unfriendly guy, and is always speaking to everybody, even when he is in the money.

But it is now a long time since The Lemon Drop Kid is in the money, or seems to have any chance of being in the money, and the landlady of the boarding-house in Saratoga where he is residing is becoming quite hostile, and making derogatory cracks about him, and also about most of her other boarders, too, so The Lemon Drop Kid is unable to really enjoy his meals there, especially as they are very bad meals to start with.

Well, The Lemon Drop Kid goes off by himself up the lawn and stands there looking out across the track, munching a lemon drop from time to time, and thinking what a harsh old world it is, to be sure, and how much better off it will be if there are no sleuths whatever around and about.

It is a day when not many citizens are present at the track, and the only one near The Lemon Drop Kid seems to be an old guy in a wheel chair, with a steamer rug over his knees, and a big, sleepy-looking stove lid who appears to be in charge of the chair.

This old guy has a big white mouser, and big white bristly eyebrows, and he is a very fierce-looking old guy, indeed, and anybody can tell at once that he is nothing but a curmudgeon, and by no means worthy of attention. But he is a familiar spectacle at the race track at Saratoga, as he comes out nearly every day in a limousine the size of a hearse, and is rolled out of the limousine in his wheel chair on a little runway by the stove lid, and pushed up to this spot where he is sitting now, so he can view the sport of kings without being bothered by the crowds.

It is well known to one and all that his name is Rarus P. Griggsby, and that he has plenty of potatoes, which he makes in Wall Street, and that he is closer than the next second with his potatoes, and furthermore, it is also well known that he hates everybody in the world, including himself, so nobody goes anywhere near him if they can help it.

The Lemon Drop Kid does not realize he is standing so close to Rarus P. Griggsby, until he hears the old guy growling at the stove lid, and then The Lemon Drop Kid looks at Rarus P. Griggsby very sympathetic and speaks to him in his low voice as follows:

'Gout?' he says.

Now of course The Lemon Drop Kid knows who Rarus P. Griggsby is, and under ordinary circumstances The Lemon Drop Kid will not think of speaking to such a character, but afterwards he explains that he is feeling so despondent that he addresses Rarus P. Griggsby just to show he does not care what happens. And under ordinary circumstances, the chances are Rarus P. Griggsby will start hollering for the gendarmes if a stranger has the gall to speak to him, but there is so much sympathy in The Lemon Drop Kid's voice and eyes, that Rarus P. Griggsby seems to be taken by surprise, and he answers like this:

'Arthritis,' Rarus P. Griggsby says. 'In my knees,' he says. 'I am not able to walk a step in three years.'

'Why,' The Lemon Drop Kid says, 'I am greatly distressed to hear this. I know just how you feel, because I am troubled from infancy with this same disease.'

Now of course this is strictly the old ackamarackus, as The Lemon Drop Kid cannot even spell arthritis, let alone have it, but he makes the above statement just by way of conversation, and furthermore he goes on to state as follows:

'In fact,' The Lemon Drop Kid says, 'I suffer so I can scarcely think, but one day I find a little remedy that fixes me up as right as rain, and I now have no trouble whatsoever.'

And with this, he takes a lemon drop out of his pocket and pops it into his mouth, and then he hands one to Rarus P. Griggsby in a most hospitable manner, and the old guy holds the lemon drop between his thumb and forefinger and looks at it as if he expects it to explode right in his pan, while the stove lid gazes at The Lemon Drop Kid with a threatening expression.

'Well,' Rarus P. Griggsby says, 'personally I consider all cures fakes. I have a standing offer of five thousand dollars to anybody that can cure me of my pain, and nobody even comes close so far. Doctors are also fakes,' he says. 'I have seven of them and they take out my tonsils, and all my teeth, and my appendix, and they keep me from eating anything I enjoy, and I only get worse. The waters here in Saratoga seem to help me some, but,' he says, 'they do not get me out of this wheel chair, and I am sick and tired of it all.'

Then, as if he comes to a quick decision, he pops the lemon drop into his mouth, and begins munching it very slow, and after a while he says it tastes just like a lemon drop to him, and of course it is a lemon drop all along, but The Lemon Drop Kid says this taste is only to disguise the medicine in it.

Now, by and by, The Lemon Drop Kid commences telling Rarus P. Griggsby the tale, and afterwards The Lemon Drop Kid says he has no idea Rarus P. Griggsby will listen to the tale, and that he only starts telling it to him in a spirit of good clean fun, just to see how he will take it, and he is greatly surprised to note that Rarus P. Griggsby is all attention.

Personally, I find nothing unusual in this situation, because I often see citizens around the race tracks as prominent as Rarus P. Griggsby, listening to the tale from guys who do not have as much as a seat in their pants, especially if the tale has any larceny in it, because it is only human nature to be deeply interested in larceny.

And the tale The Lemon Drop Kid tells Rarus P. Griggsby is that he is a brother of Sonny Saunders, the jock, and that Sonny tells him to be sure and be at the track this day to bet on a certain horse in the fifth race, because it is nothing but a boat race, and everything in it is as stiff as a plank, except this certain horse.

Now of course this is all a terrible lie, and The Lemon Drop Kid is taking a great liberty with Sonny Saunders's name, especially as Sonny does not have any brothers, anyway, and even if Sonny knows about a boat race the chances are he will never tell The Lemon Drop Kid, but then very few guys whose business is telling the tale ever stop to figure they may be committing perjury.

So The Lemon Drop Kid goes on to state that when he arrives at the track he has fifty bobs pinned to his wishbone to bet on this certain horse, but unfortunately he gets a tip on a real good thing in the very first race, and bets his fifty bobs right then and there, figuring to provide himself with a larger taw to bet on the certain horse in the fifth, but the real good thing receives practically a criminal ride from a jock who does not know one end of a horse from the other, and is beat a very dirty snoot, and there The Lemon Drop Kid is with the fifth race coming up, and an absolute cinch in it, the way his tale goes, but with no dough left to bet on it.

Well, personally I do not consider this tale as artistic as some The Lemon Drop Kid tells, and in fact The Lemon Drop Kid himself never rates it among his masterpieces, but old Rarus P. Griggsby listens to the tale quite intently without saying a word, and all the time he is munching the lemon drop and smacking his lips under his big white mouser, as if he greatly enjoys this delicacy, but when The Lemon Drop Kid concludes the tale, and is standing there gazing out across the track with a very sad expression on his face, Rarus P. Griggsby speaks as follows:

'I never bet on horse races,' Rarus P. Griggsby says. 'They are too uncertain. But this proposition you present sounds like finding money, and I love to find money. I will wager one hundred dollars on your assurance that this certain horse cannot miss.'

And with this, he outs with a leather so old that The Lemon Drop Kid half expects a cockroach to leap out at him, and produces a C note which he hands to The Lemon Drop Kid, and as he does so, Rarus P. Griggsby inquires:

'What is the name of this certain horse?'

Well, of course this is a fair question, but it happens that The Lemon Drop Kid is so busy all afternoon thinking of the injustice of the sleuths that he never even bothers to look up this particular race beforehand, and afterwards he is quite generally criticized for slovenliness in this matter, for if a guy is around telling the tale about a race, he is entitled to pick out a horse that has at least some kind of a chance.

But of course The Lemon Drop Kid is not expecting the opportunity of telling the tale to arise, so the question finds him unprepared, as off-hand he cannot think of the name of a horse in the race, as he never consults the scratches, and he does not wish to mention the name of some plug that may be scratched out, and lose the chance to make the C note. So as he seizes the C note from Rarus P. Griggsby and turns to dash for the bookmakers over in front of the grandstand, all The Lemon Drop Kid can think of to say at this moment is the following:

'Watch Number Two,' he says.

And the reason he says No. 2, is he figures there is bound to be a No. 2 in the race, while he cannot be so sure about a No. 7 or a No. 9 until he looks them over, because you understand that all The Lemon Drop Kid states in telling the tale to Rarus P. Griggsby about knowing of something doing in this race is very false.

And of course The Lemon Drop Kid has no idea of betting the C note on anything whatever in the race. In the first place, he does not know of anything to bet on, and in the second place he needs the C note, but he is somewhat relieved when he inquires of the first bookie he comes to, and learns that No. 2 is an old walrus by the name of The Democrat, and anybody knows that The Democrat has no chance of winning even in a field of mud turtles.

So The Lemon Drop Kid put the C note in his pants pocket, and walks around and about until the horses are going to the post, and you must not think there is anything dishonest in his not betting this money with a bookmaker, as The Lemon Drop Kid is only taking the bet himself, which is by no means unusual, and in fact it is so common that only guys like Cap Duhaine and his sleuths think much about it.

Finally The Lemon Drop Kid goes back to Rarus P. Griggsby, for it will be considered most ungenteel for a guy whose business is telling the tale to be absent when it comes time to explain why the tale does not stand up, and about this time the horses are turning for home, and a few seconds later they go busting past the spot where Rarus P. Griggsby is sitting in his wheel chair, and

[35]

what is in front to the wire by a Salt Lake City block but The Democrat with No. 2 on his blanket.

Well, old Rarus P. Griggsby starts yelling and waving his hands, and making so much racket that he is soon the centre of attention, and when it comes out that he bets a C note on the winner, nobody blames him for cutting up these didoes, for the horse is a twenty to one shot, but all this time The Lemon Drop Kid only stands there looking very, very sad and shaking his head, until finally Rarus P. Griggsby notices his strange attitude.

'Why are you not cheering over our winning this nice bet?' he says. 'Of course I expect to declare you in,' he says. 'In fact I am quite grateful to you.'

'But,' The Lemon Drop Kid says, 'we do not win. Our horse runs a jolly second.'

'What do you mean, *second*?' Rarus P. Griggsby says. 'Do you not tell me to watch Number Two, and does not Number Two win?'

'Yes,' The Lemon Drop Kid says, 'what you state is quite true, but what I mean when I say watch Number Two is that Number Two is the only horse I am afraid of in the race, and it seems my fear is well founded.'

Now at this, old Rarus P. Griggsby sits looking at The Lemon Drop Kid for as long as you can count up to ten, if you count slow, and his mouser and eyebrows are all twitching at once, and anybody can see that he is very much perturbed, and then all of a sudden he lets out a yell and to the great amazement of one and all he leaps right out of his wheel chair and makes a lunge at The Lemon Drop Kid.

Well, there is no doubt that Rarus P. Griggsby has murder in his heart, and nobody blames The Lemon Drop Kid when he turns and starts running away at great speed, and in fact he has such speed that finally his feet are throwing back little stones off the gravel paths of the race track with such velocity that a couple of spectators who get hit by these stones think they are shot.

For a few yards, old Rarus P. Griggsby is right at The Lemon Drop Kid's heels, and furthermore Rarus P. Griggsby is yelling and swearing in a most revolting manner. Then some of Cap Duhaine's sleuths come running up and they take after The Lemon Drop Kid too, and he has to have plenty of early foot to beat them to the race-track gates, and while Rarus P. Griggsby does not figure much in the running after the first few jumps, The Lemon Drop Kid seems to remember hearing him cry out as follows:

'Stop, there! Please stop!' Rarus P. Griggsby cries. 'I wish to see you.'

But of course The Lemon Drop Kid is by no means a chump, and he does not even slacken up, let alone stop, until he is well beyond the gates, and the sleuths are turning back, and what is more, The Lemon Drop Kid takes the road leading out of Saratoga instead of going back to the city, because he figures that Saratoga may not be so congenial to him for a while.

In fact, The Lemon Drop Kid finds himself half-regretting that he ever tells the tale to Rarus P. Griggsby, as The Lemon Drop Kid likes Saratoga in August, but of course such a thing as happens to him in calling a winner the way he does is just an unfortunate accident, and is not apt to happen again in a life-time.

Well, The Lemon Drop Kid keeps on walking away from Saratoga for quite some time, and finally he is all tuckered out and wishes to take the load off his feet. So when he comes to a small town by the name of Kibbsville, he sits down on the porch of what seems to be a general store and gas station, and while he is sitting there thinking of how nice and quiet and restful this town seems to be, with pleasant shade trees, and white houses all around and about, he sees standing in the doorway of a very little white house across the street from the store, in a gingham dress, the most beautiful young doll that ever lives, and I know this is true, because The Lemon Drop Kid tells me so afterwards.

This doll has brown hair hanging down her back, and her smile is so wonderful that when an old pappy guy with a goatee comes out of the store to sell a guy in a flivver some gas, The Lemon Drop Kid hauls off and asks him if he can use a clerk.

Well, it seems that the old guy can, at that, because it seems that a former clerk, a guy by the name of Pilloe, recently lays down and dies on the old guy from age and malnutrition, and so this is how The Lemon Drop Kid comes to be planted in Kibbsville, and clerking in Martin Potter's store for the next couple of years, at ten bobs per week.

And furthermore, this is how The Lemon Drop Kid meets up with Miss Alicia Deering, who is nobody but the beautiful little doll that The Lemon Drop Kid sees standing in the doorway of the little house across the street.

She lives in this house with her papa, her mamma being dead a long time, and her papa is really nothing but an old bum who dearly loves his applejack, and who is generally around with a good heat on. His first name is Jonas, and he is a house painter by trade, but he seldom feels like doing any painting, as he claims he never really recovers from a terrible backache he gets when he is in the Spanish-American War with the First New York, so Miss Alicia Deering supports him by dealing them off her arm in the Commercial Hotel.

But although The Lemon Drop Kid now works for a very great old skinflint who even squawks about The Lemon Drop Kid's habit of filling his side pocket now and then with lemon drops out of a jar on the shelf in the store, The Lemon Drop Kid is very happy, for the truth of the matter is he loves Miss Alicia Deering, and it is the first time in his life he ever loves anybody, or anything. And furthermore, it is the first time in his life The Lemon Drop Kid is living quietly, and in peace, and not losing sleep trying to think of ways of cheating somebody.

In fact, The Lemon Drop Kid now looks back on his old life with great repugnance, for he can see that it is by no means the proper life for any guy, and sometimes he has half a mind to write to his former associates who may still be around telling the tale, and request them to mend their ways, only The Lemon Drop Kid does not wish these old associates to know where he is.

He never as much as peeks at a racing sheet nowadays, and he spends all his spare time with Miss Alicia Deering, which is not so much time, as that, as old Martin Potter does not care to see his employees loafing between the hours of 6 a.m. and 10 p.m., and neither does the Commercial Hotel. But one day in the spring, when the apple blossoms are blooming in these parts, and the air is chock-a-block with perfume, and the grass is getting nice and green, The Lemon Drop Kid speaks of his love to Miss Alicia Deering, stating that it is such a love that he can scarcely eat.

Well, Miss Alicia Deering states that she reciprocates this love one hundred per cent., and then The Lemon Drop Kid suggests they get married up immediately, and she says she is in favour of the idea, only she can never think of leaving her papa, who has no one else in all this world but her, and while this is a little more extra weight than The Lemon Drop Kid figures on picking up, he says his love is so terrific he can even stand for her papa, too.

So they are married, and go to live in the little house across the street from Martin Potter's store with Miss Alicia Deering's papa.

When he marries Miss Alicia Deering, The Lemon Drop Kid has a bank roll of one hundred and eighteen dollars, including the C note he takes off of Rarus P. Griggsby, and eighteen bobs that he saves out of his salary from Martin Potter in a year, and three nights after the marriage, Miss Alicia Deering's papa sniffs out where The Lemon Drop Kid plants his roll and sneezes same. Then he goes on a big applejack toot, and spends all the dough.

But in spite of everything, including old man Deering, The Lemon Drop Kid and Miss Alicia Deering are very, very happy in the little house for about a year, especially when it seems that Miss Alicia Deering is going to have a baby, although this incident compels her to stop dealing them off the arm at the Commercial Hotel, and cuts down their resources.

Now one day, Miss Alicia Deering comes down with a great illness, and it is such an illness as causes old Doc Abernathy, the local croaker, to wag his head, and to state that it is beyond him, and that the only chance for her is to send her to a hospital in New York City where the experts can get a crack at her. But by this time, what with all his overhead, The Lemon Drop Kid is as clean as a jaybird, and he has no idea where he can get his dukes on any money in these parts, and it will cost a couple of C's, for low, to do what Doc Abernathy suggests.

Finally, The Lemon Drop Kid asks old Martin Potter if he can see his way clear to making him an advance on his salary, which still remains ten bobs per week, but Martin Potter laughs, and says he not only cannot see his way clear to doing such a thing, but that if conditions do not improve he is going to cut The Lemon Drop Kid off altogether. Furthermore, about this time the guy who owns the little house drops around and reminds The Lemon Drop Kid that he is now in arrears for two months' rent, amounting in all to twelve bobs, and if The Lemon Drop Kid is not able to meet this obligation shortly, he will have to vacate.

So one way and another The Lemon Drop Kid is in quite a quandary, and Miss Alicia Deering is getting worse by the minute, and finally The Lemon Drop Kid hoofs and hitch-hikes a matter of maybe a hundred and fifty miles to New York City, with the idea of going out to Belmont Park, where the giddy-aps are now running, figuring he may be able to make some kind of a scratch around there, but he no sooner lights on Broadway than he runs into a guy he knows by the name of Short Boy, and this Short Boy pulls him into a doorway, and says to him like this:

'Listen, Lemon Drop,' Short Boy says, 'I do not know what it is you do to old Rarus P. Griggsby, and I do not wish to know, but it must be something terrible, indeed, as he has every elbow around the race tracks laying for you for the past couple of years. You know Rarus P. Griggsby has great weight around these tracks, and you must commit murder the way he is after you. Why,' Short Boy says, 'only last week over in Maryland, Whitey Jordan, the track copper, asks me if ever I hear of you, and I tell him I understand you are in Australia. Keep away from the tracks,' Short Boy says, 'or you will wind up in the clink.'

So The Lemon Drop Kid hoofs and hitch-hikes back to Kibbsville, as he does not wish to become involved in any trouble at this time, and the night he gets back home is the same night a masked guy with a big six pistol in his duke steps into the lobby of the Commercial Hotel and sticks up the night clerk and half a dozen citizens who are sitting around in the lobby, including old Jonas Deering, and robs the damper of over sixty bobs, and it is also the same night that Miss Alicia Deering's baby is born dead, and old Doc Abernathy afterwards claims that it is all because the experts cannot get a crack at Miss Alicia Deering a matter of about twelve hours earlier.

And it is along in the morning after this night, around four bells, that Miss Alicia Deering finally opens her eyes, and sees The Lemon Drop Kid sitting beside her bed in the little house, crying very hard, and it is the first time The Lemon Drop Kid is levelling with his crying since the time one of the attendants in the orphans' asylum in Jersey City gives him a good belting years before.

Then Miss Alicia Deering motions to The Lemon Drop Kid to bend down so she can whisper to him, and what Miss Alicia Deering whispers, soft and low, is the following:

'Do not cry, Kid,' she whispers. 'Be a good boy after I am gone, Kid, and never forget I love you, and take good care of poor papa.'

And then Miss Alicia Deering closes her eyes for good and all, and The Lemon Drop Kid sits there beside her, watching her face until some time later he hears a noise at the front door of the little house, and he opens the door to find old Sheriff Higginbotham waiting there, and after they stand looking at each other a while, the sheriff speaks as follows:

'Well, son,' Sheriff Higginbotham says, 'I am sorry, but I guess you will have to come along with me. We find the vinegar barrel spigot wrapped in tin foil that you use for a gun in the back yard here where you throw it last night.'

'All right,' The Lemon Drop Kid says. 'All right, Sheriff. But how do you come to think of me in the first place?'

'Well,' Sheriff Higginbotham says, 'I do not suppose you recall doing it, and the only guy in the hotel lobby that notices it is nobody but your papa-in-law, Jonas Deering, but,' he says, 'while you are holding your home-made pistol with one hand last night, you reach into the side pocket of your coat with the other hand and take out a lemon drop and pop it into your mouth.'

I run into The Lemon Drop Kid out on the lawn at Hialeah in Miami last winter, and I am sorry to see that the twoer he does in Auburn leaves plenty of lines in his face, and a lot of grey in his hair.

But of course I do not refer to this, nor do I mention that he is the subject of considerable criticism from many citizens for turning over to Miss Alicia Deering's papa a purse of three C's that we raise to pay a mouthpiece for his defence.

Furthermore, I do not tell The Lemon Drop Kid that he is also criticized in some quarters for his action while in the sneezer at Auburn in sending the old guy the few bobs he is able to gather in by making and selling knick-knacks of one kind and another to visitors, until finally Jonas Deering saves him any more bother by up and passing away of too much applejack.

The way I look at it, every guy knows his own business best, so I only duke The Lemon Drop Kid, and say I am glad to see him, and we are standing there carving up a few old scores, when all of a sudden there is a great commotion and out of the crowd around us on the lawn comes an old guy with a big white mouser, and bristly white eyebrows, and as he grabs The Lemon Drop Kid by the arm, I am somewhat surprised to see that it is nobody but old Rarus P. Griggsby, without his wheel chair, and to hear him speak as follows:

'Well, well, well, well, well!' Rarus P. Griggsby says to The Lemon Drop Kid. 'At last I find you,' he says. 'Where are you hiding all these years? Do you not know I have detectives looking for you high and low because I wish to pay you the reward I offer for anybody curing me of my arthritis? Yes,' Rarus P. Griggsby says, 'the medicine you give me at Saratoga which tastes like a lemon drop, works fine, although,' he says, 'my seven doctors all try to tell me it is nothing but their efforts finally getting in their work, while the city of Saratoga is attempting to cut in and claim credit for its waters.

'But,' Rarus P. Griggsby says, 'I know it is your medicine, and if it is not your medicine, it is your scallawaggery that makes me so hot that I forget my arthritis, and never remember it since, so it is all one and the same thing. Anyway, you now have forty-nine hundred dollars coming from me, for of course I must hold out the hundred out of which you swindle me,' he says.

Well, The Lemon Drop Kid stands looking at Rarus P. Griggsby and listening to him, and finally The Lemon Drop Kid begins to laugh in his low voice, ha-ha-ha-ha-ha, but somehow there does not seem to be any laughter in the laugh, and I cannot bear to hear it, so I move away leaving Rarus P. Griggsby and The Lemon Drop Kid there together.

I look back only once, and I see The Lemon Drop Kid stop laughing long enough to take a lemon drop out of the side pocket of his coat and pop it into his mouth, and then he goes on laughing, ha-ha-ha-ha-ha.

It Comes Up Mud

PERSONALLY, I never criticize Miss Beulah Beauregard for breaking her engagement to Little Alfie, because from what she tells me she becomes engaged to him under false pretences, and I do not approve of guys using false pretences on dolls, except, of course, when nothing else will do.

It seems that Little Alfie promises to show Miss Beulah Beauregard the life of Riley following the races with him when he gets her to give up a first-class job displaying her shape to the customers in the 900 Club, although Miss Beulah Beauregard frankly admits that Little Alfie does not say what Riley, and afterward Little Alfie states that he must be thinking of Four-eyes Riley when he makes the promise, and everybody knows that Four-eyes Riley is nothing but a bum, in spades.

Anyway, the life Little Alfie shows Miss Beulah Beauregard after they become engaged is by no means exciting, according to what she tells me, as Little Alfie is always going around the race tracks with one or two crocodiles that he calls race horses, trying to win a few bobs for himself, and generally Little Alfie is broke and struggling, and Miss Beulah Beauregard says this is no existence for a member of a proud old Southern family such as the Beauregards.

In fact, Miss Beulah Beauregard often tells me that she has half a mind to leave Little Alfie and return to her ancestral home in Georgia, only she can never think of any way of getting there without walking, and Miss Beulah Beauregard says it always makes her feet sore to walk very far, although the only time anybody ever hears of Miss Beulah Beauregard doing much walking is the time she is shell-roaded on the Pelham Parkway by some Yale guys when she gets cross with them.

It seems that when Little Alfie is first canvassing Miss Beulah Beauregard to be his fiancée he builds her up to expect diamonds and furs and limousines and one thing and another, but the only diamond she ever sees is an engagement hoop that Little Alfie gives her as the old convincer when he happens to be in the money for a moment, and it is a very small diamond, at that, and needs a high north light when you look at it.

But Miss Beulah Beauregard treasures this diamond very highly just the same, and one reason she finally breaks off her engagement to Little Alfie is because he borrows the diamond one day during the Hialeah meeting at Miami without mentioning the matter to her, and hocks it for five bobs which he bets on an old caterpillar of his by the name of Governor Hicks to show.

Well, the chances are Miss Beulah Beauregard will not mind Little Alfie's borrowing the diamond so much if he does not take the twenty-five bobs he wins when Governor Hicks drops in there in the third hole and sends it to Colonel Matt Winn in Louisville to enter a three-year-old of his by the name of Last Hope in the Kentucky Derby, this Last Hope being the only other horse Little Alfie owns at this time.

Such an action makes Miss Beulah Beauregard very indignant indeed, because she says a babe in arms will know Last Hope cannot walk a mile and a quarter, which is the Derby distance, let alone run so far, and that even if Last Hope can run a mile and a quarter, he cannot run it fast enough to get up a sweat.

In fact, Miss Beulah Beauregard and Little Alfie have words over this proposition, because Little Alfie is very high on Last

Hope and will not stand for anybody insulting this particular horse, not even his fiancée, although he never seems to mind what anybody says about Governor Hicks, and, in fact, he often says it himself.

Personally, I do not understand what Little Alfie sees in Last Hope, because the horse never starts more than once or twice since it is born, and then has a tough time finishing last, but Little Alfie says the fifty G's that Colonel Winn gives to the winner of the Kentucky Derby is just the same as in the jug in his name, especially if it comes up mud on Derby Day, for little Alfie claims that Last Hope is bred to just naturally eat mud.

Well, Miss Beulah Beauregard says there is no doubt Little Alfie blows his topper, and that there is no percentage in her remaining engaged to a crack-pot, and many citizens put in with her on her statement because they consider entering Last Hope in the Derby very great foolishness, no matter if it comes up mud or what, and right away Tom Shaw offers 1,000 to 1 against the horse in the future book, and everybody says Tom is underlaying the price at that.

Miss Beulah Beauregard states that she is very discouraged by the way things turn out, and that she scarcely knows what to do, because she fears her shape changes so much in the four or five years she is engaged to Little Alfie that the customers at the 900 Club may not care to look at it any more, especially if they have to pay for this privilege, although personally I will pay any reasonable cover charge to look at Miss Beulah Beauregard's shape any time, if it is all I suspect. As far as I can see it is still a very nice shape indeed, if you care for shapes.

Miss Beulah Beauregard is at this time maybe twenty-five or twenty-six, and is built like a first baseman, being tall and rangy. She has hay-coloured hair, and blue eyes, and lots of health, and a very good appetite. In fact, I once see Miss Beulah Beauregard putting on the fried chicken in the Seven Seas Restaurant in a way that greatly astonishes me, because I never knew before that members of proud old Southern families are such hearty eaters.

[47]

Furthermore, Miss Beulah Beauregard has a very Southern accent, which makes her sound quite cute, except maybe when she is a little excited and is putting the zing on somebody, such as Little Alfie.

Well, Little Alfie says he regrets exceedingly that Miss Beulah Beauregard sees fit to break their engagement, and will not be with him when he cuts up the Derby dough, as he is planning a swell wedding for her at French Lick after the race, and even has a list all made out of the presents he is going to buy her, including another diamond, and now he has all this bother of writing out the list for nothing.

Furthermore, Little Alfie says he is so accustomed to having Miss Beulah Beauregard as his fiancée that he scarcely knows what to do without her, and he goes around with a very sad puss, and is generally quite low in his mind, because there is no doubt that Little Alfie loves Miss Beulah Beauregard more than somewhat.

But other citizens are around stating that the real reason Miss Beulah Beauregard breaks her engagement to Little Alfie is because a guy by the name of Mr. Paul D. Veere is making a powerful play for her, and she does not wish him to know that she has any truck with a character such as Little Alfie, for of course Little Alfie is by no means anything much to look at, and, furthermore, what with hanging out with his horses most of the time, he never smells like any rose geranium.

It seems that this Mr. Paul D. Veere is a New York banker, and he has a little moustache, and plenty of coconuts, and Miss Beulah Beauregard meets up with him one morning when she is displaying her shape on the beach at the Roney Plaza for nothing, and it also seems that there is enough of her shape left to interest Mr. Paul D. Veere no little.

In fact, the next thing anybody knows, Mr. Paul D. Veere is taking Miss Beulah Beauregard here and there, and around and about, although at this time Miss Beulah Beauregard is still engaged to Little Alfie, and the only reason Little Alfie does not notice Mr. Paul D. Veere at first is because he is busy training Last Hope to win the Kentucky Derby, and hustling around trying to get a few bobs together every day to stand off the overhead, including Miss Beulah Beauregard, because naturally Miss Beulah Beauregard cannot bear the idea of living in a fleabag, such as the place where Little Alfie resides, but has to have a nice room at the Roney Plaza.

Well, personally, I have nothing against bankers as a class, and in fact I never meet up with many bankers in my life, but somehow I do not care for Mr. Paul D. Veere's looks. He looks to me like a stony-hearted guy, although, of course, nobody ever sees any banker who does not look stony-hearted, because it seems that being bankers just naturally makes them look this way.

But Mr. Paul D. Veere is by no means an old guy, and the chances are he speaks of something else besides horses to Miss Beulah Beauregard, and furthermore he probably does not smell like horses all the time, so nobody can blame Miss Beulah Beauregard for going around and about with him, although many citizens claim she is a little out of line in accepting Mr. Paul D. Veere's play while she is still engaged to Little Alfie. In fact, there is great indignation in some circles about this, as many citizens feel that Miss Beulah Beauregard is setting a bad example to other fiancées.

But after Miss Beulah Beauregard formally announces that their engagement is off, it is agreed by one and all that she has a right to do as she pleases, and that Little Alfie himself gets out of line in what happens at Hialeah a few days later when he finally notices that Miss Beulah Beauregard seems to be with Mr. Paul D. Veere, and on very friendly terms with him, at that. In fact, Little Alfie comes upon Mr. Paul D. Veere in the act of kissing Miss Beulah Beauregard behind a hibiscus bush out near the paddock, and this scene is most revolting to Little Alfie as he never cares for hibiscus, anyway.

He forgets that Miss Beulah Beauregard is no longer his fiancée, and tries to take a punch at Mr. Paul D. Veere, but he is stopped by a number of detectives, who are greatly horrified at the idea of anybody taking a punch at a guy who has as many coco-nuts as Mr. Paul D. Veere, and while they are expostulating with Little Alfie, Miss Beulah Beauregard disappears from the scene and is observed no more in Miami. Furthermore, Mr. Paul D. Veere also disappears, but of course nobody minds this very much, and, in fact, his disappearance is a great relief to all citizens who have fiancées in Miami at this time.

But it seems that before he disappears Mr. Paul D. Veere calls on certain officials of the Jockey Club and weighs in the sacks on Little Alfie, stating that he is a most dangerous character to have loose around a race track, and naturally the officials are bound to listen to a guy who has as many coco-nuts as Mr. Paul D. Veere.

So a day or two later old Cap Duhaine, the head detective around the race track, sends for Little Alfie and asks him what he thinks will become of all the prominent citizens such as bankers if guys go around taking punches at them and scaring them half to death, and Little Alfie cannot think of any answer to this conundrum off-hand, especially as Cap Duhaine then asks Little Alfie if it will be convenient for him to take his two horses elsewhere.

Well, Little Alfie can see that Cap Duhaine is hinting in a polite way that he is not wanted around Hialeah any more, and Little Alfie is a guy who can take a hint as well as the next guy, especially when Cap Duhaine tells him in confidence that the racing stewards do not seem able to get over the idea that some scalawag slips a firecracker into Governor Hicks the day old Governor Hicks runs third, because it seems from what Cap Duhaine says that the stewards consider it practically supernatural for Governor Hicks to run third anywhere, any time.

So there Little Alfie is in Miami, as clean as a jaybird, with two horses on his hands, and no way to ship them to any place where horses are of any account, and it is quite a predicament indeed, and causes Little Alfie to ponder quite some. And the upshot of his pondering is that Little Alfie scrapes up a few bobs here and there, and a few oats, and climbs on Governor Hicks one day and boots him in the slats and tells him to giddyup, and away he goes out of Miami, headed north, riding Governor Hicks and leading Last Hope behind him on a rope.

Naturally, this is considered a most unusual spectacle by one and all who witness it and, in fact, it is the first time anybody can remember a horse owner such as Little Alfie riding one of his own horses off in this way, and Gloomy Gus is offering to lay plenty of 5 to 1 that Governor Hicks never makes Palm Beach with Little Alfie up, as it is well known that the old Governor has bum legs and is half out of wind and is apt to pig it any time.

But it seems that Governor Hicks makes Palm Beach all right with Little Alfie up and going so easy that many citizens are around asking Gloomy for a price against Jacksonville. Furthermore, many citizens are now saying that Little Alfie is a pretty smart guy, at that, to think of such an economical idea, and numerous other horse owners are looking their stock over to see if they have anything to ride up north themselves.

Many citizens are also saying that Little Alfie gets a great break when Miss Beulah Beauregard runs out on him, because it takes plenty of weight off him in the way of railroad fare and one thing and another; but it seems Little Alfie does not feel this way about the matter at all.

It seems that Little Alfie often thinks about Miss Beulah Beauregard as he goes jogging along to the north, and sometimes he talks to Governor Hicks and Last Hope about her, and especially to Last Hope, as Little Alfie always considers Governor Hicks somewhat dumb. Also Little Alfie sometimes sings sad love songs right out loud as he is riding along, although the first time he starts to sing he frightens Last Hope and causes him to break loose from the lead rope and run away, and Little Alfie is an hour catching him. But after this Last Hope gets so he does not mind Little Alfie's voice so much, except when Little Alfie tries to hit high C.

Well, Little Alfie has a very nice ride, at that, because the weather is fine and the farmers along the road feed him and his horses, and he has nothing whatever to worry about except a few saddle galls, and about getting to Kentucky for the Derby in May, and here it is only late in February, and anyway Little Alfie does not figure to ride any farther than maybe Maryland where he is bound to make a scratch so he can ship from there.

Now, one day Little Alfie is riding along a road through a stretch of piny woods, a matter of maybe ninety-odd miles north of Jacksonville, which puts him in the State of Georgia, when he passes a half-ploughed field on one side of the road near a ramshackly old house and beholds a most unusual scene:

A large white mule hitched to a plough is sitting down in the field and a tall doll in a sunbonnet and a gingham dress is standing beside the mule crying very heartily.

Naturally, the spectacle of a doll in distress, or even a doll who is not in distress, is bound to attract Little Alfie's attention, so he tells Governor Hicks and Last Hope to whoa, and then he asks the doll what is eating her, and the doll looks up at him out of her sunbonnet, and who is this doll but Miss Beulah Beauregard.

Of course Little Alfie is somewhat surprised to see Miss Beulah Beauregard crying over a mule, and especially in a sunbonnet, so he climbs down off of Governor Hicks to inquire into this situation, and right away Miss Beulah Beauregard rushes up to Little Alfie and chucks herself into his arms and speaks as follows:

'Oh, Alfie,' Miss Beulah Beauregard says, 'I am so glad you find me. I am thinking of you day and night, and wondering if you forgive me. Oh, Alfie, I love you,' she says. 'I am very sorry I go away with Mr. Paul D. Veere. He is nothing but a great rapscallion,' she says. 'He promises to make me his ever-loving wife when he gets me to accompany him from Miami to his shooting-lodge on the Altamaha River, twenty-five miles from here, although,' she says, 'I never know before he has such a lodge in these parts.

'And,' Miss Beulah Beauregard says, 'the very first day I have to pop him with a pot of cold cream and render him half unconscious to escape his advances. Oh, Alfie,' she says, 'Mr. Paul D. Veere's intentions towards me are by no means honourable. Furthermore,' she says, 'I learn he already has an ever-loving wife and three children in New York.'

Well, of course Little Alfie is slightly perplexed by this matter and can scarcely think of anything much to say, but finally he says to Miss Beulah Beauregard like this:

'Well,' he says, 'but what about the mule?'

'Oh,' Miss Beulah Beauregard says, 'his name is Abimelech, and I am ploughing with him when he hauls off and sits down and refuses to budge. He is the only mule we own,' she says, 'and he is old and ornery, and nobody can do anything whatever with him when he wishes to sit down. But,' she says, 'my papa will be very angry because he expects me to get this field all ploughed up by supper-time. In fact,' Miss Beulah Beauregard says, 'I am afraid my papa will be so angry he will give me a whopping, because he by no means forgives me as yet for coming home, and this is why I am shedding tears when you come along.'

Then Miss Beulah Beauregard begins crying again as if her heart will break, and if there is one thing Little Alfie hates and despises it is to see a doll crying, and especially Miss Beulah Beauregard, for Miss Beulah Beauregard can cry in a way to wake the dead when she is going good, so Little Alfie holds her so close to his chest he ruins four cigars in his vest pocket, and speaks to her as follows:

'Tut, tut,' Little Alfie says. 'Tut, tut, tut, tut, tut,' he says. 'Dry your eyes and we will just hitch old Governor Hicks here to the plough and get this field ploughed quicker than you can say scat, because,' Little Alfie says, 'when I am a young squirt, I am the best plougher in Columbia County, New York.'

Well, this idea cheers Miss Beulah Beauregard up no little, and so Little Alfie ties Last Hope to a tree and takes the harness off Abimelech, the mule, who keeps right on sitting down as if he does not care what happens, and puts the harness on Governor Hicks and hitches Governor Hicks to the plough, and the way the old Governor carries on when he finds out they wish him to pull a plough is really most surprising. In fact, Little Alfie has to get a club and reason with Governor Hicks before he will settle down and start pulling the plough.

It turns out that Little Alfie is a first-class plougher, at that, and while he is ploughing, Miss Beulah Beauregard walks along with him and talks a blue streak, and Little Alfie learns more things from her in half an hour than he ever before suspects in some years, and especially about Miss Beulah Beauregard herself.

It seems that the ramshackly old house is Miss Beulah Beauregard's ancestral home, and that her people are very poor, and live in these piny woods for generations, and that their name is Benson and not Beauregard at all, this being nothing but a name that Miss Beulah Beauregard herself thinks up out of her own head when she goes to New York to display her shape.

Furthermore, when they go to the house it comes out that Miss Beulah Beauregard's papa is a tall, skinny old guy with a goatee, who can lie faster than Little Alfie claims Last Hope can run. But it seems that the old skeezicks takes quite an interest in Last Hope when Little Alfie begins telling him what a great horse this horse is, especially in the mud, and how he is going to win the Kentucky Derby.

In fact, Miss Beulah Beauregard's papa seems to believe everything Little Alfie tells him, and as he is the first guy Little Alfie ever meets up with who believes anything he tells about anything whatever, it is a privilege and a pleasure for Little Alfie to talk to him. Miss Beulah Beauregard also has a mamma who turns out to be very fat, and full of Southern hospitality, and quite handy with a skillet.

Then there is a grown brother by the name of Jeff, who is practically a genius, as he knows how to disguise skimmin's so it makes a person only a little sick when they drink it, this skimmin's being a drink which is made from skimmings that come to the top on boiling sugar cane, and generally it tastes like gasoline, and is very fatal indeed.

Now, the consequences are Little Alfie finds this place very pleasant, and he decides to spend a few weeks there, paying for his keep with the services of Governor Hicks as a plough horse, especially as he is now practically engaged to Miss Beulah Beauregard all over again and she will not listen to him leaving without her. But they have no money for her railroad fare, and Little Alfie becomes very indignant when she suggests she can ride Last Hope on north while he is riding Governor Hicks, and wishes to know if she thinks a Derby candidate can be used for a truck horse.

Well, this almost causes Miss Beulah Beauregard to start breaking the engagement all over again, as she figures it is a dirty crack about her heft, but her papa steps in and says they must remain until Governor Hicks gets through with the ploughing anyway, or he will know the reason why. So Little Alfie stays, and he puts in all his spare time training Last Hope and wondering who he can write to for enough dough to send Miss Beulah Beauregard north when the time comes.

He trains Last Hope by walking him and galloping him along the country roads in person, and taking care of him as if he is a baby, and what with this work, and the jog up from Miami, Last Hope fills out very strong and hearty, and anybody must admit that he is not a bad-looking beetle, though maybe a little more leggy than some like to see.

Now, it comes a Sunday, and all day long there is a very large storm with rain and wind that takes to knocking over big trees, and one thing and another, and no one is able to go outdoors much. So late in the evening Little Alfie and Miss Beulah Beauregard and all the Bensons are gathered about the stove in the kitchen drinking skimmin's, and Little Alfie is telling them all over again about how Last Hope will win the Kentucky Derby, especially if it comes up mud, when they hear a hammering at the door.

[55]

When the door is opened, who comes in but Mr. Paul D. Veere, sopping wet from head to foot, including his little moustache, and limping so he can scarcely walk, and naturally his appearance nonplusses Miss Beulah Beauregard and Little Alfie, who can never forget that Mr. Paul D. Veere is largely responsible for the saddle galls he gets riding up from Miami.

In fact, several times since he stops at Miss Beulah Beauregard's ancestral home, Little Alfie thinks of Mr. Paul D. Veere, and every time he thinks of him he is in favour of going over to Mr. Paul D. Veere's shooting-lodge on the Altamaha and speaking to him severely.

But Miss Beulah Beauregard always stops him, stating that the proud old Southern families in this vicinity are somewhat partial to the bankers and other rich guys from the North who have shooting-lodges around and about in the piny woods, and especially on the Altamaha, because these guys furnish a market to the local citizens for hunting guides, and corn liquor, and one thing and another.

Miss Beulah Beauregard says if a guest of the Bensons speaks to Mr. Paul D. Veere severely, it may be held against the family, and it seems that the Benson family cannot stand any more beefs against it just at this particular time. So Little Alfie never goes, and here all of a sudden is Mr. Paul D. Veere right in his lap.

Naturally, Little Alfie steps forward and starts winding up a large right hand with the idea of parking it on Mr. Paul D. Veere's chin, but Mr. Paul D. Veere seems to see that there is hostility afoot, and he backs up against the wall, and raises his hand, and speaks as follows:

'Folks,' Mr. Paul D. Veere says, 'I just go into a ditch in my automobile half a mile up the road. My car is a wreck,' he says, 'and my right leg seems so badly hurt I am just barely able to drag myself here. Now, folks,' he says, 'it is almost a matter of life or death with me to get to the station at Tillinghast in time to flag the Orange Blossom Special. It is the last train to-night to Jacksonville, and I must be in Jacksonville before midnight so I can hire an aeroplane and get to New York by the time my bank opens at ten o'clock in the morning. It is about ten hours by plane from Jacksonville to New York,' Mr. Paul D. Veere says, 'so if I can catch the Orange Blossom, I will be able to just about make it!'

Then he goes on speaking in a low voice and states that he receives a telephone message from New York an hour or so before at his lodge telling him he must hurry home, and right away afterward, while he is trying to telephone the station at Tillinghast to make sure they will hold the Orange Blossom until he gets there, no matter what, all the telephone and telegraph wires around and about go down in the storm.

So he starts for the station in his car, and just as it looks as if he may make it, his car runs smack-dab into a ditch and Mr. Paul D. Veere's leg is hurt so there is no chance he can walk the rest of the way to the station, and there Mr. Paul D. Veere is.

'It is a very desperate case, folks,' Mr. Paul D. Veere says. 'Let me take your automobile, and I will reward you liberally.'

Well, at this Miss Beulah Beauregard's papa looks at a clock on the kitchen wall and states as follows:

'We do not keep an automobile, neighbour,' he says, 'and anyway,' he says, 'it is quite a piece from here to Tillinghast and the Orange Blossom is due in ten minutes, so I do not see how you can possibly make it. Rest your hat, neighbour,' Miss Beulah Beauregard's papa says, 'and have some skimmin's, and take things easy, and I will look at your leg and see how bad you are bunged up.'

Well, Mr. Paul D. Veere seems to turn as pale as a pillow as he hears this about the time, and then he says:

'Lend me a horse and buggy,' he says. 'I must be in New York in person in the morning. No one else will do but me,' he says, and as he speaks these words he looks at Miss Beulah Beauregard and then at Little Alfie as if he is speaking to them personally, although up to this time he does not look at either of them after he comes into the kitchen.

'Why, neighbour,' Miss Beulah Beauregard's papa says, 'we do not keep a buggy, and even if we do keep a buggy we do not have time to hitch up anything to a buggy. Neighbour,' he says, 'you are certainly on a bust if you think you can catch the Orange Blossom now.'

'Well, then,' Mr. Paul D. Veere says, very sorrowful, 'I will have to go to jail.'

Then he flops himself down in a chair and covers his face with his hands, and he is a spectacle such as is bound to touch almost any heart, and when she sees him in this state Miss Beulah Beauregard begins crying because she hates to see anybody as sorrowed up as Mr. Paul D. Veere, and between sobs she asks Little Alfie to think of something to do about the situation.

'Let Mr. Paul D. Veere ride Governor Hicks to the station,' Miss Beulah Beauregard says. 'After all,' she says, 'I cannot forget his courtesy in sending me half-way here in his car from his shooting-lodge after I pop him with the pot of cold cream, instead of making me walk as those Yale guys do the time they red-light me.'

'Why,' Little Alfie says, 'it is a mile and a quarter from the gate out here to the station. I know,' he says, 'because I get a guy in an automobile to clock it on his metre one day last week, figuring to give Last Hope a workout over the full Derby route pretty soon. The road must be fetlock deep in mud at this time, and,' Little Alfie says, 'Governor Hicks cannot as much as stand up in the mud. The only horse in the world that can run fast enough through this mud to make the Orange Blossom is Last Hope, but,' Little Alfie says, 'of course I'm not letting anybody ride a horse as valuable as Last Hope to catch trains.'

Well, at this Mr. Paul D. Veere lifts his head and looks at Little Alfie with great interest and speaks as follows:

'How must is this valuable horse worth?' Mr. Paul D. Veere says.

'Why,' Little Alfie says, 'he is worth anyway fifty G's to me, because,' he says, 'this is the sum Colonel Winn is giving to the winner of the Kentucky Derby, and there is no doubt whatever that Last Hope will be this winner, especially,' Little Alfie says, 'if it comes up mud.'

'I do not carry any such large sum of money as you mention on my person,' Mr. Paul D. Veere says, 'but,' he says, 'if you are willing to trust me, I will give you my IOU for same, just to let me ride your horse to the station. I am once the best amateur steeplechase rider in the Hunts Club,' Mr. Paul D. Veere says, 'and if your horse can run at all there is still a chance for me to keep out of jail.'

Well, the chances are Little Alfie will by no means consider extending a line of credit for fifty G's to Mr. Paul D. Veere or any other banker, and especially a banker who is once an amateur steeplechase jock, because if there is one thing Little Alfie does not trust it is an amateur steeplechase jock, and furthermore Little Alfie is somewhat offended because Mr. Paul D. Veere seems to think he is running a livery stable.

But Miss Beulah Beauregard is now crying so loud nobody can scarcely hear themselves think, and Little Alfie gets to figuring what she may say to him if he does not rent Last Hope to Mr. Paul D. Veere at this time and it comes out later that Last Hope does not happen to win the Kentucky Derby after all. So he finally says all right, and Mr. Paul D. Veere at once outs with a little gold pencil and a notebook, and scribbles off a marker for fifty G's to Little Alfie.

And the next thing anybody knows, Little Alfie is leading Last Hope out of the barn and up to the gate with nothing on him but a bridle as Little Alfie does not wish to waste time saddling, and as he is boosting Mr. Paul D. Veere on to Last Hope Little Alfie speaks as follows:

'You have three minutes left,' Little Alfie says. 'It is almost a straight course, except for a long turn going into the last quarter. Let this fellow run,' he says. 'You will find plenty of mud all the way, but,' Little Alfie says, 'this is a mud-running fool. In fact,' Little Alfie says, 'you are pretty lucky it comes up mud.'

Then he gives Last Hope a smack on the hip and away goes Last Hope lickity-split through the mud and anybody can see from the way Mr. Paul D. Veere is sitting on him that Mr. Paul D. Veere knows what time it is when it comes to riding. In fact, Little Alfie himself says he never sees a better seat anywhere in his life, especially for a guy who is riding bareback.

Well, Little Alfie watches them go down the road in a gob of mud, and it will always be one of the large regrets of Little Alfie's life that he leaves his split-second super in hock in Miami, because he says he is sure Last Hope runs the first quarter through the mud faster than any quarter is ever run before in this world. But of course Little Alfie is more excited than somewhat at this moment, and the chances are he exaggerates Last Hope's speed.

However, there is no doubt that Last Hope goes over the road very rapidly, indeed, as a coloured party who is out squirrel hunting comes along a few minutes afterward and tells Little Alfie that something goes past him on the road so fast he cannot tell exactly what it is, but he states that he is pretty sure it is old Henry Devil himself, because he smells smoke as it passes him, and hears a voice yelling hi-yah. But of course the chances are this voice is nothing but the voice of Mr. Paul D. Veere yelling words of encouragement to Last Hope.

It is not until the station-master at Tillinghast, a guy by the name of Asbury Potts, drives over to Miss Beulah Beauregard's ancestral home an hour later that Little Alfie hears that as Last Hope pulls up at the station and Mr. Paul D. Veere dismounts with so much mud on him that nobody can tell if he is a plaster cast or what, the horse is gimping as bad as Mr. Paul D. Veere himself, and Asbury Potts says there is no doubt Last Hope bows a tendon, or some such, and that if they are able to get him to the races again he will eat his old wool hat.

'But, personally,' Asbury Potts says as he mentions this sad news, 'I do not see what Mr. Paul D. Veere's hurry is, at that, to be pushing a horse so hard. He has fifty-seven seconds left by my watch when the Orange Blossom pulls in right on time to the dot,' Asbury Potts says.

Well, at this Little Alfie sits down and starts figuring, and finally he figures that Last Hope runs the mile and a quarter in around 2.03 in the mud, with maybe one hundred and sixty pounds up, for Mr. Paul D. Veere is no feather duster, and no horse ever runs a mile and a quarter in the mud in the Kentucky Derby as fast as this, or anywhere else as far as anybody knows, so Little Alfie claims that this is practically flying.

But of course few citizens ever accept Little Alfie's figures as strictly official, because they do not know if Asbury Potts's watch is properly regulated for timing race horses, even though Asbury Potts is 100 per cent right when he says they will never be able to get Last Hope to the races again.

Well, I meet up with Little Alfie one night this summer in Mindy's Restaurant on Broadway, and it is the first time he is observed in these parts in some time, and he seems to be looking very prosperous, indeed, and after we get to cutting up old touches, he tells me the reason for this prosperity.

It seems that after Mr. Paul D. Veere returns to New York and puts back in his bank whatever it is that it is advisable for him to put back, or takes out whatever it is that seems best to take out, and gets himself all rounded up so there is no chance of his going to jail, he remembers that there is a slight difference between him and Little Alfie, so what does Mr. Paul D. Veere do but sit down and write out a cheque for fifty G's to Little Alfie to take up his IOU, so Little Alfie is nothing out on account of losing the Kentucky Derby, and, in fact, he is stone rich, and I am glad to hear of it, because I always sympathize deeply with him in his bereavement over the loss of Last Hope. Then I ask Little Alfie what he is doing in New York at this time, and he states to me as follows:

'Well,' Little Alfie says, 'I will tell you. The other day,' he says, 'I get to thinking things over, and among other things I get to thinking that after Last Hope wins the Kentucky Derby, he is a sure thing to go on and also win the Maryland Preakness, because,' Little Alfie says, 'the Preakness is a sixteenth of a mile shorter than the Derby, and a horse that can run a mile and a quarter in the mud in around 2.03 with a brick house on his back is bound to make anything that wears hair look silly at a mile and three-sixteenths, especially,' Little Alfie says, 'if it comes up mud.

'So,' Little Alfie says, 'I am going to call on Mr. Paul D. Veere and see if he does not wish to pay me the Preakness stake, too, because,' he says, 'I am building the finest house in South Georgia at Last Hope, which is my stock farm where Last Hope himself is on public exhibition, and I can always use a few bobs here and there.'

'Well, Alfie,' I says, 'this seems to me to be a very fair proposition, indeed, and,' I says, 'I am sure Mr. Paul D. Veere will take care of it as soon as it is called to his attention, as there is no doubt you and Last Hope are of great service to Mr. Paul D. Veere. By the way, Alfie,' I say, 'whatever becomes of Governor Hicks?'

'Why,' Little Alfie says, 'do you know Governor Hicks turns out to be a terrible disappointment to me as a plough horse? He learns how to sit down from Abimelech, the mule, and nothing will make him stir, not even the same encouragement I give him the day he drops down there third at Hialeah.

'But,' Little Alfie says, 'my ever-loving wife is figuring on using the old Governor as a saddle-horse for our twins, Beulah and Little Alfie, Junior, when they get old enough, although,' he says, 'I tell her the Governor will never be worth a dime in such a way especially,' Little Alfie says, 'if it comes up mud.'

That Ever-Loving Wife of Hymie's

I F anybody ever tells me I will wake up some morning to find myself sleeping with a horse, I will consider them very daffy indeed, especially if they tell me it will be with such a horse as old Mahogany, for Mahogany is really not much horse. In fact, Mahogany is nothing but an old bum, and you can say it again, and many horse players wish he is dead ten thousand times over.

But I will think anybody is daffier still if they tell me I will wake up some morning to find myself sleeping with Hymie Banjo Eyes, because as between Mahogany and Hymie Banjo Eyes to sleep with, I will take Mahogany every time, even though Mahogany snores more than somewhat when he is sleeping. But Mahogany is by no means as offensive to sleep with as Hymie Banjo Eyes, as Hymie not only snores when he is sleeping, but he hollers and kicks around and takes on generally.

He is a short, pudgy little guy who is called Hymie Banjo Eyes because his eyes bulge out as big and round as banjos, although his right name is Weinstein, or some such, and he is somewhat untidy-looking in spots, for Hymie Banjo Eyes is a guy who does not care if his breakfast gets on his vest, or what. Furthermore, he gabs a lot and thinks he is very smart, and many citizens

consider him a pest, in spades. But personally I figure Hymie
Banjo Eyes as very harmless, although he is not such a guy as I
will ordinarily care to have much truck with.

But there I am one morning waking up to find myself sleeping
with both Mahogany and Hymie, and what are we sleeping in but
a horse car bound for Miami, and we are passing through North
Carolina in a small-time blizzard when I wake up, and Mahogany
is snoring and shivering, because it seems Hymie cops the poor
horse's blanket to wrap around himself, and I am half frozen and
wishing I am back in Mindy's Restaurant on Broadway, where all
is bright and warm, and that I never see either Mahogany or
Hymie in my life.

Of course it is not Mahogany's fault that I am sleeping with him
and Hymie, and in fact, for all I know, Mahogany may not consider me any bargain whatever to sleep with. It is Hymie's fault
for digging me up in Mindy's one night and explaining to me how
wonderful the weather is in Miami in the winter-time, and how
we can go there for the races with his stable and make plenty of
potatoes for ourselves, although of course I know when Hymie is
speaking of his stable he means Mahogany, for Hymie never has
more than one horse at any one time in his stable.

Generally it is some broken-down lizard that he buys for about
the price of an old wool hat and patches up the best he can, as
Hymie Banjo Eyes is a horse trainer by trade, and considering
the kind of horses he trains he is not a bad trainer, at that. He is
very good indeed at patching up cripples and sometimes winning
races with them until somebody claims them on him or they fall
down dead, and then he goes and gets himself another cripple
and starts all over again.

I hear he buys Mahogany off a guy by the name of O'Shea for
a hundred bucks, although the chances are if Hymie waits a while
the guy will pay him at least two hundred to take Mahogany away
and hide him, for Mahogany has bad legs and bum feet, and is
maybe nine years old, and does not win a race since the summer
of 1924, and then it is an accident. But anyway, Mahogany is the

stable Hymie Banjo Eyes is speaking of taking to Miami when he digs me up in Mindy's.

'And just think,' Hymie says, 'all we need to get there is the price of a drawing-room on the Florida Special.'

Well, I am much surprised by this statement, because it is the first time I ever hear of a horse needing a drawing-room, especially such a horse as Mahogany, but it seems the drawing-room is not to be for Mahogany, or even for Hymie or me. It seems it is to be for Hymie's ever-loving wife, a blonde doll by the name of 'Lasses, which he marries out of some night-club where she is what is called an adagio dancer.

It seems that when 'Lasses is very young somebody once says she is just as sweet as Molasses, and this is how she comes to get the name of 'Lasses, although her right name is Maggie Something, and I figure she must change quite a lot since they begin calling her 'Lasses because at the time I meet her she is sweet just the same as green grapefruit.

She has a partner in the adagio business by the name of Donaldo, who picks her up and heaves her around the night-club as if she is nothing but a baseball, and it is very thrilling indeed to see Donaldo giving 'Lasses a sling as if he is going to throw her plumb away, which many citizens say may not be a bad idea, at that, and then catching her by the foot in mid-air and hauling her back to him.

But one night it seems that Donaldo takes a few slugs of gin before going into this adagio business, and he muffs 'Lasses' foot, although nobody can see how this is possible, because 'Lasses' foot is no more invisible than a box car, and 'Lasses keeps on sailing through the air. She finally sails into Hymie Banjo Eyes' stomach as he is sitting at a table pretty well back, and this is the way Hymie and 'Lasses meet, and a romance starts, although it is nearly a week before Hymie recovers enough from the body beating he takes off 'Lasses to go around and see her.

The upshot of the romance is 'Lasses and Hymie get married, although up to the time Donaldo slings her into Hymie's stomach, 'Lasses is going around with Brick McCloskey, the bookmaker, and is very loving with him indeed, but they have a row about something and are carrying the old torch for each other when Hymie happens along.

Some citizens say the reason 'Lasses marries Hymie is because she is all sored up on Brick and that she acts without thinking, as dolls often do, especially blonde dolls, although personally I figure Hymie takes all the worst of the situation, as 'Lasses is not such a doll as any guy shall marry without talking it over with his lawyer. 'Lasses is one of these little blondes who is full of short answers, and personally I will just as soon marry a porcupine. But Hymie loves her more than somewhat, and there is no doubt Brick McCloskey is all busted up because 'Lasses takes this run-out powder on him, so maybe after all 'Lasses has some kind of appeal which I cannot notice off-hand.

'But,' Hymie explains to me when he is speaking to me about this trip to Miami, "Lasses is not well, what with nerves and one thing and another, and she will have to travel to Miami along with her Pekingese dog, Sooey-pow, because,' Hymie says, 'it will make her more nervous than somewhat if she has to travel with anybody else. And of course,' Hymie says, 'no one can expect 'Lasses to travel in anything but a drawing-room on account of her health.'

Well, the last time I see 'Lasses she is making a sucker of a big sirloin in Bobby's Restaurant, and she strikes me as a pretty healthy doll, but of course I never examine her close, and anyway, her health is none of my business.

'Now,' Hymie says, 'I get washed out at Empire, and I am pretty much in hock here and there and have no dough to ship my stable to Miami, but,' he says, 'a friend of mine is shipping several horses there and he has a whole car, and he will kindly let me have room in one end of the car for my stable, and you and I can ride in there, too.

'That is,' Hymie says, 'we can ride in there if you will dig up the price of a drawing-room and the two tickets that go with it so

'Lasses' nerves will not be disturbed. You see,' Hymie says, 'I happen to know you have two hundred and fifty bucks in the jug over here on the corner, because one of the tellers in the jug is a friend of mine, and he tips me off you have this sugar, even though,' Hymie says, 'you have it in there under another name.'

Well, a guy goes up against many daffy propositions as he goes along through life, and the first thing I know I am waking up, like I tell you, to find myself sleeping with Mahogany and Hymie, and as I lay there in the horse car slowly freezing to death, I get to thinking of 'Lasses in a drawing-room on the Florida Special, and I hope and trust that she and the Peke are sleeping nice and warm.

The train finally runs out of the blizzard and the weather heats up somewhat, so it is not so bad riding in the horse car, and Hymie and I pass the time away playing two-handed pinochle. Furthermore, I get pretty well acquainted with Mahogany, and I find he is personally not such a bad old pelter as many thousands of citizens think.

Finally we get to Miami, and at first it looks as if Hymie is going to have a tough time finding a place to keep Mahogany, as all the stable room at the Hialeah track is taken by cash customers, and Hymie certainly is not a cash customer and neither is Mahogany. Personally, I am not worried so much about stable room for Mahogany as I am about stable room for myself, because I am now down to a very few bobs and will need same to eat on.

Naturally, I figure Hymie Banjo Eyes will be joining his ever-loving wife 'Lasses, as I always suppose a husband and wife are an entry, but Hymie tells me 'Lasses is parked in the Roney Plaza over on Miami Beach, and that he is going to stay with Mahogany, because it will make her very nervous to have people around her, especially people who are training horses every day, and who may not smell so good.

Well, it looks as if we will wind up camping out with Mahogany under a palm-tree, although many of the palm-trees are already taken by other guys camping out with horses, but finally Hymie finds a guy who has a garage back of his house right near the race track, and having no use for this garage since his car blows away in the hurricane of 1926, the guy is willing to let Hymie keep Mahogany in the garage. Furthermore, he is willing to let Hymie sleep in the garage with Mahogany, and pay him now and then.

So Hymie borrows a little hay and grain, such as horses love to eat, off a friend who has a big string at the track, and moves into the garage with Mahogany, and about the same time I run into a guy by the name of Pottsville Legs, out of Pottsville, Pa., and he has a room in a joint down-town, and I move in with him, and it is no worse than sleeping with Hymie Banjo Eyes and Mahogany, at that.

I do not see Hymie for some time after this, but I hear of him getting Mahogany ready for a race. He has the old guy out galloping on the track every morning, and who is galloping him but Hymie himself, because he cannot get any stable-boys to do the galloping for him, as they do not wish to waste their time. However, Hymie rides himself when he is a young squirt, so galloping Mahogany is not such a tough job for him, except that it gives him a terrible appetite, and it is very hard for him to find anything to satisfy this appetite with, and there are rumours around that Hymie is eating most of Mahogany's hay and grain.

In the meantime, I am going here and there doing the best I can, and this is not so very good, at that, because never is there such a terrible winter in Miami or so much suffering among the horse players. In the afternoon I go out to the race track, and in the evening I go to the dog tracks, and later to the gambling joints trying to pick up a few honest bobs, and wherever I go I seem to see Hymie's ever-loving wife 'Lasses, and she is always dressed up more than somewhat, and generally she is with Brick McCloskey, for Brick shows up in Miami figuring to do a little business in bookmaking at the track.

When they turn off the books there and put in the mutuels, Brick still does a little booking to big betters who do not wish to put their dough in the mutuels for fear of ruining a price, for

Brick is a very large operator at all times. He is not only a large operator, but he is a big, good-looking guy, and how 'Lasses can ever give him the heave-o for such a looking guy as Hymie Banjo Eyes is always a great mystery to me. But then this is the way blondes are.

Of course Hymie probably does not know 'Lasses is running around with Brick McCloskey, because Hymie is too busy getting Mahogany ready for a race to make such spots as 'Lasses and Brick are apt to be, and nobody is going to bother to tell him, because so many ever-loving wives are running around with guys who are not their ever-loving husbands in Miami this winter that nobody considers it any news.

Personally, I figure 'Lasses' running around with Brick is a pretty fair break for Hymie, at that, as it takes plenty of weight off him in the way of dinners, and maybe breakfasts for all I know, although it seems to me 'Lasses cannot love Hymie as much as Hymie thinks to be running around with another guy. In fact, I am commencing to figure 'Lasses does not care for Hymie Banjo Eyes whatever.

Well, one day I am looking over the entries, and I see where Hymie has old Mahogany in a claiming race at a mile and an eighth, and while it is a cheap race, there are some pretty fair hides in it. In fact, I can figure at least eight out of the nine that are entered to beat Mahogany by fourteen lengths.

Well, I go out to Hialeah very early, and I step around to the garage where Mahogany and Hymie are living, and Hymie is sitting out in front of the garage on a bucket looking very sad, and Mahogany has his beezer stuck out through the door of the garage, and he is looking even sadder than Hymie.

'Well,' I say to Hymie Banjo Eyes, 'I see the big horse goes to-day.'

'Yes,' Hymie says, 'the big horse goes to-day if I can get ten bucks for the jockey fee, and if I can get a jock after I get the fee. It is a terrible situation,' Hymie says. 'Here I get Mahogany all readied up for the race of his life in a spot where he can win by as far as from here to Palm Beach and grab a purse worth six hundred fish, and me without as much as a sawbuck to hire one of these hop-toads that are putting themselves away as jocks around here.'

'Well,' I say, 'why do you not speak to 'Lasses your ever-loving wife, about this situation? I see 'Lasses playing the wheel out at Hollywood last night,' I say, 'and she has a stack of cheques in front of her a grey-hound cannot hurdle, and,' I say, 'it is not like 'Lasses to go away from there without a few bobs off such a start.'

'Now there you go again,' Hymie says, very impatient indeed. 'You are always making cracks about 'Lasses, and you know very well it will make the poor little doll very nervous if I speak to her about such matters as a sawbuck, because 'Lasses needs all the sawbucks she can get hold of to keep herself and Sooey-pow at the Roney Plaza. By the way,' Hymie says, 'how much scratch do you have on your body at this time?'

Well, I am never any hand for telling lies, especially to an old friend such as Hymie Banjo Eyes, so I admit I have a ten-dollar note, although naturally I do not mention another tenner which I also have in my pocket, as I know Hymie will wish both of them. He will wish one of my tenners to pay the jockey fee, and he will wish the other to bet on Mahogany, and I am certainly not going to let Hymie throw my dough away betting it on such an old crocodile as Mahogany, especially in a race which a horse by the name of Side Burns is a sure thing to win.

In fact, I am waiting patiently for several days for a chance to bet on Side Burns. So I hold out one sawbuck on Hymie, and then I go over to the track and forget all about him and Mahogany until the sixth race is coming up, and I see by the jockey board that Hymie has a jock by the name of Scroon riding Mahogany, and while Mahogany is carrying only one hundred pounds, which is the light-weight of the race, I will personally just as soon have Paul Whiteman up as Scroon. Personally I do not think Scroon can spell 'horse,' for he is nothing but a dizzy little guy who gets a mount about once every Pancake Tuesday.

But of course Hymie is not a guy who can pick and choose his jocks, and the chances are he is pretty lucky to get anybody to ride Mahogany.

I see by the board where it tells you the approximate odds that Mahogany is 40 to 1, and naturally nobody is paying any attention to such a horse, because it will not be good sense to pay any attention to Mahogany in this race, what with it being his first start in months, and Mahogany not figuring with these horses, or with any horses, as far as this is concerned. In fact, many citizens think Hymie Banjo Eyes is either crazy, or is running Mahogany in this race for exercise, although nobody who knows Hymie will figure him to be spending dough on a horse just to exercise him.

The favourite in the race is this horse named Side Burns, and from the way they are playing him right from taw you will think he is Twenty Grand. He is even money on the board, and I hope and trust that he will finally pay as much as this, because at even money I consider him a very sound investment, indeed. In fact, I am willing to take 4 to 5 for my dough, and will consider it money well found, because I figure this will give me about eighteen bobs to bet on Tony Joe in the last race, and anybody will tell you that you can go to sleep on Tony Joe winning, unless something happens.

There is a little action on several other horses in the race, but of course there is none whatever for Mahogany and the last time I look he is up to fifty. So I buy my ticket on Side Burns, and go out to the paddock to take a peek at the horses, and I see Hymie Banjo Eyes in there saddling Mahogany with his jockey, this dizzy Scroon, standing alongside him in Hymie's colours of red, pink and yellow, and making wise-cracks to the guys in the next stall about Mahogany.

Hymie Banjo Eyes sees me and motions me to come into the paddock, so I go in and give Mahogany a pat on the snoot, and the old guy seems to remember me right away, because he rubs his beezer up and down my arm and lets out a little snicker. But it seems to me the old plug looks a bit peaked, and I can see his ribs very plain indeed, so I figure maybe there is some truth in the rumour about Hymie sharing Mahogany's hay and grain, after all.

Well, as I am standing there, Hymie gives this dizzy Scroon his riding instructions, and they are very short, for all Hymie says is as follows:

'Listen,' Hymie says, 'get off with this horse and hurry right home.'

And Scroon looks a little dizzier than somewhat and nods his head, and then turns and tips a wink to Kurtsinger, who is riding the horse in the next stall.

Well, finally the post bugle goes, and Hymie walks back with me to the lawn as the horses are coming out on the track, and Hymie is speaking about nothing but Mahogany.

'It is just my luck,' Hymie says, 'not to have a bob or two to bet on him. He will win this race as far as you can shoot a rifle, and the reason he will win this far,' Hymie says, 'is because the track is just soft enough to feel nice and soothing to his sore feet. Furthermore,' Hymie says, 'after lugging my one hundred and forty pounds around every morning for two weeks, Mahogany will think it is Christmas when he finds nothing but this Scroon's one hundred pounds on his back.

'In fact,' Hymie says, 'if I do not need the purse money, I will not let him run-to-day, but will hide him for a bet. But,' he says, "Lasses must have five yards at once, and you know how nervous she will be if she does not get the five yards. So I am letting Mahogany run,' Hymie says, 'and it is a pity.'

'Well,' I says, 'why do you not promote somebody to bet on him for you?'

'Why,' Hymie says, 'if I ask one guy I ask fifty. But they all think I am out of my mind to think Mahogany can beat such horses as Side Burns and the rest. Well,' he says, 'they will be sorry. By the way,' he says, 'do you have a bet down of any kind?'

Well, now, I do not wish to hurt Hymie's feelings by letting him know I bet on something else in the race, so I tell him I do not play this race at all, and he probably figures it is because I have nothing to bet with after giving him the sawbuck. But he keeps on talking as we walk over in front of the grandstand, and all he is talking about is what a tough break it is for him not to have any dough to bet on Mahogany. By this time the horses are at the post a little way up the track, and as we are standing there watching them, Hymie Banjo Eyes goes on talking, half to me and half to himself, but out loud.

'Yes,' he says, 'I am the unluckiest guy in all the world. Here I am,' he says, 'with a race that is a kick in the pants for my horse at fifty to one, and me without a quarter to bet. It is certainly a terrible thing to be poor,' Hymie says. 'Why,' he says, 'I will bet my life on my horse in this race, I am so sure of winning. I will bet my clothes. I will bet all I ever hope to have. In fact,' he says, 'I will even bet my ever-loving wife, this is how sure I am.'

Now of course this is only the way horse players rave when they are good and heated up about the chances of a horse, and I hear such conversations as this maybe a million times, and never pay any attention to it whatever, but as Hymie makes this crack about betting his ever-loving wife, a voice behind us says as follows:

'Against how much?'

Naturally, Hymie and I look around at once, and who does the voice belong to but Brick McCloskey. Of course I figure Brick is kidding Hymie Banjo Eyes, but Brick's voice is as cold as ice as he says to Hymie like this:

'Against how much will you bet your wife your horse wins this race?' he says. 'I hear you saying you are sure this old buzzard meat you are running will win,' Brick says, 'so let me see how sure you are. Personally,' Brick says, 'I think they ought to prosecute you for running a broken-down hound like Mahogany on the ground of cruelty to animals, and furthermore,' Brick says, 'I think they ought to put you in an insane asylum if you really believe your old dog has a chance. But I will give you a bet,' he says. 'How much do you wish me to lay against your wife?'

Well, this is very harsh language indeed, and I can see that Brick is getting something off his chest he is packing there for some time. The chances are he is putting the blast on poor Hymie Banjo Eyes on account of Hymie grabbing 'Lasses from him, and of course Brick McCloskey never figures for a minute that Hymie will take his question seriously. But Hymie answers like this:

'You are a price-maker,' he says. 'What do you lay?'

Now this is a most astonishing reply, indeed, when you figure that Hymie is asking what Brick will bet against Hymie's everloving wife 'Lasses, and I am very sorry to hear Hymie ask, especially as I happen to turn around and find that nobody but 'Lasses herself is listening in on the conversation, and the chances are her face will be very white, if it is not for her make-up, 'Lasses being a doll who goes in for make-up more than somewhat.

'Yes,' Brick McCloskey says, 'I am a price-maker, all right, and I will lay you a price. I will lay you five C's against your wife that your plug does not win,' he says.

Brick looks at 'Lasses as he says this, and 'Lasses looks at Brick, and personally I will probably take a pop at a guy who looks at my ever-loving wife in such a way, if I happen to have any ever-loving wife, and maybe I will take a pop at my ever-loving wife, too, if she looks back at a guy in such a way, but of course Hymie is not noticing such things as looks at this time, and in fact he does not see 'Lasses as yet. But he does not hesitate in answering Brick.

'You are a bet,' says Hymie. 'Five hundred bucks against my ever-loving wife 'Lasses. It is a chiseller's price such as you always lay,' he says, 'and the chances are I can do better if I have time to go shopping around but as it is,' he says, 'it is like finding money and I will not let you get away. But be ready to pay cash right after the race, because I will not accept your paper.'

Well, I hear of many a strange bet on horse races, but never before do I hear of a guy betting his ever-loving wife, although to tell you the truth I never before hear of a guy getting the opportunity to bet his wife on a race. For all I know, if bookmakers take wives as a steady thing there will be much action in such matters at every track.

But I can see that both Brick McCloskey and Hymie Banjo Eyes are in dead earnest, and about this time 'Lasses tries to cop a quiet sneak, and Hymie sees her and speaks to her as follows:

'Hello, Baby,' Hymie says. 'I will have your five yards for you in a few minutes and five more to go with it, as I am just about to clip a sucker. Wait here with me, Baby,' Hymie says.

'No,' 'Lasses says, 'I am too nervous to wait here. I am going down by the fence to root your horse in,' she says, but as she goes away I see another look pass between her and Brick McCloskey.

Well, all of a sudden Cassidy gets the horses in a nice line and lets them go, and as they come busting down past the stand the first time who is right there on top but old Mahogany, with this dizzy Scroon kicking at his skinny sides and yelling in his ears. As they make the first turn, Scroon has Mahogany a length in front, and he moves him out another length as they hit the back side.

Now I always like to watch the races from a spot away up the lawn, as I do not care to have anybody much around me when the tough finishes come along in case I wish to bust out crying, so I leave Hymie Banjo Eyes and Brick McCloskey still glaring at each other and go to my usual place, and who is standing there, too, all by herself but 'Lasses. And about this time the horses are making the turn into the stretch and Mahogany is still on top, but something is coming very fast on the outside. It looks as if Mahogany is in a tough spot, because half-way down the stretch the outside horse nails him and looks him right in the eye, and who is it but the favourite, Side Burns.

They come on like a team, and I am personally giving Side Burns a great ride from where I am standing, when I hear a doll yelling out loud, and who is the doll but 'Lasses, and what is she yelling but the following:

'Come on with him, jock!'

Furthermore, as she yells, 'Lasses snaps her fingers like a crap shooter and runs a couple of yards one way and then turns and runs a couple of yards back the other way, so I can see that 'Lasses is indeed of a nervous temperament, just as Hymie Banjo Eyes is always telling me, although up to this time I figure her nerves are the old alzo.

'Come on!' 'Lasses yells again. 'Let him roll!' she yells. 'Ride him, boy!' she yells. 'Come on with him, Frankie!'

Well, I wish to say that 'Lasses' voice may be all right if she is selling tomatoes from door to door, but I will not care to have her using it around me every day for any purpose whatever, because she yells so loud I have to move off a piece to keep my ear-drums from being busted wide open. She is still yelling when the horses go past the finish line, the snozzles of old Mahogany and Side Burns so close together that nobody can hardly tell which is which.

In fact, there is quite a wait before the numbers go up, and I can see 'Lasses standing there with her programme all wadded up in her fist as she watches the board, and I can see she is under a very terrible nervous strain indeed, and I am very sorry I go around thinking her nerves are the old alzo. Pretty soon the guy hangs out No. 9, and No. 9 is nobody but old Mahogany, and at this I hear 'Lasses screech, and all of a sudden she flops over in a faint, and somebody carries her under the grandstand to revive her, and I figure her nerves bog down entirely, and I am sorrier than ever for thinking bad thoughts of her.

I am also very, very sorry I do not bet my sawbuck on Mahogany, especially when the board shows he pays $102, and I can see where Hymie Banjo Eyes is right about the weight and all, but I am glad Hymie wins the purse and also the five C's off of Brick McCloskey and that he saves his ever-loving wife, because I figure Hymie may now pay me back a few bobs.

I do not see Hymie or Brick or 'Lasses again until the races are over, and then I hear of a big row going on under the stand, and go to see what is doing, and who is having the row but Hymie Banjo Eyes and Brick McCloskey. It seems that Hymie hits Brick a clout on the breezer that stretches Brick out, and it seems that

Hymie hits Brick this blow because as Brick is paying Hymie the five C's he makes the following crack:

'I do not mind losing the dough to you, Banjo Eyes,' Brick says, 'but I am sore at myself for overlaying the price. It is the first time in all the years I am booking that I make such an overlay. The right price against your wife,' Brick says, 'is maybe two dollars and a half.'

Well, as Brick goes down with a busted beezer from Hymie's punch, and everybody is much excited, who steps out of the crowd around them and throws her arms around Hymie Banjo Eyes but his ever-loving wife 'Lasses, and as she kisses Hymie smack-dab in the mush, 'Lasses says as follows:

'My darling Hymie,' she says, 'I hear what this big flannel-mouth says about the price on me, and,' she says, 'I am only sorry you do not cripple him for life. I know now I love you, and only you, Hymie,' she says, 'and I will never love anybody else. In fact,' 'Lasses says, 'I just prove my love for you by almost wrecking my nerves in rooting Mahogany home. I am still weak,' she says, 'but I have strength enough left to go with you to the Sunset Inn for a nice dinner, and you can give me my money then. Furthermore,' 'Lasses says, 'now that we have a few bobs, I think you better find another place for Mahogany to stay, as it does not look nice for my husband to be living with a horse.'

Well, I am going by the jockey house on my way home, thinking how nice it is that Hymie Banjo Eyes will no longer have to live with Mahogany, and what a fine thing it is to have a loyal, ever-loving wife such as 'Lasses, who risks her nerves rooting for her husband's horse, when I run into this dizzy Scroon in his street clothes, and wishing to be friendly, I say to him like this:

'Hello, Frankie,' I say. 'You put up a nice ride to-day.'

'Where do you get this "Frankie"?' Scroon says. 'My name is Gus.'

'Why,' I say, commencing to think of this and that, 'so it is, but is there a jock called Frankie in the sixth race with you this afternoon?'

[77]

'Sure,' Scroon says. 'Frankie Madeley. He rides Side Burns, the favourite; and I make a sucker of him in the stretch run.'

But of course I never mention to Hymie Banjo Eyes that I figure his ever-loving wife roots herself into a dead faint for the horse that will give her to Brick McCloskey, because for all I know she may think Scroon's name is Frankie, at that.

All Horse Players Die Broke

I T is during the last race meeting at Saratoga, and one evening I am standing out under the elms in front of the Grand Union Hotel thinking what a beautiful world it is, to be sure, for what do I do in the afternoon at the track but grab myself a piece of a 10–to–1 shot.

I am thinking what a beautiful moon it is, indeed, that is shining down over the park where Mr. Dick Canfield once deals them higher than a cat's back, and how pure and balmy the air is, and also what nice-looking Judys are wandering around and about, although it is only the night before that I am standing in the same spot wondering where I can borrow a Betsy with which to shoot myself smack-dab through the pimple.

In fact, I go around to see a character I know by the name of Solly something, who owns a Betsy, but it seems he has only one cartridge to his name for this Betsy and he is thinking some of either using the cartridge to shoot his own self smack-dab through the pimple, or of going out to the race course and shooting an old catfish by the name of Pair of Jacks that plays him false in the fifth race, and therefore Solly is not in a mood to lend his Betsy to anybody else.

So we try to figure out a way we can make one cartridge do for two pimples, and in the meantime Solly outs with a bottle of applejack, and after a couple of belts at this bottle we decide that the sensible thing to do is to take the Betsy out and peddle it for whatever we can, and maybe get a taw for the next day.

Well, it happens that we run into an Italian party from Passaic, N.J., by the name of Guiseppe Palladino, who is called Joe for short, and this Joe is in the money very good at the moment, and he is glad to lend us a pound note on the Betsy, because Joe is such a character as never knows when he may need an extra Betsy, and anyway it is the first time in his experience around the race tracks that anybody ever offers him collateral for a loan.

So there Solly and I are with a deuce apiece after we spend the odd dollar for breakfast the next day, and I run my deuce up to a total of twenty-two slugs on the 10–to–1 shot in the last heat of the day, and everything is certainly all right with me in every respect.

Well, while I am standing there under the elms, who comes along but a raggedy old Dutchman by the name of Unser Fritz, who is maybe seventy-five years old, come next grass, and who is following the giddyaps since the battle of Gettysburg, as near as anybody can figure out. In fact, Unser Fritz is quite an institution around the race tracks, and is often written up by the newspaper scribes as a terrible example of what a horse player comes to, although personally I always say that what Unser Fritz comes to is not so tough when you figure that he does not do a tap of work in all these years.

In his day, Unser Fritz is a most successful handicapper, a handicapper being a character who can dope out from the form what horses ought to win the races, and as long as his figures turn out all right, a handicapper is spoken of most respectfully by one and all, although of course when he begins missing out for any length of time as handicappers are bound to do, he is no longer spoken of respectfully, or even as a handicapper. He is spoken of as a bum.

It is a strange thing how a handicapper can go along for years doing everything right, and then all of a sudden he finds himself doing everything wrong, and this is the way it is with Unser Fritz. For a long time his figures on the horse races are considered most remarkable indeed, and as he will bet till the cows come home on his own figures, he generally has plenty of money, and a fiancée by the name of Emerald Em.

She is called Emerald Em because she has a habit of wearing a raft of emeralds in rings, and pins, and bracelets, and one thing and another, which are purchased for her by Unser Fritz to express his love, an emerald being a green stone that is considered most expressive of love, if it is big enough. It seems that Emerald Em is very fond of emeralds, especially when they are surrounded by large, coarse diamonds.

I hear the old-timers around the race tracks say that when Emerald Em is young, she is a tall, good-looking Judy with yellow hair that is by no means a phony yellow, at that, and with a shape that does not require a bustle such as most Judys always wear in those days.

But then nobody ever hears an old-timer mention any Judy that he remembers from back down the years who is not good-looking, and in fact beautiful. To hear the old-timers tell it, every pancake they ever see when they are young is a double Myrna Loy, though the chances are, figuring in the law of averages, that some of them are bound to be rutabagas, the same as now. Anyway, for years this Emerald Em is known on every race track from coast to coast as Unser Fritz's fiancée, and is considered quite a remarkable scene, what with her emeralds, and not requiring any bustle, and everything else.

Then one day Unser Fritz's figures run plumb out on him, and so does his dough, and so does Emerald Em, and now Unser Fritz is an old pappy guy, and it is years since he is regarded as anything but a crumbo around the race tracks, and nobody remembers much of his story, or cares a cuss about it, for if there is anything that is a drug on the market around the tracks it is the story of a broker.

How he gets from place to place, and how he lives after he gets there, is a very great mystery to one and all, although I hear he often rides in the horsecars with the horses, when some owner or trainer happens to be feeling tender-hearted, or he hitchhikes in automobiles, and sometimes he even walks, for Unser Fritz is still fairly nimble, no matter how old he is.

He always has under his arm a bundle of newspapers that somebody throws away, and every night he sits down and handicaps the horses running the next day according to his own system, but he seldom picks any winners, and even if he does pick any winners, he seldom has anything to bet on them.

Sometimes he promotes a stranger, who does not know he is bad luck to a good hunting dog, to put down a few dibs on one of his picks, and once in a while the pick wins, and Unser Fritz gets a small stake, and sometimes an old-timer who feels sorry for him will slip him something. But whatever Unser Fritz gets hold of, he bets off right away on the next race that comes up, so naturally he never is holding anything very long.

Well, Unser Fritz stands under the elms with me a while, speaking of this and that, and especially of the races, and I am wondering to myself if I will become as dishevelled as Unser Fritz if I keep on following the races, when he gazes at the Grand Union Hotel, and says to me like this:

'It looks nice,' he says. 'It looks cheery-like, with the lights, and all this and that. It brings back memories to me. Emma always lives in this hotel whenever we make Saratoga for the races back in the days when I am in the money. She always has a suite of two or three rooms on this side of the hotel. Once she has four.

'I often stand here under these trees,' Unser Fritz says, 'watching her windows to see what time she puts out her lights, because, while I trust Emma implicitly, I know she has a restless nature, and sometimes she cannot resist returning to scenes of gaiety after I bid her good night, especially,' he says, 'with a party by the name of Pete Shovelin, who runs the restaurant where she once deals them off the arm.'

[82]

'You mean she is a biscuit shooter?' I say.

'A waitress,' Unser Fritz says. 'A good waitress. She comes of a family of farm folks in this very section, although I never know much about them,' he says. 'Shovelin's is a little hole-in-the-wall up the street here somewhere which long since disappears. I go there for my morning java in the old days.

'I will say one thing for Shovelin,' Unser Fritz says, 'he always has good java. Three days after I first clap eyes on Emma, she is wearing her first emerald, and is my fiancée. Then she moves into a suite in the Grand Union. I only wish you can know Emma in those days,' he says. 'She is beautiful. She is a fine character. She is always on the level, and I love her dearly.'

'What do you mean – always on the level?' I say. 'What about this Shovelin party you just mention?'

'Ah,' Unser Fritz says, 'I suppose I am dull company for a squab, what with having to stay in at night to work on my figures, and Emma likes to go around and about. She is a highly nervous type, and extremely restless, and she cannot bear to hold still very long at a time. But,' he says, 'in those days it is not considered proper for a young Judy to go around and about without a chaperon, so she goes with Shovelin for her chaperon. Emma never goes anywhere without a chaperon,' he says.

Well, it seems that early in their courtship, Unser Fritz learns that he can generally quiet her restlessness with emeralds, if they have diamonds on the side. It seems that these stones have a very soothing effect on her, and this is why he purchases them for her by the bucket.

'Yes,' Unser Fritz says, 'I always think of Emma whenever I am in New York City, and look down Broadway at night with the go lights on.'

But it seems from what Unser Fritz tells me that even with the emeralds her restless spells come on her very bad, and especially when he finds himself running short of ready, and is unable to purchase more emeralds for her at the moment, although Unser Fritz claims this is nothing unusual. In fact, he says anybody with any experience with nervous female characters knows that it becomes very monotonous for them to be around people who are short of ready.

'But,' he says, 'not all of them require soothing with emeralds. Some require pearls,' he says.

Well, it seems that Emma generally takes a trip without Unser Fritz to break the monotony of his running short of ready, but she never takes one of these trips without a chaperon, because she is very careful about her good name, and Unser Fritz's, too. It seems that in those days Judys have to be more careful about such matters than they do now.

He remembers that once when they are in San Francisco she takes a trip through the Yellowstone with Jockey Gus Kloobus as her chaperon, and is gone three weeks and returns much refreshed, especially as she gets back just as Unser Fritz makes a nice score and has a seidel of emeralds waiting for her. He remembers another time she goes to England with a trainer by the name of Blootz as her chaperon and comes home with an English accent that sounds right cute, to find Unser Fritz going like a house afire at Belmont.

'She takes a lot of other trips without me during the time we are engaged,' Unser Fritz says, 'but,' he says, 'I always know Emma will return to me as soon as she hears I am back in the money and can purchase more emeralds for her. In fact,' he says, 'this knowledge is all that keeps mè struggling now.'

'Look, Fritz,' I say, 'what do you mean, keeps you going? Do you mean you think Emma may return to you again?'

'Why, sure,' Unser Fritz says. 'Why, certainly, if I get my rushes again. Why not?' he says. 'She knows there will be a pail of emeralds waiting for her. She knows I love her and always will,' he says.

Well, I ask him when he sees Emerald Em last, and he says it is 1908 in the old Waldorf-Astoria the night he blows a hundred and sixty thousand betting on a hide called Sir Martin to win the Futurity, and it is all the dough Unser Fritz has at the moment.

In fact, he is cleaner than a jay bird, and he is feeling somewhat discouraged.

It seems he is waiting on his floor for the elevator, and when it comes down Emerald Em is one of the several passengers, and when the door opens, and Unser Fritz starts to get in, she raises her foot and plants it in his stomach, and gives him a big push back out the door and the elevator goes on down without him.

'But, of course,' Unser Fritz says, 'Emma never likes to ride in the same elevator with me, because I am not always tidy enough to suit her in those days, what with having so much work to do on my figures, and she claims it is a knock to her socially. Anyway,' he says, 'this is the last I see of Emma.'

'Why, Fritz,' I say, 'nineteen-eight is nearly thirty years back, and if she ever thinks of returning to you, she will return long before this.'

'No,' Unser Fritz says. 'You see, I never make a scratch since then. I am never since in the money, so there is no reason for Emma to return to me. But,' he says 'wait until I get going good again and you will see.'

Well, I always figure Unser Fritz must be more or less of an old screwball for going on thinking there is still a chance for him around the tracks, and now I am sure of it, and I am about to bid him good evening, when he mentions that he can use about two dollars if I happen to have a deuce on me that is not working, and I will say one thing for Unser Fritz, he seldom comes right out and asks anybody for anything unless things are very desperate with him, indeed.

'I need it to pay something on account of my landlady,' he says. 'I room with old Mrs. Crob around the corner for over twenty years, and,' he says, 'she only charges me a finnif a week, so I try to keep from getting too far to the rear with her. I will return it to you the first score I make.'

Well, of course I know this means practically never, but I am feeling so good about my success at the track that I slip him a deucer, and it is half an hour later before I fully realize what I do, and go looking for Fritz to get anyway half of it back. But by this time he disappears, and I think no more of the matter until the next day out at the course when I hear Unser Fritz bets two dollars on a thing by the name of Speed Cart, and it bows down at 50 to 1, so I know Mrs. Crob is still waiting for hers.

Now there is Unser Fritz with one hundred slugs, and this is undoubtedly more money than he enjoys since Hickory Slim is a two-year-old. And from here on the story becomes very interesting, and in fact remarkable, because up to the moment Speed Cart hits the wire, Unser Fritz is still nothing but a crumbo, and you can say it again, while from now on he is somebody to point out and say can you imagine such a thing happening?

He bets a hundred on a centipede called Marchesa, and down pops Marchesa like a trained pig at 20 to 1. Then old Unser Fritz bets two hundred on a caterpillar by the name of Merry Soul, at 4 to 1, and Merry Soul just laughs his way home. Unser Fritz winds up the day betting two thousand more on something called Sharp Practice, and when Sharp Practice wins by so far it looks as if he is a shoo-in, Fritz finds himself with over twelve thousand slugs, and the way the bookmakers in the betting ring are sobbing is really most distressing to hear.

Well, in a week Unser Fritz is a hundred thousand dollars in front, because the way he sends it in is quite astonishing to behold, although the old-timers tell me it is just the way he sends it when he is younger. He is betting only on horses that he personally figures out, and what happens is that Unser Fritz's figures suddenly come to life again, and he cannot do anything wrong.

He wins so much dough that he even pays off a few old touches, including my two, and he goes so far as to lend Joe Palladino three dollars on the Betsy that Solly and I hock with Joe for the pound note, as it seems that by this time Joe himself is practically on his way to the poorhouse, and while Unser Fritz has no use whatsoever for a Betsy he cannot bear to see a character such as Joe go to the poorhouse.

But with all the dough Unser Fritz carries in his pockets, and plants in a safe-deposit box in the jug downtown, he looks just the same as ever, because he claims he cannot find time from working on his figures to buy new clothes and dust himself off, and if you tell anybody who does not know who he is that this old crutch is stone rich, the chances are they will call you a liar.

In fact, on a Monday around noon, the clerk in the branch office that a big Fifth Avenue jewellery firm keeps in the lobby of the States Hotel is all ready to yell for the constables when Unser Fritz leans up against the counter and asks to see some jewellery on display in a showcase, as Unser Fritz is by no means the clerk's idea of a customer for jewellery.

I am standing in the lobby of the hotel on the off chance that some fresh money may arrive in the city on the late trains that I may be able to connect up with before the races, when I notice Unser Fritz and observe the agitation of the clerk, and presently I see Unser Fritz waving a fistful of bank notes under the clerk's beak, and the clerk starts setting out the jewellery with surprising speed.

I go over to see what is coming off, and I can see that the jewellery Unser Fritz is looking at consists of a necklace of emeralds and diamonds, with a centrepiece the size of the home plate, and some eardrops, and bracelets, and clips of same, and as I approach the scene I hear Unser Fritz ask how much for the lot as if he is dickering for a basket of fish.

'One hundred and one thousand dollars, sir,' the clerk says. 'You see, sir, it is a set, and one of the finest things of the kind in the country. We just got it in from our New York store to show a party here, and,' he says, 'she is absolutely crazy about it, but she states she cannot give us a final decision until five o'clock this afternoon. Confidentially, sir,' the clerk says, 'I think the real trouble is financial, and doubt that we will hear from her again. In fact,' he says, 'I am so strongly of this opinion that I am prepared to sell the goods without waiting on her. It is really a bargain at the price,' he says.

[87]

'Dear me,' Unser Fritz says to me, 'this is most unfortunate as the sum mentioned is just one thousand dollars more than I possess in all this world. I have twenty thousand on my person, and eighty thousand over in the box in the jug, and not another dime. But,' he says, 'I will be back before five o'clock and take the lot. In fact,' he says, 'I will run in right after the third race and pick it up.'

Well, at this the clerk starts putting the jewellery back in the case, and anybody can see that he figures he is on a lob and that he is sorry he wastes so much time, but Unser Fritz says to me like this:

'Emma is returning to me,' he says.

'Emma who?' I say.

'Why,' Unser Fritz says, 'my Emma. The one I tell you about not long ago. She must hear I am in the money again, and she is returning just as I always say she will.'

'How do you know?' I say. 'Do you hear from her, or what?'

'No,' Unser Fritz says, 'I do not hear from her direct, but Mrs. Crob knows some female relative of Emma's that lives at Ballston Spa a few miles from here, and this relative is in Saratoga this morning to do some shopping, and she tells Mrs. Crob and Mrs. Crob tells me. Emma will be here to-night. I will have these emeralds waiting for her.'

Well, what I always say is that every guy knows his own business best, and if Unser Fritz wishes to toss his dough off on jewellery, it is none of my put-in, so all I remark is that I have no doubt Emma will be very much surprised indeed.

'No,' Unser Fritz says. 'She will be expecting them. She always expects emeralds when she returns to me. I love her,' he says. 'You have no idea how I love her. But let us hasten to the course,' he says. 'Cara Mia is a right good thing in the third, and I will make just one bet to-day to win the thousand I need to buy these emeralds.'

'But, Fritz,' I say, 'you will have nothing left for operating expenses after you invest in the emeralds.'

'I am not worrying about operating expenses now,' Unser Fritz says. 'The way my figures are standing up, I can run a spool of thread into a pair of pants in no time. But I can scarcely wait to see the expression on Emma's face when she sees her emeralds. I will have to make a fast trip into town after the third to get my dough out of the box in the jug and pick them up,' he says. 'Who knows but what this other party that is interested in the emeralds may make her mind up before five o'clock and pop in there and nail them?'

Well, after we get to the race track, all Unser Fritz does is stand around waiting for the third race. He has his figures on the first two races, and ordinarily he will be betting himself a gob on them, but he says he does not wish to take the slightest chance on cutting down his capital at this time, and winding up short of enough dough to buy the emeralds.

It turns out that both of the horses Unser Fritz's figures make on top in the first and second races bow down, and Unser Fritz will have his thousand if he only bets a couple of hundred on either of them, but Unser Fritz says he is not sorry he does not bet. He says the finishes in both races are very close, and prove that there is an element of risk in these races. And Unser Fritz says he cannot afford to tamper with the element of risk at this time.

He states that there is no element of risk whatever in the third race, and what he states is very true, as everybody realizes that this mare Cara Mia is a stick-out. In fact, she is such a stick-out that it scarcely figures to be a contest. There are three other horses in the race, but it is the opinion of one and all that if the owners of these horses have any sense they will leave them in the barn and save them a lot of unnecessary lather.

The opening price offered by the bookmakers on Cara Mia is 2 to 5, which means that if you wish to wager on Cara Mia to win you will have to put up five dollars to a bookmaker's two dollars, and everybody agrees that this is a reasonable thing to do in this case unless you wish to rob the poor bookmaker.

In fact, this is considered so reasonable that everybody starts running at the bookmakers all at once, and the bookmakers can see if this keeps up they may get knocked off their stools in the betting ring and maybe seriously injured, so they make Cara Mia 1 to 6, and out, as quickly as possible to halt the rush and give them a chance to breathe.

This 1 to 6 means that if you wish to wager on Cara Mia to win, you must wager six of your own dollars to one of the bookmaker's dollars, and means that the bookies are not offering any prices whatsoever on Cara Mia running second or third. You can get almost any price you can think of right quick against any of the other horses winning the race, and place and show prices, too, but asking the bookmakers to lay against Cara Mia running second or third will be something like asking them to bet that Mr. Roosevelt is not President of the United States.

Well, I am expecting Unser Fritz to step in and partake of the 2 to 5 on Cara Mia for all the dough he has on his person the moment it is offered, because he is very high indeed on this mare, and in fact I never see anybody any higher on any horse, and it is a price Unser Fritz will not back off from when he is high on anything.

Moreover, I am pleased to think he will make such a wager, because it will give him plenty over and above the price of the emeralds, and as long as he is bound to purchase the emeralds, I wish to see him have a little surplus, because when anybody has a surplus there is always a chance for me. It is when everybody runs out of surpluses that I am handicapped no little. But instead of stepping in and partaking, Unser Fritz keeps hesitating until the opening price gets away from him, and finally he says to me like this:

'Of course,' he says, 'my figures show Cara Mia cannot possibly lose this race, but,' he says, 'to guard against any possibility whatever of her losing, I will make an absolute cinch of it. I will bet her third.'

'Why, Fritz,' I say, 'I do not think there is anybody in this world outside of an insane asylum who will give you a price on the peek. Furthermore,' I say, 'I am greatly surprised at this sign of weakening on your part on your figures.'

'Well,' Unser Fritz says, 'I cannot afford to take a chance on not having the emeralds for Emma when she arrives. Let us go through the betting ring and see what we can see,' he says.

So we walk through the betting ring, and by this time it seems that many of the books are so loaded with wagers on Cara Mia to win that they will not accept any more under any circumstances, and I figure that Unser Fritz blows the biggest opportunity of his life in not grabbing the opening. The bookmakers who are loaded are now looking even sadder than somewhat, and this makes them a pitiful spectacle indeed.

Well, one of the saddest-looking is a character by the name of Slow McCool, but he is a character who will usually give you a gamble and he is still taking Cara Mia at 1 to 6, and Unser Fritz walks up to him and whispers in his ear, and what he whispers is he wishes to know if Slow McCool cares to lay him a price on Cora Mia third. But all that happens is that Slow McCool stops looking sad a minute and looks slightly perplexed, and then he shakes his head and goes on looking sad again.

Now Unser Fritz steps up to another sad-looking bookmaker by the name of Pete Phozzler and whispers in his ear and Pete also shakes his head, and after we leave him I look back and see that Pete is standing up on his stool watching Unser Fritz and still shaking his head.

Well, Unser Fritz approaches maybe a dozen other sad-looking bookmakers, and whispers to them, and all he gets is the old head-shake, but none of them seem to become angry with Unser Fritz, and I always say that this proves that bookmakers are better than some people think, because, personally, I claim they have a right to get angry with Unser Fritz for insulting their intelligence, and trying to defraud them, too, by asking a price on Cara Mia third.

Finally we come to a character by the name of Willie the Worrier, who is called by this name because he is always worrying about something, and what he is generally worrying about is a short bank roll, or his ever-loving wife, and sometimes both, though mostly it is his wife. Personally, I always figure she is something to worry about, at that, though I do not consider details necessary.

She is a red-headed Judy about half as old as Willie the Worrier, and this alone is enough to start any guy worrying, and what is more she is easily vexed, especially by Willie. In fact, I remember Solly telling me that she is vexed with Willie no longer ago than about 11 a.m. this very day, and gives him a public reprimanding about something or other in the telegraph office downtown when Solly happens to be in there hoping maybe he will receive an answer from a mark in Pittsfield, Mass., that he sends a tip on a horse.

Solly says the last he hears Willie the Worrier's wife say is that she will leave him for good this time, but I just see her over on the clubhouse lawn wearing some right classy-looking garments, so I judge she does not leave him as yet, as the clubhouse lawn is not a place to be waiting for a train.

Well, when Unser Fritz sees that he is in front of Willie's stand, he starts to move on, and I nudge him and motion at Willie, and ask him if he does not notice that Willie is another bookmaker, and Unser Fritz says he notices him all right, but that he does not care to offer him any business because Willie insults him ten years ago. He says Willie calls him a dirty old Dutch bum, and while I am thinking what a wonderful memory Unser Fritz has to remember insults from bookmakers for ten years, Willie the Worrier, sitting there on his stool looking out over the crowd, spots Unser Fritz and yells at him as follows:

'Hello, Dirty Dutch,' he says. 'How is the soap market? What are you looking for around here, Dirty Dutch? Santa Claus?'

Well, at this Unser Fritz pushes his way through the crowd around Willie the Worrier's stand, and gets close to Willie, and says:

'Yes,' he said, 'I am looking for Santa Claus. I am looking for a show price on number two horse, but,' he says, 'I do not expect to get it from the shoemakers who are booking nowadays.'

Now the chances are Willie the Worrier figures Unser Fritz is just trying to get sarcastic with him for the benefit of the crowd around his stand in asking for such a thing as a price on Cara Mia third, and in fact the idea of anybody asking a price third on a horse that some bookmakers will not accept any more wagers on first, or even second, is so humorous that many characters laugh right out loud.

'All right,' Willie the Worrier says. 'No one can ever say he comes to my store looking for a market on anything and is turned down. I will quote you a show price, Dirty Dutch,' he says. 'You can have 1 to 100.'

This means that Willie the Worrier is asking Unser Fritz for one hundred dollars to the book's one dollar if Unser Fritz wishes to bet on Cara Mia dropping in there no worse than third, and of course Willie has no idea Unser Fritz or anybody else will ever take such a price, and the chances are if Willie is not sizzling a little at Unser Fritz, he will not offer such a price, because it sounds foolish.

Furthermore, the chances are if Unser Fritz offers Willie a comparatively small bet at this price, such as may enable him to chisel just a couple of hundred out of Willie's book, Willie will find some excuse to wiggle off, but Unser Fritz leans over and says in a low voice to Willie the Worrier:

'A hundred thousand.'

Willie nods his head and turns to a clerk alongside him, and his voice is as low as Unser Fritz's as he says to the clerk:

'A thousand to a hundred thousand, Cara Mia third.'

The clerk's eyes pop open and so does his mouth, but he does not say a word. He just writes something on a pad of paper in his hand, and Unser Fritz offers Willie the Worrier a package of thousand-dollar bills, and says:

'Here is twenty,' he says. 'The rest is in the jug.'

'All right, Dutch,' Willie says, 'I know you have it, although,' he says, 'this is the first crack you give me at it. You are on, Dutch,' he says. 'P.S.,' Willie says, 'the Dirty does not go any more.'

Well, you understand Unser Fritz is betting one hundred thousand dollars against a thousand dollars that Cara Mia will run in the money, and personally I consider this wager a very sound business proposition indeed, and so does everybody else, for all it amounts to is finding a thousand dollars in the street.

There is really nothing that can make Cara Mia run out of the money, the way I look at it, except what happens to her, and what happens is she steps in a hole fifty yards from the finish when she is on top by ten, and breezing, and down she goes all spread out, and of course the other three horses run on past her to the wire, and all this is quite a disaster to many members of the public, including Unser Fritz.

I am standing with him on the rise of the grandstand lawn watching the race, and it is plain to be seen that he is slightly surprised at what happens, and personally, I am practically dumbfounded because, to tell the truth, I take a nibble at the opening price of 2 to 5 on Cara Mia with a total of thirty slugs, which represents all my capital, and I am thinking what a great injustice it is for them to leave holes in the track for horses to step in, when Unser Fritz says like this:

'Well,' he says, 'it is horse racing.'

And this is all he ever says about the matter, and then he walks down to Willie the Worrier, and tells Willie if he will send a clerk with him, he will go to the jug and get the balance of the money that is now due Willie.

'Dutch,' Willie says, 'it will be a pleasure to accompany you to the jug in person.'

As Willie is getting down off his stool, somebody in the crowd who hears of the wager gazes at Unser Fritz, and remarks that he is really a game guy, and Willie says:

'Yes,' he says, 'he is a game guy at that. But,' he says, 'what about me?'

And he takes Unser Fritz by the arm, and they walk away together, and anybody can see that Unser Fritz picks up anyway twenty years or more, and a slight stringhalt, in the last few minutes.

Then it comes on night again in Saratoga, and I am standing out under the elms in front of the Grand Union, thinking that this world is by no means as beautiful as formerly, when I notice a big, fat old Judy with snow-white hair and spectacles standing near me, looking up and down the street. She will weigh a good two hundred pounds, and much of it is around her ankles, but she has a pleasant face, at that, and when she observes me looking at her, she comes over to me, and says:

'I am trying to fix the location of a restaurant where I work many years ago,' she says. 'It is a place called Shovelin's. The last thing my husband tells me is to see if the old building is still here, but,' she says, 'it is so long since I am in Saratoga I cannot get my bearings.'

'Ma'am,' I say, 'is your name Emma by any chance and do they ever call you Emerald Em?'

Well, at this the old Judy laughs, and says:

'Why, yes,' she says. 'That is what they call me when I am young and foolish. But how do you know?' she says. 'I do not remember ever seeing you before in my life.'

'Well' I say, 'I know a party who once knows you. A party by the name of Unser Fritz.'

'Unser Fritz?' she says. 'Unser Fritz? Oh,' she says, 'I wonder if you mean a crazy Dutchman I run around with many years ago? My gracious,' she says, 'I just barely remember him. He is a great hand for giving me little presents such as emeralds. When I am young I think emeralds are right pretty, but,' she says, 'otherwise I cannot stand him.'

'Then you do not come here to see him?' I say.

'Are you crazy, too?' she says. 'I am on my way to Ballston Spa to see my grandchildren. I live in Macon, Georgia. If ever you are in Macon, Georgia, drop in at Shovelin's restaurant and get some real Southern fried chicken. I am Mrs. Joe Shovelin,' she says. 'By the way,' she says, 'I remember more about that crazy Dutchman. He is a horse player. I always figure he must die long ago and that the chances are he dies broke, too. I remember I hear people say all horse players die broke.'

'Yes,' I say, 'he dies all right, and he dies as you suggest, too,' for it is only an hour before that they find old Unser Fritz in a vacant lot over near the railroad station with the Betsy he gets off Joe Palladino in his hand and a bullet-hole smack-dab through his pimple.

Nobody blames him much for taking this out, and in fact I am standing there thinking long after Emerald Em goes on about her business that it will be a good idea if I follow his example, only I cannot think where I can find another Betsy, when Solly comes along and stands there with me. I ask Solly if he knows anything new.

'No,' Solly says, 'I do not know anything new, except,' he says, 'I heard Willie the Worrier and his ever-loving make up again, and she is not going to leave him after all. I hear Willie takes home a squarer in the shape of a batch of emeralds and diamonds that she orders sent up here when Willie is not looking, and that they are fighting about all day. Well,' Solly says, 'maybe this is love.'

Money From Home

I T comes on a pleasant morning in the city of Baltimore, Md., and a number of citizens are standing in front of the Cornflower Hotel in Calvert Street, speaking of this and that, and one thing and another, and especially of the horse races that are to take place in the afternoon at Pimlico, because these citizens are all deeply interested in horse races, and in fact they are not interested in much of anything else in this world.

Among these citizens is The Seldom Seen Kid, who is called The Seldom Seen because he is seldom seen after anything comes off that anybody may wish to see him about, as he has a most retiring disposition, although he can talk a blue streak whenever talking becomes really necessary. He is a young guy of maybe twenty-five years of age, and he always chucks a good front, and has a kind face that causes people to trust him implicitly.

Then there is Hot Horse Herbie, who is called Hot Horse Herbie because he generally knows about some horse that is supposed to be hotter than a base-burner, a hot horse being a horse that is all heated up to win a horse race, although sometimes Hot Horse Herbie's hot horses turn out to be as cold as a landlord's heart. And there is also Big Reds, who is known to one and all as an excellent handicapper if his figures are working right.

Now these are highly respected characters, and if you ask them what they do, they will tell you that they are turf advisers, a turf adviser being a party who advises the public about horse races, and their services are sometimes quite valuable, even if the coppers at the race-tracks do say that turf advisers are nothing but touts, and are always jerking them around, and sometimes going so far as to bar them off the tracks altogether, which is a grave injustice, as it deprives many worthy citizens of a chance to earn a livelihood.

In fact, the attitude of these coppers is so odious towards turf advisers that there is some talk of organizing a National Turf Advisers' Association, for mutual protection, and bringing the names of the coppers up at the meetings and booing them for ten minutes each.

There is another guy standing in front of the Cornflower Hotel with The Seldom Seen Kid and Hot Horse Herbie and Big Reds, and this guy is a little, dark complected, slippery-looking guy by the name of Philly the Weeper, and he is called by this name because he is always weeping about something, no matter what. In fact, Philly the Weeper is such a guy as will go around with a loaf of bread under his arm weeping because he is hungry.

He is generally regarded as a most unscrupulous sort of guy, and in fact some people claim Philly the Weeper is downright dishonest, and ordinarily The Seldom Seen Kid, and Hot Horse Herbie and Big Reds do not associate with parties of this calibre, but of course they cannot keep Philly the Weeper from standing around in front of the Cornflower Hotel with them, because he resides there the same as they do.

In fact, Philly the Weeper is responsible at this time for The Seldom Seen Kid, and Hot Horse Herbie and Big Reds being able to continue residing in the Cornflower, as conditions are very bad with them, what with so few of the public being willing to take their advice about the horse races, and the advice turning out the wrong way even when the public takes it, and they are all in the hotel stakes, and the chances are the management will be putting hickeys in their keyholes if it is not for Philly the Weeper okaying them.

The reason Philly the Weeper is able to okay them is because a musical show by the name of 'P's and Q's' is trying out in Baltimore, and Philly the Weeper's fiancée, Miss Lola Ledare, is a prominent member of the chorus, and the company is stopping at the Cornflower Hotel, and Philly the Weeper lets on that he has something to do with them being there, so he stands first-class with the hotel management, which does not think to ask anybody connected with the 'P's and Q's' company about the matter.

If the hotel management does ask, the chances are it will find out that the company regard Philly the Weeper as a wrong gee, the same as everybody else, although it thinks well of his fiancée, Miss Lola Ledare, who is one of these large, wholesome blondes, and by no means bad-looking, if you like them blonde. She is Philly the Weeper's fiancée for several years, but nobody holds this against her, as it is well known to one and all that love is something that cannot be explained, and, anyway, Miss Lola Ledare does not seem to let it bother her very much.

She is such a doll as enjoys going around and about, being young, and full of vitality, as well as blonde, and if Philly the Weeper is too busy, or does not have enough dough to take her around and about, Miss Lola Ledare always seems able to find somebody else who has a little leisure time on their hands for such a purpose, and if Philly the Weeper does not like it, he can lump it, and usually he lumps it, for Miss Lola Ledare can be very, very firm when it comes to going around and about.

In fact, Philly the Weeper is telling The Seldom Seen Kid and Hot Horse Herbie and Big Reds, the very morning in question, about Miss Lola Ledare and nine other members of the 'P's and Q's' company being around and about the night before with an English guy who checks in at the Cornflower early in the evening, and who is in action in the matter of going around and about before anybody can say Jack Robinson.

'He is a young guy,' Philly the Weeper says, 'and from what Lola tells me, he is a very fast guy with a dollar. His name is the Honourable Bertie Searles, and he has a valet, and enough luggage to sink a barge. Lola says he takes quite a fancy to her, but,' Philly the Weeper says, 'every guy Lola meets takes quite a fancy to her, to hear her tell it.'

Well, nobody is much interested in the adventures of Miss Lola Ledare, or any of the other members of the 'P's and Q's' company, but when Philly the Weeper mentions the name of the English guy, The Seldom Seen Kid, who is reading the sport page of the *News*, looks up and speaks as follows:

'Why,' he says, 'there is a story about the Honourable Searles right here in this paper. He is the greatest amateur steeplechase rider in England, and he is over here to ride his own horse, Trafalgar, in some of our steeplechase races, including the Gold Vase at Belmont next week. It says here they are giving a fox hunt and a big dinner in his honour to-day at the Oriole Hunts Club.'

Then he hands the *News* to Philly the Weeper, and Philly the Weeper reads the story himself, and says like this:

'Well,' he says, 'from what Lola tells me of the guy's condition when they get him back to the hotel about six bells this a.m., they will have to take him to the Oriole Hunts Club unconscious. He may be a great hand at kicking them over the sticks, but I judge he is also quite a rum-pot.'

'Anyway,' Hot Horse Herbie says, 'he is wasting his time riding anything in the Gold Vase. Personally,' he says, 'I do not care for amateur steeplechase riders, because I meet up with several in my time who have more larceny in them than San Quentin. They call them gentleman riders, but many of them cannot even spell gentleman. I will take Follow You and that zig-gaboo jock of his in the Gold Vase for mine against any horse and any amateur rider in the world, including Marsh Preston's Sweep Forward.'

'Yes,' Big Reds says, 'if there is any jumper alive that can lick Follow You, with the coon up, I will stand on my head in front of Mindy's restaurant on Broadway for twenty-four hours hand running, and I do not like standing on my head. Any time they go to the post,' Big Reds says, 'they are just the same as money from home.'

Well, of course it is well known to one and all that what Hot Horse Herbie and Big Reds say about Follow You in the Gold Vase is very true, because this Follow You is a Maryland horse that is a wonderful jumper, and furthermore he is a very popular horse because he is owned by a young Maryland doll by the name of Miss Phyllis Richie, who comes of an old family on the Eastern Shore.

It is such an old family as once has plenty of dough, and many great race horses, but by the time the family gets down to Miss Phyllis Richie, the dough is all gone, and about all that is left is a house with a leaky roof on the Tred Avon River, and this horse, Follow You, and a coon by the name of Roy Snakes, who always rides the horse, and everybody in Maryland knows that Follow You supports Miss Phyllis Richie and her mother and the house with the leaky roof by winning jumping races here and there.

In fact, all this is quite a famous story of the Maryland turf, and nobody is violating any secrets or poking their nose into private family affairs in speaking of it, and any time Follow You walks out on a race-track in Maryland with Roy Snakes on his back in the red and white colours of the Richie stable, the band always plays 'My Maryland', and the whole State of Maryland gets up and yells.

Well, anyway, jumping races do not interest such characters as The Seldom Seen Kid and Hot Horse Herbie and Big Reds, or even Philly the Weeper, very much, so they get to talking about something else, when all of a sudden down the street comes a spectacle that is considered most surprising.

It consists of a young guy who is dressed up in a costume such as is worn by fox hunters when they are out chasing foxes, including a pink coat, and tight pants, and boots, and a peaked cap, and moreover, the guy is carrying a whip in one hand, and a horn in the other, and every now and then he puts this horn to his mouth and goes ta-ta-tee-ta-ta-tee-ta-dah.

But this is not as surprising as the fact that behind the guy are maybe a dozen dogs of one kind and another, such as a dachshund, a Boston bull terrier, a Scottie, a couple of fox hounds, and a lot of just plain every-day dogs, and they are yipping, and making quite a fuss about the guy in the costume, and the reason is that between ta-ta-dees he tucks his horn under one arm and reaches into a side pocket of his pink coat, and takes out some little brown crackers, which he chucks to the dogs.

Well, the first idea anybody is bound to have about a guy going around in such an outfit baiting dogs to follow him, is that he is slightly daffy, and this is the idea The Seldom Seen Kid, and Hot Horse Herbie, and Big Reds, and Philly the Weeper have as they watch the guy, until he turns around to chide a dog that is nibbling at the seat of his tight pants, and they see that the guy has a sign on his back that reads as follows:

Barker's Dog Crullers

Then of course they know the guy is only up to an advertising dodge, and Hot Horse Herbie laughs right out loud, and says like this:

'Well,' Herbie says, 'I will certainly have to be in tough shape to take such a job as this, especially for a guy like old Barker. I know him well,' Herbie says. 'He has a factory down here on Lombard Street, and he likes to play the horses now and then, but he is the toughest, meanest old guy in Maryland, and will just as soon bat your brains out as not. In fact, he is thinking some of batting my brains out one day at Laurel last year when I lay him on the wrong horse. But,' Herbie says, 'they tell me he makes a wonderful dog cruller, at that, and he is certainly a great hand for advertising.'

By this time, the young guy in the fox hunter's costume is in front of the hotel with his dogs, and nothing will do but The Seldom Seen Kid must stop him, and speak to him.

'Hello,' The Seldom Seen Kid says, 'where is your horse?'

Well, the young guy seems greatly surprised at being accosted in this manner by a stranger, and he looks at The Seldom Seen Kid for quite a spell, as if he is trying to figure out where he sees him before, and finally he says like this:

'Why,' the young guy says, 'it is very strange that you ask me such a question, as I not only do not have a horse, but I hate horses. I am afraid of horses since infancy. In fact,' he says, 'one reason I leave my home town is because my father wishes me to give up my musical career and drive the delivery waggon for his grocery-store, although he knows how I loathe and despise horses.'

Now, of course, The Seldom Seen Kid is only joking when he asks the young guy about his horse, and does not expect to get all this information, but the young guy seems so friendly, and so innocent, that The Seldom Seen Kid keeps talking to him, although the dogs bother the young guy quite some, while he is standing there, by trying to climb up his legs, and he has to keep feeding them the little brown crackers out of his pocket, and it seems that these crackers are Barker's Dog Crullers, and Hot Horse Herbie personally tries several and pronounces them most nutritious.

The young guy says his name is Eddie Yokum, and he comes from a town in Delaware that is called Milburn, and another reason he comes to Baltimore besides wishing to avoid contact with horses is that he reads in a paper that the 'P's and Q's' company is there, and he wishes to get a position with the show, because it seems that back in Milburn he is considered quite an excellent singer, and he takes a star part in the Elks' minstrel show in the winter of 1933, and even his mother says it will be a sin and a shame to waste such talent on a delivery waggon, especially by a guy who can scarcely bear the sight of a horse.

Well, Eddie Yokum then starts telling The Seldom Seen Kid all about the Elks' minstrel show, and how he gives imitations of Eddie Cantor and Al Jolson in black face; and in fact he gives these imitations for The Seldom Seen right then and there, and both are exactly alike, except of course Eddie Yokum is not in black face, and The Seldom Seen Kid confesses the imitations are really wonderful, and Eddie Yokum says he thinks so, too, especially when you consider he never even sees Eddie Cantor or Al Jolson.

He offers to render a song by the name of 'Silver Threads Among the Gold,' which it seems is the song he renders in the Elks' minstrels in Milburn, while imitating Eddie Cantor and Al Jolson, but Hot Horse Herbie and Big Reds tell The Seldom Seen Kid that this will be going too far, and he agrees with them, although Eddie Yokum seems greatly disappointed.

He is a very nice-looking young guy, with big round eyes, and a pleasant smile, but he is so innocent that it is really surprising to think he can walk around Baltimore, Md., safe and sound, even made up as a fox hunter.

Well, it seems that when Eddie Yokum arrives in Baltimore, Md., from Milburn, he goes around to the theatre where the 'P's and Q's' company is playing to see about getting a position with the show, but nobody wishes to listen to him, and in fact the stage doorman finally speaks very crossly to Eddie, and tells him that if he does not desire a bust in the beezer, he will go away from there. So Eddie goes away, as he does not desire a bust in the beezer.

By and by he has a great wish to eat food, and as he is now all out of money, there is nothing for him to do but go to work, so he gets this job with Barker's Dog Crullers, and here he is.

'But,' Eddie Yokum says, 'I hesitate at taking it at first because I judge from the wardrobe that a horse goes with it, but Mr. Barker says if I think he is going to throw in a horse after spending a lot of money on this outfit, I am out of my head, and in fact Mr. Barker tells me not to walk fast, so as not to wear out these boots too soon. I am commencing to suspect that Mr. Barker is a trifle near.'

By this time, no one except The Seldom Seen Kid is paying much attention to Eddie Yokum, as anybody can see that he is inclined to be somewhat gabby, and quite a bore, and anyway there cannot possibly be any percentage in talking to such a guy.

Hot Horse Herbie and Big Reds are chatting with each other, and Philly the Weeper is reading the paper, while Eddie Yokum goes right along doing a barber, and the dogs are still climbing up his legs after the Barker's Dog Crullers, when all of a sudden Philly the Weeper looks at the dogs, and speaks to Eddie Yokum in a most severe tone of voice as follows:

'See here, young fellow,' Philly says, 'where do you get the two fox hounds you have with you? I just notice them, and I will thank you to answer me promptly, and without quibbling.'

Well, it seems from what Eddie Yokum says that he does not get the fox hounds anywhere in particular, but that they just up and follow him as he goes along the street. He explains that the Boston bull, the dachsund, and the Scottie are what you might call stooges, because they belong to Mr. Barker personally, and Eddie has to see that they get back to the factory with him every day, but all the other dogs are strays that join out with him here and there on account of the crullers, and he shoos them away when his day's work is done.

'To tell the truth,' Eddie Yokum says, 'I am always somewhat embarrassed to have so many dogs following me, but Mr. Barker sometimes trails me in person, and if I do not have a goodly throng of dogs in my wake eagerly partaking of Barker's Dog Crullers, he is apt to become very peevish. But,' Eddie says, 'I consider these fox hounds a great feather in my cap, because they are so appropriate to my costume, and I am sure that Mr. Barker will be much pleased when he sees them. In fact, he may raise my salary, which will be very pleasant, indeed.'

'Well,' Philly the Weeper says, 'your story sounds very fishy to me. These fox hounds undoubtedly belong to my old friend, Mr.

Prendergast, and how am I to know that you do not steal them from his country place? In fact, now that I look at you closely, I can see that you are such a guy as is apt to sneeze a dog any time, and for two cents I will call a cop and give you in charge.'

He is gazing at Eddie Yokum most severely, and at this crack about his friend Mr. Prendergast, and a country place, The Seldom Seen Kid reaches over and takes the newspaper out of Philly the Weeper's hands, because he knows Philly has no friend by the name of Mr. Prendergast, and that even if he does have such a friend, Mr. Prendergast has no more country place than a jay-bird, but he can see that Philly has something on his mind, and right away The Seldom Seen Kid raps to what it is, because there in the paper in black type is an advertisement that reads as follows:

'LOST, STRAYED, OR STOLEN. TWO LIVER-AND-WHITE FOX HOUNDS ANSWERING TO THE NAMES OF NIP AND TUCK. $200 REWARD AND NO QUESTIONS ASKED IF RETURNED TO THE ORIOLE HUNTS CLUB.'

Hot Horse Herbie and Big Reds read the advertisement over The Seldom Seen Kid's shoulder, and each makes a lunge at a fox hound, Hot Horse Herbie grabbing one around the neck, and Big Reds snaring the other by the hind legs; and this unexpected action causes some astonishment and alarm among the other dogs, and also frightens Eddie Yokum no little, especially as The Seldom Seen Kid joins Philly the Weeper in gazing at Eddie very severely, and The Seldom Seen Kid speaks as follows:

'Yes,' he says, 'this is a most suspicious case. There is only one thing to do with a party who stoops so low as to steal a dog, and especially two dogs, and that is to clap him in the clink.'

Now of course The Seldom Seen Kid has no idea whatever of clapping anybody in the clink, because as a matter of fact he is greatly opposed to clinks, and if he has his way about it, they will all be torn down and thrown away, but he figures that it is just as well to toss a good scare into Eddie Yokum and get rid of him before Eddie discovers what this interest in the fox hounds is all about, as The Seldom Seen Kid feels that if there is any reward money to be cut up, it is best not to spread it around any more than is necessary.

Well, by this time, Eddie Yokum has a very good scare in him, indeed, and he is backing away an inch or two at a time from The Seldom Seen Kid and Philly the Weeper, while Hot Horse Herbie and Big Reds are struggling with the fox hounds, and just about holding their own, when who comes walking up very briskly but a plain-clothes copper by the name of Detective Wilbert Schmalz, because it seems that the manager of the Cornflower Hotel gets sick and tired of the dogs out in front of his joint, and telephones to the nearest station-house and wishes to know if there is no justice.

So the station-house gets hold of Detective Wilbert Schmalz and tells him to see about this proposition; and here he is, and naturally Detective Schmalz can see by Eddie Yokum's costume and by the dogs around him that he is undoubtedly very unlawful, and as he comes walking up Detective Schmalz speaks to Eddie Yokum as follows:

'Come with me,' he says. 'You are under arrest.'

Now what Eddie Yokum thinks he is under arrest for is stealing the fox hounds, and by the time Detective Schmalz gets close to him, Eddie Yokum is near one of the two entrances to the Cornflower Hotel that open on Calvert Street, and both of these entrances have revolving doors.

So all of a sudden, Eddie Yokum makes a jump into one of these entrances, and at the same time Detective Schmalz makes a grab for him, as Detective Schmalz can see by Eddie Yokum's attempt to escape that he is undoubtedly a very great malefactor, but all Detective Schmalz gets is the sign off Eddie's back that reads 'Barker's Dog Crullers.'

Then Detective Schmalz finds himself tangled up in the revolving door with the dachsund, which is trying to follow Eddie

Yokum, and crying in a way that will break your heart, while Eddie is dashing out the other entrance, and there is a great confusion all around and about, with Hot Horse Herbie and Big Reds using language to the fox hounds that is by no means fit for publication.

In fact, there is so much confusion that very few people notice that as Eddie Yokum pops out the other entrance and heads for the middle of the street where he will have plenty of racing room, a big, shiny town car with a chauffeur and a footman pulls up at the kerb in front of the hotel, and the footman leaps off the seat and yanks open the door of the car right under Eddie Yokum's nose, and the next thing anybody knows, Eddie is inside the town car, and the car is tearing down the street.

Afterwards Eddie Yokum remembers hearing the footman mumble something about being sorry, they are late, but Eddie is too bewildered by his strange experience, and too happy to escape the law, to think of much of anything else for a while, and it does not come to him that he must be mistaken for somebody else until the town car is rolling up the driveway of the Oriole Hunts Club, a few miles out of Baltimore, and he sees a raft of guys and dolls strolling around and about, with the guys dressed up as fox hunters, just the same way he is.

Now, of course the guy Eddie Yokum is mistaken for is nobody but the Honourable Bertie Searles, who at this time is pounding his ear back in the Cornflower Hotel, and the chances are glad of it, but nobody can scarcely blame the chauffeur and the footman for the mistake when they see a guy dressed up as a fox hunter come bouncing out of a hotel, where they are sent to pick up an English gentleman rider, because anybody is apt to look like an Englishman, and a gentleman, too, if they are dressed up as a fox hunter.

Naturally, Eddie Yokum knows that a mistake is going on the minute he gets out of the car and finds himself surrounded by guys and dolls all calling him the Honourable Bertie Searles, and he realizes that there is nothing for him to do but to explain and apologize, and get away from there as quick as he can, and the chances are he will do this at once, as Eddie Yokum is really an honest, upright young guy, but before he can say a word, what does he see on the clubhouse veranda in riding clothes but the most beautiful doll he ever claps eyes on in his whole life.

In fact, this doll is so beautiful that Eddie Yokum is practically tongue-tied at once, and when she is introduced to him as Miss Phyllis Richie, he does not care what happens if he can only hang around here a little while, for this is undoubtedly love at first sight as far as Eddie Yokum is concerned, and Miss Phyllis Richie is by no means displeased with him, either, although she remarks that he is the first Englishman she ever sees who does not have an English accent.

So Eddie Yokum says to himself he will just keep his trap closed until the real Honourable Bertie Searles bobs up, or somebody who knows the real Honourable Bertie Searles comes around, and enjoy the sunshine of Miss Phyllis Richie's smile as long as possible; and to show you what a break he gets, it seems that nobody in the club ever sees the Honourable Bertie Searles in person, and they are all too busy getting the fox hunt in his honour going to bother to ask Eddie any questions that he cannot answer yes or no.

Anyway, Eddie Yokum keeps so close to Miss Phyllis Richie that nobody has much chance to talk to her, although a tall young guy with a little moustache and a mean look keeps trying, and Miss Phyllis Richie explains that this guy is nobody but Mr. Marshall Preston, who is as great an amateur rider in America as the Honourable Bertie Searles himself is in England.

Furthermore, she explains that Mr. Marshall Preston is the owner of a horse by the name of Sweet Forward, that is the only horse in this country that figures a chance to beat her horse, Follow You, in the Gold Vase, unless maybe the Honourable Bertie Searles' horse, Trafalgar, is an extra-good horse.

Then she commences asking Eddie Yokum about his horse, Trafalgar, and of course Eddie not only does not know he has such a horse, but he hates just even talking about horses, and he has quite a time switching the conversation, because Miss Phyllis Richie seems bound and determined to talk about horses, and especially her horse.

'I am only sorry,' Miss Phyllis Richie says, 'that it is not possible to let you ride Follow You over a course, just so you can see what a wonderful horse he is, but,' she says, 'it is a well-known peculiarity of his that he will not permit any one to ride him except a coloured boy, not even myself. In fact, several times we try to put white riders on Follow You, and he half kills them. It is most unfortunate, because you will really appreciate him.'

Well, naturally Eddie Yokum does not consider this unfortunate by any means, as the last thing in the world he wishes to do is to ride a horse, but of course he does not mention the matter to Miss Phyllis Richie, as he can see that a guy who does not wish to ride horses is not apt to get to first base with her.

What bothers Eddie Yokum more than somewhat, however, is the way this Mr. Marshall Preston keeps scowling at him, and finally he asks Miss Phyllis Richie if she can figure out what is eating the guy, and Miss Phyllis Richie laughs heartily, and says like this:

'Oh,' she says, 'Mr. Marshall Preston seems to have an idea that he loves me, and wishes to marry me. He hates anybody that comes near me. He hates my poor horse, Follow You, because he thinks if it is not for Follow You coming along and winning enough money to support us, I will have to marry him out of sheer poverty.

'But,' Miss Phyllis Richie says, 'I do not love Mr. Marshall Preston, and I will never marry except for love, and while things are not so good with us right now, everything will be all right after Follow You wins the Gold Vase, because it is a $25,000 stake. But no matter what happens, I do not think I will ever marry Mr. Marshall Preston, as he is very wild in his ways, and is unkind to horses.'

Well, this last is really a boost for Mr. Marshall Preston with

Eddie Yokum, but naturally he does not so state to Miss Phyllis Richie, and in fact he says that now he takes a second peek at Mr. Marshall Preston he can see that he may be a wrong gee in more ways than one, and that Miss Phyllis Richie is quite right in playing the chill for such a guy.

Now there is a great commotion about the premises, with guys coming up leading horses, and a big pack of fox hounds yapping around, and it seems that the fox hunt in honour of the Honourable Bertie Searles is ready to start, and Eddie Yokum is greatly horrified when he realizes that he is expected to take part in the fox hunt, and ride a horse, and in fact Miss Phyllis Richie tells him they pick out the very finest horse in the club stables for him to ride, although she says she is afraid it will not compare to the horses he is accustomed to riding in England.

Well, at this, Eddie Yokum is greatly nonplussed, and he figures that here is the blow-off sure enough, especially as a guy who seems to be a groom comes up leading a tall, fierce-looking horse, and hands Eddie the bridle-reins. But Eddie cannot think of words in which to put his confession, so when nobody seems to be noticing him, he walks off by himself towards the club stables, and naturally the horse follows him, because Eddie has hold of the reins.

Now the presence of this horse at his heels is very disquieting to Eddie Yokum, so when he gets behind the stables which shut him off from the sight of the crowd, Eddie looks around for something to tie the horse to, and finally drops the reins over the handle of a motor-cycle that is leaning up against a wall, this motor-cycle being there for the grooms to run errands on to and from the city.

Well, it seems that in the excitement over getting the fox hunt started, nobody missed Eddie Yokum at first, and away goes the crowd on their horses with the hounds yapping quite some, while Eddie is standing there behind the stables thinking of how to break the news about himself to one and all, and especially to Miss Phyllis Richie.

Then Eddie Yokum happens to look up, and who does he see coming up the driveway in such a direction that they cannot miss seeing him if he remains where he is, but Philly the Weeper and Hot Horse Herbie, leading a pair of hounds, which are undoubtedly the fox hounds they get from Eddie Yokum and which they are now delivering to claim the reward.

Naturally, the sight of these parties is most distasteful to Eddie Yokum, because all he can think of is that in addition to everything else, he will now be denounced as a dog thief, and Eddie can scarcely bear to have Miss Phyllis Richie see him in such a light, so he grabs up the motor-cycle, and starts it going, and leaps in the saddle, and away he sprints down a country lane in the opposite direction from the driveway, for if there is one thing Eddie Yokum can do, it is ride a motor-cycle.

He forgets about the horse being hooked to the motor-cycle, and of course the poor horse has to follow him, and every time Eddie Yokum looks around, there is the horse, and Eddie gets the idea that maybe the horse is chasing him, so he gives the motor-cycle plenty of gas, and makes it zing. But it is very bumpy going along the country lane, and Eddie cannot lose the horse, and, besides, Eddie is personally becoming very tired, so finally he pulls up to take a rest.

By this time, the horse has enough lather on him to shave the House of David, and seems about ready to drop dead, and Eddie Yokum will not care a cuss if he does, as Eddie is sick and tired of the horse, although the horse is really not to blame for anything whatever.

Anyway, Eddie Yokum is lying stretched out on the ground taking a rest, when he hears the fox hounds barking away off, but coming closer right along, and he figures the fox hunters will also be moving in his direction, and as he does not wish to ever again be seen by Miss Phyllis Richie after ducking the hunt, he unhooks the horse from the motor-cycle, and gives it a good kick in the vestibule, and tells it to go on about its business, and then he crawls in under a big brush-heap beside the lane, dragging the motor-cycle in after him.

Well, what is under the brush-heap but a little bitsy fox, all tuckered out, and very much alarmed, and this little bitsy fox seems glad to see such a kind and sympathetic face as Eddie Yokum possesses, and it crawls into Eddie Yokum's lap, and roosts there shivering and shaking, and the next thing Eddie knows the brush-heap is surrounded by fox hounds, who are very anxious to get at the little bitsy fox, and maybe at Eddie Yokum, too, but Eddie remembers that he has some of Barker's Dog Crullers still left in his pocket, and he cools the hounds out no little by feeding them these appetizers.

By and by the fox hunters come up, following the hounds, and they are greatly surprised when Eddie Yokum comes crawling out from under the brush-heap with the little bitsy fox in his arms, especially as they meet up with Eddie's horse all covered with perspiration, and figure he must just finish a terrible run, because of course they do not know about the motor-cycle hidden under the brush-heap.

They are all the more surprised when Eddie Yokum tells them that he does not believe in killing foxes, and that he always personally catches them with his bare hands after the dogs locate them, but Eddie feels rewarded when Miss Phyllis Richie smiles at him, and says he is the most humane guy she ever meets, especially when Eddie says his horse is too tired for him to ride him home, and insists on walking, carrying the little bitsy fox.

Well, Eddie is commencing to wonder again how he can confess what an impostor he is, and get away from this company, but the more he looks at Miss Phyllis Richie, the more he hates to do it, especially as she is talking about what a wonderful time they will have at the dinner in his honour later on in the evening, as it seems that this is to be a very fine affair, indeed, and Harry Richman and several other stars of the 'P's and Q's' company are expected to be present to entertain, and Eddie Yokum can see where he may be missing a great opportunity to come in contact with such parties.

But by the time he gets back to the clubhouse, Eddie's mind is pretty well made up to get himself out of this predicament, no matter what, especially as the clubhouse doorman calls him aside, and says to him like this:

'Mr. Searles,' the doorman says, 'a most obnoxious character is here just a little while ago claiming he is you. Yes, sir,' the doorman says, 'he has the gall to claim he is the Honourable Bertie Searles, and he is slightly under the influence, and has several dolls with him, including a very savage blonde. Of course we know he is not you, and so we throw him out.

'He is very cheerful about it, at that, Mr. Searles,' the doorman says. 'He says it does not strike him as a very lively place, anyway, and that he is having more fun where he is. But the savage blonde is inclined to make much of the matter. In fact, she tries to bite me. It is a very strange world, Mr. Searles.'

Well, Eddie Yokum figures right away that this must be the guy they mistake him for, and he also figures that the guy is a sure thing to be coming back sooner or later, and as it is now coming on dusk, Eddie starts easing himself down the driveway, although they tell him there is a nice room ready for him at the club where he can clean up and take a rest before dinner; but he does not get very far down the driveway, when who steps out of some bushes but Philly the Weeper, who speaks as follows:

'Well, well, well,' Philly the Weeper says. 'I know my eyes do not deceive me when I see you springing away on a motor-cycle, but,' he says, 'imagine my astonishment when I describe you to the doorman, and he tells me you are the Honourable Bertie Searles. Why, you can knock me over with the eighth pole, I am so surprised, because of course I know you are nothing but a dog thief, and I am waiting around here for hours to get an explanation from you for such goings on.'

Naturally, Philly the Weeper does not mention that he already has Hot Horse Herbie collect two C's from the club secretary for returning the hounds, and that he sends Herbie on back to Baltimore, for Philly the Weeper has a nose like a beagle, and he smells something here the minute he sees Eddie Yokum going away on the motor-cycle, and he keeps himself in the background, while Hot Horse Herbie is collecting the dough, although Philly does not neglect to take the two C's off of Herbie afterwards, for safe-keeping.

Of course, Philly the Weeper has no idea Eddie Yokum is trying to run away entirely on the motor-cycle, or he will not be hanging around waiting for him to come back, but there Eddie is, and Philly the Weeper gets the whole story out of him in no time, because Eddie figures the best thing for him to do is to throw himself on the mercy of Philly the Weeper as far as the stolen dogs are concerned.

Well, Philly the Weeper is greatly interested and amused at Eddie's story of how he is mistaken for the Honourable Bertie Searles, and has to go fox hunting, and of his sudden and great love for Miss Phyllis Richie; but when Eddie gets down to telling him about how he is now trying to slip away from the scene, Philly the Weeper becomes very severe again, and speaks as follows:

'No, no,' Philly says, 'you are not to go away, at all. You are to remain here at the club for the dinner in your honour to-night, and, moreover, you are to take me into the club with you as your valet, because,' Philly says, 'I wish to play a joke on certain members of this organization, including my old friend, Mr. Prendergast, who will undoubtedly be present. If you will do this for me, I will forget about you stealing Mr. Prendergast's fox hounds, although he is inclined to be very drastic about the matter.'

Now, of course, if Eddie Yokum is such a guy as does a little serious thinking now and then, the chances are he will see that there is something unusual about all this, but Eddie is not only very innocent, but by this time he is greatly confused, and all he can think of to say to Philly the Weeper is that he is afraid the real Honourable Bertie Searles will come back and expose him.

'You need not worry about this,' Philly the Weeper says. 'I am present in ambush when the Honourable Bertie Searles and his party, including my fiancée, Miss Lola Ledare, are given the bum's rush out of here a short time ago, and as they depart I hear him promising to give Lola and her friends a big party downtown to-night after the show to reimburse them for the churlish treatment they received here. Remember,' Philly says, 'you will not only be rounding yourself up for stealing Mr. Prendergast's dogs, but you will be able to be with the doll you love so dearly all evening.'

So the upshot of it all is, Eddie Yokum goes back to the club, taking Philly the Weeper with him and explaining that Philly is his valet; and one thing about it, Philly makes Eddie more important than somewhat, at that, which is a good thing, as some of the members are commencing to wonder about Eddie, especially Mr. Marshall Preston, who is all burned up at the way Eddie is pitching to Miss Phyllis Richie.

Now, the reason Philly the Weeper wishes to get inside the clubhouse is not to play any jokes on anybody, as he says, especially on his friend Mr. Prendergast, because in the first place he has no friend named Mr. Prendergast, and in the second place, Philly the Weeper has no friends by any names whatever. The reason he wishes to get inside the clubhouse is to collect any little odds and ends of jewellery that he may find lying about the premises later on, for collecting articles of this kind is really one of Philly the Weeper's regular occupations, though naturally he does not mention it to Eddie Yokum.

As a matter of fact, he is of quite some service to Eddie Yokum when they go to the room that is assigned to Eddie, as he coaches Eddie in the way a guy shall act at dinner, and in talking to such a doll as Miss Phyllis Richie, and he also fixes Eddie's clothes up for him a little, as the dinner is to be in fox hunting costume, which is a good thing for Eddie, as he does not have any other costume.

The only argument they have is about the little bitsy fox, which

Eddie Yokum is still carrying around with him, and which he wishes to keep with him at all times, as he is now very fond of the little creature, but Philly the Weeper convinces him that it is better to turn it loose, and let it return to its native haunts, and when Eddie does same the little bitsy fox creates a riot in the club kennels when it goes streaking past them headed for the woods.

Well, Eddie Yokum is a very hospitable soul, and he wishes Philly the Weeper to attend the dinner with him, but Philly says no, a valet is supposed to be a sort of hired hand, and does not go in for social functions with his boss, so Eddie goes down to dinner alone, leaving Philly the Weeper in the room, and Eddie is greatly delighted to find Miss Phyllis Richie is waiting for him to escort her in, and for the next couple of hours he is in a sort of trance, and cannot remember that he is not the Honourable Bertie Searles, but only Eddie Yokum, of Milburn, Del.

All he can remember is that he hauls off and tells Miss Phyllis Richie that he is in love with her, and she says she loves him right back, and the only trouble with this conversation is that Mr. Marshall Preston accidentally overhears it, and is so unhappy he can scarcely think, because it is only a couple of hours before that Mr. Marshall Preston asks Miss Phyllis Richie to please marry him.

Mr. Marshall Preston is so unhappy that he goes out to the bar before dinner is over and has a few drinks, and then goes upstairs to a room he is occupying for the evening, just in time to catch Philly the Weeper collecting a job lot of trinkets in the room to add to a bundle he already collects from other rooms.

Naturally, this unexpected intrusion is most embarrassing to Philly the Weeper, especially as Mr. Marshall Preston recognizes him as the Honourable Bertie Searles' valet, and it is perhaps just as well for Mr. Marshall Preston that Philly the Weeper is not rodded up at this time, as Philly never cares to be embarrassed. But Mr. Marshall Preston turns out to be very broad-minded, and instead of making a scene over finding Philly the Weeper at his collecting, he speaks to Philly as follows:

'Sit down,' he says. 'Sit down, and let us talk this over. What is there about this party who calls himself the Honourable Bertie Searles that causes me to wonder, and what is your real connection with him, and why does your face seem so familiar to me? Tell me your tale, and tell me true,' Mr. Marshall Preston says, 'or shall I call the gendarmes?'

Well, Philly the Weeper can see that Mr. Marshall Preston is no sucker, so he tells him that the Honourable Bertie Searles at the club is 100 per cent phoney, because he is nobody but Eddie Yokum, and he explains how he gets there, and that the real Honourable Bertie Searles is downtown enjoying himself with members of the 'P's and Q's' company.

'And,' Philly says, 'the reason my face seems familiar to you may be because I am around the race-tracks quite often, although I never have much truck with the steeplechasers.'

Now, Mr. Marshall Preston listens to all this with great interest, and when Philly the Weeper gets through, Mr. Marshall Preston sits there quiet for awhile, as if he is studying something out, and finally he says like this:

'I will call up the Honourable Bertie Searles, and we will have him come here and expose this impostor,' he says. 'It will be a good lesson to Miss Phyllis Richie for taking up with such a character without first finding out something about him. But in the meantime,' he says, 'let us continue talking while I make up my mind about handing you over to the cops.'

They continue talking until Mr. Marshall Preston forgets about calling the Honourable Bertie Searles until an hour later, and then he may just as well save himself the trouble, for at the moment he is telephoning, the Honourable Bertie Searles is on his way to the Oriole Hunts Club with Miss Lola Ledare, and a taxi-load of other blondes, and a few brunettes, because right in the middle of a nice party, some of the blondes remember they are due at the club to help Harry Richman put on a number, and the Honourable Bertie Searles says he will go along and demand an explanation from the club for his treatment earlier in the day, although the Honourable Bertie Searles says he does not really care a whoop, as he is treated worse in better clubs.

Well, while all this is happening, the dinner is going along very nicely, and it is a gala scene, to be sure, what with the decorations, and music, and all, and Eddie Yokum is in more of a trance than ever over Miss Phyllis Richie, when all of a sudden an old phflug by the name of Mrs. Abernathy comes running into the dining-hall letting out a squawk that she is robbed. It seems that she leaves a purse containing some dough, and other valuables, with her wraps in the dolls' dressing-room upstairs, and when she goes up there to powder her nose, or some such, she finds somebody knocks off her poke.

Now, this causes other dolls to remember leaving their leathers laying around upstairs, and some of them investigate at once, and find they are clipped, too, and presently guys who occupy rooms in the club are also letting out bleats and it becomes apparent that some thievery is going on around and about, and the club manager telephones for the police, because the beefs are commencing to be most upsetting.

Well, naturally Eddie Yokum is paying little attention to this commotion, because he is too greatly interested in Miss Phyllis Richie, but all of a sudden a bunch of coppers walk into the room, and who is among them but Detective Wilbert Schmalz, and the minute Eddie sees him, he becomes alarmed, as he is afraid Detective Schmalz may recognize him and put the arm on him for stealing the fox hounds, even though this matter is now supposed to be rounded up with Philly the Weeper.

So Eddie Yokum excuses himself to Miss Phyllis Richie and steps in back of a stand of potted plants, where he will not be conspicuous, and about this time he hears a familiar voice asking what is the trouble here, and why are all the coppers present, and somebody speaks up and says:

'Why, we are robbed.'

Then Eddie Yokum hears the familiar voice again, which he recognizes as the voice of Mr. Barker, who makes the dog crullers, and it is quite a loud voice, at that, and very unpleasant, and in fact it is such a loud voice that it causes Eddie Yokum to tremble in his top-boots, for Mr. Barker states as follows:

'You are robbed?' he says. 'Well, think of me, and how I am robbed, too. I am robbed of my hunting clothes, and I have to appear here at a hunts dinner for the first time in all the years I am a member of this club, the way you see me. If they do not happen to have sense enough to find their way home, I will also be robbed of Adolph, my dachshund, and Boggie, my Boston, and McTavish, my Scottie. But,' Mr. Barker says, 'if it takes me the rest of my life, I will find the young squirt who runs off with my hunting clothes and choke the tongue out of his head.'

Well, at this, Eddie Yokum peeks around the potted plants, and he sees Mr. Barker standing nearby in a dinner jacket, and apparently very angry, indeed, and this is quite a situation for Eddie Yokum, because he is between Detective Schmalz, who may wish to put the arm on him, and Mr. Barker, who wishes to choke the tongue out of his head, and as if this is not enough, there is now a great commotion at the front door, with dolls squealing, and guys yelling, and Eddie Yokum hears somebody say that a guy is out there claiming he is the Honourable Bertie Searles, and trying to fight his way in.

The racket is so great it attracts everybody's attention, and Eddie Yokum sees his chance and slips away quietly, popping into the first door he comes to, and this door leads down a stairway into the furnace-room, so Eddie hides himself behind a furnace for awhile.

In the meantime, there is much excitement upstairs, as it seems that the Honourable Bertie Searles finally battles his way inside against great odds, and is identified by all the members of the 'P's and Q's' company who are with him, including Harry Richman and the other stars, as the guy he claims he is, and he is demanding apologies from everybody connected with the club, while a search is going on for the phoney Honourable Bertie Searles.

Finally, Detective Schmalz, who joins the search, frisks the room that Eddie occupies, and finds a couple of missing purses, now empty, and everybody is saying that there is no doubt Eddie is not only an impostor, but that he and his valet are thieves; although Mr. Marshall Preston puts in here, and says he does not think the valet is a party to the crime, as he personally sees the valet leaving the premises some time before the robbery can possibly take place.

So then everybody agrees that Eddie must be a lone hand criminal, and Miss Phyllis Richie is so mortified she gets her wraps and goes out on the veranda, especially after somebody describes Eddie Yokum, and Mr. Barker says he is surely the guy who cops his hunting costume, and Detective Schmalz, who listens in on the description, states that he is positive the guy is a much wanted dog snatcher.

Mr. Marshall Preston goes out on the veranda and tries to console Miss Phyllis Richie, and in fact he tells her that it is now time for her to make up her mind to marry him and find safety from adventurers such as Eddie Yokum, but Miss Phyllis Richie gives him a very short answer, and there are undoubtedly large tears in her eyes as she speaks, and anybody can see that she is feeling very downhearted, so Mr. Marshall Preston leaves her to her sorrow.

Well, pretty soon the entertainment goes into action, and the real Honourable Bertie Searles becomes the guest of honour in place of Eddie Yokum, and everybody forgets the unpleasant incidents of the evening, because the Honourable Bertie Searles is full of life and spirits and does not centre his attention on any one doll, as Eddie does when he is guest of honour, but scatters his shots around and about, although it is plain to be seen that the Honourable Bertie Searles cares for Miss Lola Ledare more than somewhat, even if she does keep wishing to go back and fight the doorman all over again.

Meantime, Eddie Yokum is down in the furnace-room, and how to get out and away from the club without being observed becomes something of a problem, as Eddie is still in the fox hunting costume, and such a costume is bound to attract attention at all times, and, furthermore, the only entrance to the furnace-room seems to be the room through which Eddie comes in the first place.

Well, Eddie sits there behind the furnace thinking things over, and he can hear the music and the laughter upstairs, and he is wishing he is back in Milburn, Del., where he has a home, and friends, and thinking of Milburn, Del., reminds Eddie of the time he blacks up his face and gives imitations of Al Jolson and Eddie Cantor; and thinking of this gives him a brand-new idea.

This idea is to black up his face right there and walk out to safety, because Eddie figures that anybody who sees him is bound to take him as an employee of the furnace-room, so he peeks into the furnace, and finds a lot of soot, and he makes his face blacker than a yard up a chimney.

Moreover, Eddie gets another break when he finds a suit of blue overalls left by some guy who works in the furnace-room, and also an old cap, and when he sneaks out the door a little later, he is nothing but a boogie, as far as anybody can see, and not a very clean boogie, at that, and the chances are he will be out of the club and gone in two minutes, if he does not happen to run into the Honourable Bertie Searles, who is teetering around looking for Miss Lola Ledare, who is absent from the scene longer than the Honourable Bertie Searles thinks is necessary.

As a matter of fact, Miss Lola Ledare is at this time off in a corner with Mr. Barker, giving Mr. Barker quite a canvass one way and another, for Miss Lola Ledare is a doll who believes in scattering her play, but of course this has nothing to do with the story.

Well, when he runs into Eddie Yokum, naturally the Honourable Bertie Searles thinks Eddie is really a coloured guy, and right away the Honourable Bertie Searles get a big idea, as guys who are rummed up a little always do. The Honourable Bertie Searles says that so far the entertainment in his honour lacks the old Southern touch he is led to believe he will find in such spots as Baltimore, Md., especially by coloured parties, and he considers Eddie a great capture, and insists on leading him out on the floor where the entertainment is going on, and presenting him to the crowd as a bit of real Southern atmosphere.

Naturally, Eddie Yokum is somewhat embarrassed, and alarmed, because he is afraid he will be recognized by somebody, but no one gives him a tumble for who he is, and everybody laughs heartily at what they consider the Honourable Bertie Searles' humour. Then the Honourable Bertie Searles says his protégé will now sing, and there is nothing for Eddie Yokum to do but sing, so he goes into 'Silver Threads Among the Gold,' and the orchestra picks him up nicely, and accompanies his singing.

Ordinarily, Eddie will be very glad to sing before such an audience, and even now he has a notion to give them Al Jolson and Eddie Cantor, then he commences thinking of what will happen to him if he is recognized, and he gets so alarmed he sings a little flat.

As he is singing, Eddie Yokum makes sure of the direction of the front entrance to the club, and he keeps edging in this direction as his song comes to a close, so it seems very natural when he finishes to bow himself off in an aisle leading to the entrance; only Eddie keeps right on going out the entrance, and he is on the veranda, and flying, when who does he run into but Miss Phyllis Richie.

Well, at the sight of Miss Phyllis Richie, Eddie Yokum forgets he is all sooted up, and looks like a smudge, and in fact all he can think of is how much he loves Miss Phyllis Richie, and he rushes up to her and speaks as follows:

'Darling,' Eddie Yokum says, 'I am in a bit of a hurry right now, and do not have time to explain matters, but do not believe anything you hear about me, because it is by no means true; and, anyway,' Eddie says, 'I adore you.'

Naturally, Miss Phyllis Richie thinks at first that Eddie is a real jig, and she is somewhat startled for a moment, but then she recognizes his voice, and she becomes very indignant, indeed.

'Why,' Miss Phyllis Richie says, 'you impostor! You cad! You liar! Why,' she says, 'you dog stealer! You common burglar! If you do not get away from here at once, I will call Mr. Marshall Preston and he will thrash you within an inch of your life, and turn you over to the police!'

And with this, she hauls off and biffs Eddie Yokum a hard slap in the kisser, and then she bursts out crying, and there is nothing for Eddie Yokum to do but to continue on his way, because he hears the Honourable Bertie Searles yelling for him, and he does not desire any further complications at this time.

All Eddie Yokum wishes to do is to go away somewhere and sit down and rest, and get his nerves composed again, as he is feeling greatly fatigued; and the first thing he does is to go to his rooming-house and wash himself up, and put on his best suit of clothes, which he brings with him from Milburn, Del., and then he starts thinking things over, and what he especially thinks over is why Miss Phyllis Richie calls him a common burglar, for of course Eddie Yokum does not know he is suspected of prowling the Oriole Hunts Club, although he knows it the next morning when he reads all about the robbery in the paper, and also about how the coppers are looking for a guy who impersonates the Honourable Bertie Searles to get into the club for the purpose of committing the crime.

Well, this is a very great shock to Eddie Yokum, and he can see at once why he stands like a broken leg with Miss Phyllis Richie. Moreover, he can see that there is just one guy who can state that he does not get into the club to commit any crimes, and this guy is nobody but Philly the Weeper, so Eddie figures the thing for him to do is to find Philly the Weeper, and get him to straighten this matter out, although of course if Eddie is well acquainted with Philly the Weeper he will know that getting Philly to straighten anything out is just the same thing as asking a gimlet to straighten out.

But Eddie Yokum has great faith in human nature and honesty, so the next morning he goes around in front of the Cornflower Hotel looking for Philly the Weeper; but Philly is by no means there, although The Seldom Seen Kid and Hot Horse Herbie and Big Reds are present; and at first none of them recognize Eddie without his fox hunter's costume until he asks The Seldom Seen Kid where Philly is, and The Seldom Seen Kid says like this:

'Well,' he says, 'if you can tell us, we will be greatly obliged, for we are seeking him ourselves to cut his ears off unless he kicks in with our share of a small score we make on some dogs. Yes,' The Seldom Seen Kid says, 'we will just love to see Philly the Weeper, but the 'P's and Q's' company goes to New York this morning, and the chances are he goes there, too, because he never gets far away from his fiancée, Miss Lola Ledare, for fear he will starve to death. But we will catch up with him sooner or later.'

Then The Seldom Seen Kid seems to remember Eddie Yokum's face, and he starts to laugh, because the last time he sees Eddie Yokum it is a very humorous spectacle, to be sure; but Eddie Yokum does not see anything to laugh about, and he starts in telling The Seldom Seen Kid and Hot Horse Herbie and Big Reds how Philly the Weeper makes him take him into the club as his valet, and what happens, and how he wishes to find Philly to prove his innocence; and Hot Horse Herbie is especially horrified, and states as follows:

'Why,' he says, 'I ought to know this fink has something on his mind that spells larceny when he tells me he is going to stick around out there at the club awhile and sends me back to town. But,' Herbie says, 'it does not occur to me it is anything more serious than maybe stealing a couple of dogs over again to collect another reward. There is no doubt but what he prowls the joint and leaves this poor guy to take the fall.'

'Philly the Weeper is a wrong gee,' The Seldom Seen Kid says. 'I know he is a wrong gee because he means to defraud us of our end of the two C's he gets yesterday, but I never figure he is wrong enough to do such a trick as he does to this guy here. It is really most preposterous. Well,' The Seldom Seen Kid says, 'the races are over here tomorrow and the best thing for you to do is to go with us and see if we can find Philly the Weeper. Anyway,' he says, 'if you stick around here you will be picked up and placed in the sneezer, and it is very, very difficult to get out of a Baltimore sneezer, once you are in.'

So this is how Eddie Yokum comes to be in New York and around Mindy's restaurant on Broadway the next week with The Seldom Seen Kid, and Hot Horse Herbie, and Big Reds, and also with other prominent turf advisers, and followers of the sport of kings, for Mindy's restaurant is a great resort for such characters.

But although he looks high and low, Eddie Yokum do not see hide or hair of Philly the Weeper, and neither does The Seldom Seen Kid and Hot Horse Herbie and Big Reds, although his fiancée, Miss Lola Ledare, is around in different spots nearly every night with the Honourable Bertie Searles, and the price against the Honourable Bertie Searles' horse, Trafalgar, in the Gold Vase Steeplechase goes up by the minute, and some bookmakers will give you as good as 10 to 1 that the Honourable Bertie cannot even sit on a horse Saturday, let alone ride one.

Most of the conversation around Mindy's at this time is about the Gold Vase Steeplechase, but it is conceded by one and all that it is a set-up for Miss Phyllis Richie's Follow You, and every time Eddie Yokum hears her name he has a pain in his heart, because he even forgets to think of Philly the Weeper when he is thinking of Miss Phyllis Richie.

What with being around with parties interested in horse racing, Eddie Yokum takes to reading the sport pages quite some, and when it comes to the day before the Gold Vase, he reads about Miss Phyllis Richie arriving at the Savoy-Plaza with a party of friends from all over Maryland to see the race, and he hangs around in front of the hotel for three hours just to get a peek at her, although he is somewhat discouraged when he sees Miss Phyllis Richie with Mr. Marshall Preston.

In the evening, he hears the citizens around Mindy's speaking of Mr. Marshall Preston's horse, Sweep Forward, and of other horses, but the conversation makes no impression on Eddie Yokum, because he does not know anything about racing, and in fact he never sees a race, because he hates horses so much, but there is so much excitement over the Gold Vase that finally he feels a desire to see this race, and he asks The Seldom Seen Kid and Hot Horse Herbie and Big Reds if they will take him with them the next day.

Well, they say they will, although they will much rather take somebody that has something, because the truth of the matter is, they are getting a little tired of Eddie Yokum, as he is strictly a non-producer at this time, and they have to sustain him as he goes along, and the only reason they do this is they feel sorry for him, and The Seldom Seen Kid and Hot Horse Herbie and Big Reds are noted for their kind hearts.

The Seldom Seen Kid is especially sorry for Eddie Yokum, because he knows of Eddie's love for Miss Phyllis Richie, as Eddie confides same to The Seldom Seen Kid one evening, and as The Seldom Seen often carries the old torch himself, he knows how it feels.

But he is wishing Eddie Yokum will get a job and forget Miss Phyllis Richie, as The Seldom Seen Kid regards it as a hopeless passion, especially as he reads in a paper that Miss Phyllis Richie is planning to go abroad with a party that will include Mr. Marshall Preston immediately after the race for the Gold Vase, although The Seldom Seen Kid does not show this item to Eddie Yokum.

Well, the day of the Gold Vase Steeplechase is always a great day at Belmont Park, as it brings together all the greatest steeplechasers in the country, and the best riders, including gentleman jocks and professionals, and the finest society crowd, and Eddie Yokum is quite bewildered by what he sees and hears as he wanders around and about, although he cannot help a feeling of loathing that all this is over horses.

He looks around for Miss Phyllis Richie, and asks The Seldom Seen Kid where she is apt to be at such a place as a race-track, and The Seldom Seen says the chances are she will be out under the trees behind the grandstand where the horses are walked around and saddled not long before the big race, to take a peek at her horse, and furthermore The Seldom Seen Kid says:

'I only wish you are on speaking terms with her, at that,' he says. 'There is a rumour that Miss Phyllis Richie's nigger jockey, Roy Snakes, is off on a bender, or something to this effect. Anyway, they say he is missing, and if they cannot find him, or get another jig jock, they will have to scratch Follow You, because no white guy alive can ride Follow You in a race.

'Now,' The Seldom Seen Kid goes on, 'I hear there is not another coon steeplechaser in these parts just now, and if you can find out if Roy Snakes is really absent, I can get a fair price on Sweep Forward. With Follow You out, he is a triple-plated pipe. It will really be quite a favour to me, and some of my customers if you can secure this information for me before the rush sets in.'

Well, Eddie Yokum does not understand what this is all about, but he does get the idea that Miss Phyllis Richie may be in some sort of predicament, so he goes out under the trees behind the grandstand, and waits around there awhile, and sure enough he finally sees Miss Phyllis Richie standing under a tree around which an old guy by the name of Ike is leading a big chestnut horse, and there is a large ring of guys and dolls around the tree looking at the horse, and furthermore he sees that Miss Phyllis Richie's eyes are all red and swollen as if she is weeping.

Now at this spectacle, Eddie Yokum's heart goes out to Miss Phyllis Richie, and he will walk right up to her as bold as a lion if he is not afraid of the horse, so he waits awhile longer, and pretty soon Miss Phyllis Richie leaves the group and goes across the grass to the jockey-house, and what Miss Phyllis Richie is going to the jockey-house for is to ask if Roy Snakes shows up, or if they find another darky jockey for her.

But it seems the answer is no both ways, and Miss Phyllis Richie is turning away looking most despondent when Eddie Yokum steps up to her and speaks to her as follows:

'Miss Richie,' Eddie says, 'if there is anything I can do to help you out in this situation, kindly so state. I know you despise me,' he says, 'but I will gladly lay down my life for you.'

Well, at this, Miss Phyllis Richie stops and gazes at him awhile, and there is great sarcasm in her voice when she finally says:

'Why, the last time I see you, you are coloured. It is a pity you are not the same way now, or you might take Roy Snakes' place in this race. Good-day to you, Mr. Burglar, or I will call a Pinkerton.'

She turns away, and goes back to where the old guy is walking the horse around, and Eddie Yokum follows her at a distance, but gets up in time to hear her telling Ike it is no use waiting on Roy Snakes, or anybody else, and to go ahead and declare Follow You out of the Gold Vase Steeplechase.

Then she disappears in the crowd, but Eddie Yokum can see that she is very sad, and he is sad himself, and he gets to talking to Ike, and he asks him what about a guy blacking himself up and fooling Follow You into thinking he is a smoke, and Ike says it is undoubtedly a great idea.

'In fact,' Ike says, 'if I am younger, I will do it myself, just to save Miss Phyllis Richie, because I hear if she does not win this stake, she is going to marry Mr. Marshall Preston, and this is a sad fate for a young doll, to be sure. Between you and me, Mr. Marshall Preston is far from being all right.'

Well, at this news, Eddie Yokum becomes greatly agitated, and he tells Ike to get him some cork, and he will ride Follow You, and old Ike is so delighted that he does not bother to ask Eddie Yokum if he is a good rider. He leaves Follow You in charge of a stable boy, and takes Eddie Yokum over to the secretary's office and announces him as a gentleman jockey from Delaware, who is willing to help Miss Phyllis Richie out of her predicament about a jockey, and when they suggest that Eddie Yokum seems to be as white as any of the other white guys who try to ride Follow You and fail, and Ike says Eddie is going to ride blackface, there is quite a looking up of the rules.

But there is nothing in the rules against such a thing, although an old guy in the office with a big white mouser says it seems quite irregular, and that he does not recall a similar case in fifty years of experience. However, he says the office is willing to establish a precedent in the case of such a great horse as Follow You, though he cannot figure what on earth becomes of Roy Snakes, or why the only other two coloured steeplechase jockeys in the East, Washington and Lincoln, find it necessary to go to Aiken two days before this race.

He is still muttering about the matter when Ike takes Eddie Yokum to the jockey-house, and then Ike sends in to Frank Stevens' bar in the clubhouse and buys several bottles of liquor to get corks for Eddie to burn and black up with, although Ike personally drinks all the liquor himself.

Well, all the time Eddie Yokum is blacking up, he is saying every prayer he knows that Roy Snakes, or one of the other dinge jockeys appears to ride Follow You, but no such thing happens, and by and by Eddie is out in the Richie colours, and is as black as anything, and maybe blacker, and while Follow You gives him quite a snuffing over when Eddie approaches him, the horse seems satisfied he is dealing with a smoke, and afterwards some people claim this is a knock to the way Eddie smells.

No one will ever know what Eddie Yokum suffers when he is hoisted up on Follow You, and there is considerable criticism of his riding technique, as he does not seem to be sure which is the front end and which is the back end of a horse.

But by this time, Eddie is determined to go through with this proposition if he gets killed, and it looks as if he will, at that, although it does not look as if he will get killed any sooner than the Honourable Bertie Searles, who arrives at the course slightly mulled, and who insists on practising a few tricks he once observes at a rodeo in England, when the horses are going to the post, because the Honourable Bertie Searles thinks Miss Lola Ledare is in the grandstand watching him, and he warns her to be sure and take note of his fancy riding.

Now, the Honourable Bertie Searles is riding along next to Eddie Yokum, and he seems such a good-natured sort of guy that Eddie figures it may not be a bad idea to get a little advice from him, so he asks the Honourable Bertie Searles what are the rules of such a race, and what is the best thing for a guy who does not know much about it to do; and while the Honourable Bertie Searles is somewhat surprised at the question, especially from a smudge rider, he answers as follows:

'Why,' he says, 'all you do is to try and keep going. If you fall off your horse, do not worry, but just get back on again, and take the jump all over and keep going, unless your neck is broken. Personally, I generally let my horse, Trafalgar, do the thinking for me in a race, because Trafalgar is quite a thinker, and maybe your horse is a thinker, too. But,' he says, 'keep going.'

The most astonished guy around at seeing Eddie Yokum on Follow You is undoubtedly Mr. Marshall Preston, who is riding his horse Sweep Forward, but he is no more astonished than Miss Phyllis Richie, who is sitting in a box in the grandstand with a party of friends from Baltimore, Md., and who is still weeping, thinking her horse is out of the race.

She stops weeping when she sees her colours on the track, and looks at the jockey-board to see who is riding her horse, but the name E. Yokum on the board means nothing to her, as she never hears Eddie's real name before, and she does not recognize him at first, and figures he is some new coloured jockey old Ike digs up at the last minute.

The horse players on the lawn and the bookies under the stand are also somewhat astonished, because there nobody ever hears of E. Yokum before, either, except maybe The Seldom Seen Kid, and Hot Horse Herbie, and Big Reds, and even they do not know Eddie in his make-up until they run down to the rail to watch the post parade, and Eddie Yokum tips them a large wink, although the reason Eddie tips them this wink is to squeeze a large tear out of his eye, because Eddie is so alarmed he is half crying, and only love sustains him in the saddle.

Well, when The Seldom Seen Kid and Hot Horse Herbie and Big Reds see who is on Follow You, and see Eddie's wink, they figure that there must be something very special doing in this race, and they start running around everywhere, hoping they may be able to raise a few bobs to bet on Follow You, but of course nobody is going to let them have a few bobs for any purpose, and they are greatly discouraged about the matter, when who do they run into but Miss Lola Ledare, who is not in the grandstand at all, as the Honourable Bertie Searles thinks, but is standing on the edge of the betting ring with some large coarse banknotes in her hand.

Naturally, when they see Miss Lola Ledare in possession of funds, they are greatly interested, and they surround her and ask her what seems to be troubling her, and Miss Lola Ledare speaks freely to them, as she is not aware of any coolness between them and her fiancée, Philly the Weeper, and what she speaks is as follows:

'Why,' she says, 'they do not allow ladies in the betting ring, and I am waiting here for some one to come along and bet this money for me on Sweep Forward, so your arrival is most timely. The bet is for Philly. He raises this money on some old family heirlooms that I never know he possesses, and he requests me to place it for him. Personally,' she says, 'I think the Honourable Bertie Searles will win this race on Trafalgar, because he tells me so himself, and I have half a notion to bet some of the money on him, only I am afraid of what Philly will say if Trafalgar does not come in.'

Well, The Seldom Seen Kid takes the dough out of Miss Lola Ledare's hand, and says to her like this:

'Lola,' he says, 'it will be a privilege and a pleasure for me to do Philly the service of betting this money for him – and by the way, where is Philly?'

'Why,' Lola says, 'he asks me not to mention to anybody that he is present, but I know he will not mind you knowing. He is sitting away up in one corner of the grandstand all by himself. To tell the truth, Philly has become somewhat solitary of late, and I am commencing to get somewhat displeased with him, because I like sociable guys, like the Honourable Bertie Searles.'

Well, The Seldom Seen Kid is somewhat surprised to find that he takes ten large C's off of Miss Lola Ledare, because he does not know there is this much money in the world, and he hurries into the ring and bets it all on Follow You and gets 6 to 5 for the money, as Follow You is favourite, even with somebody by the name of E. Yokum up, which shows what the public thinks of the horse, although with Roy Snakes riding, the price will be 7 to 10.

There is a ton of money for Sweep Forward at the last minute, and some very, very smart guys are betting on him, and further-more there is a rumour that Sweep Forward has help in the race, which is a way of saying that some of the others will be trying to assist Sweep Forward to win, and there is also a rumour that Follow You is a stiff in the race, and this is why Roy Snakes is not riding; but one thing about a race-track, you can always hear any-thing, and the public sticks to Follow You, no matter what.

There are ten other horses in the Gold Vase, and there is money for all of them, including Trafalgar, although Trafalgar is 15 to 1, as nobody seems to care for the way the Honourable Bertie Searles is riding the horse going to the post, what with the Honourable Bertie Searles doing handstands in the saddle, and otherwise carrying on.

Now the Gold Vase Steeplechase is a race of about three miles, or about two and a half times around the course, and the horses have to make about nineteen jumps over hedges and a water jump, and everybody that knows about these matters will tell you that this is the toughest race in this country, especially with a big field of starters, and many things can happen in the race, includ-ing death. In fact, a steeplechaser rider is regarded as a very poor risk, indeed, by all insurance companies, although it is perhaps just as well that Eddie Yokum does not know this as he goes to the post.

But Eddie is smart enough to remember what the Honourable Bertie Searles tells him about letting the horse do the thinking, and it happens that Follow You is quite a thinker, indeed, and very experienced, so when the starter tells them to come on, Eddie just hangs on to Follow You's mane and lets him do as he feels best, and Follow You feels that it is best to go right to the front.

At least Eddie Yokum hangs on to Follow You's mane until the horse hits the first jump, when Mr. Marshall Preston, on Sweep Forward, comes out of the pack with a rush, and yells look out, and Eddie is looking out as Follow You jumps with Sweep Forward, and Eddie lets go the mane so he can look out better, and the next thing Eddie knows he is on the grass, and the rest of the field is going past him, and Follow You is standing there looking greatly surprised.

Well, there is a groan from the grandstand, for here is the public choice apparently out of the race before it really starts, but Eddie suddenly remembers what the Honourable Bertie Searles tells him about keeping going, and taking all the jumps, so he gets on his feet, and backs Follow You up against the fence and climbs on him and sends him at the jump again, and this time Eddie does not forget to hang on to the horse's mane.

But all this takes up some time, and the rest of the field is anyway half a mile ahead, but three horses go down at the second jump, and two more at the third, and at both these jumps, Eddie Yokum falls off Follow You as the horse is jumping, and the public is commencing to marvel about Follow You making every jump twice, and wondering if it is a handicap he is giving the others, or what.

Sweep Forward is out in front going easy, and fencing like a bird, with Mr. Marshall Preston looking very graceful in the saddle, and who is laying right close to him all the time but the Honourable Bertie Searles, on Trafalgar. The rest are strung out all along the course, and it looks like a parade more than anything else.

Well, the real tough jump on the course is the water jump in front of the grandstand, and they take this jump twice during the race, and the first time Eddie Yokum falls off Follow You into the water he is so long coming up that many customers think maybe he is drowned, and most of them hope he is, at that.

But one thing about Follow You, he never runs away when he loses his rider, but stands perfectly still until Eddie is on his back again, although Follow You is commencing to look very pained, especially when it appears to be a sure thing that he will be lapped by Sweep Forward and Trafalgar, anyway, before the race is over.

However, other horses keep going down at the various jumps, and at the end of the second mile, only Sweep Forward and Trafalgar, and a horse that is called Great Shakes, with a professional jockey by the name of Smithers up, and Follow You are left in the race, although of course you cannot say Follow You is really in the race because he is now almost a full mile to the rear, and Miss Phyllis Richie faints three different times in the grandstand, once out of dismay, and twice out of vexation.

It seems that Miss Phyllis Richie does not recognize Eddie Yokum even yet, but she can see that the guy on her horse does not have any great knack for riding, and she is annoyed no little, especially as everybody on the premises is now uniting in a Bronx cheer for Follow You and his jockey.

The way Eddie Yokum is riding Follow You when he is not falling off is really something remarkable, as he is all over the horse, and sometimes halfway under him, and when the Honourable Bertie Searles sees this exhibition, he gets sored up, because he figures Eddie is trying to show him up as a trick rider, although of course Eddie has no such idea whatever.

Now Trafalgar is never more than two lengths off Sweep Forward at any stage of the race, and anybody can see that the Honourable Bertie Searles has a great horse under him, and in fact it looks as if he can go to the front whenever he is ready, and when Great Shakes falls with Smithers at about the fourteenth jump, it is strictly a two-horse race, because by this time Eddie Yokum is in the water jump again, and, anyway, Follow You is getting pretty much fagged out, because the way the race figures, Follow You does twice as much work as any of the other horses, and he is carrying top weight of 175 pounds, at that, counting Eddie's 150 and the lead in his saddle slots.

In fact, Follow You is so fagged out that he is just able to jog along, and the jumps in the last mile are as tough for him as they are for Eddie, and in fact once when Eddie is stretched out on the grass after a jump, it looks as if Follow You wishes to lay down beside him.

Well, in the meantime, Mr. Marshall Preston on Sweep Forward and the Honourable Bertie Searles on Trafalgar, are tearing for the last jump neck and neck, because the Honourable Bertie Searles now makes his serious challenge, and the crowd is up and yelling and nobody even thinks of Eddie Yokum and Follow You plugging along away back yonder, except maybe Miss Phyllis Richie.

Sweep Forward and Trafalgar take off for the final jump just like a team, and as Trafalgar jumps, Mr. Marshall Preston gives him a smack across the nose with his riding bat, which upsets Trafalgar no little, and in fact causes him to stumble and fall as he clears the jump, but not before the Honourable Bertie Searles can reach out almost in mid-air and tweak Mr. Marshall Preston's saddle pad in such a way that Sweep Forward falls, too, because naturally the Honourable Bertie Searles is slightly irked by Mr. Marshall Preston playing such a dirty trick on Trafalgar.

Well, Mr. Marshall Preston lets out a loud cry as Sweep Forward falls, because Mr. Marshall Preston finds himself pinned down under the horse with a broken leg, and he is in great pain at once, and while the Honourable Bertie Searles is not hurt, Trafalgar gets up and runs off so fast there is no chance that the Honourable Bertie Searles can catch him, and by and by along the course comes Eddie Yokum on Follow You, the only horse left in the race, with one jump to go.

Well, the Honourable Bertie Searles runs up the course, somewhat excited, and begins coaching Eddie Yokum, telling him to take it easy, and to bear a little to the left going over the jump to keep from landing on Mr. Marshall Preston and Sweep Forward, and Eddie tries to do as he is told, but Follow You is now a mighty weary horse, and for the first time in years he falls taking a hurdle, and Eddie finds himself on the turf alongside Mr. Marshall Preston, who stops groaning long enough to look at Eddie Yokum in great surprise, and to speak to him as follows:

'I am dying,' Mr. Marshall Preston says. 'Tell Miss Phyllis Richie that with my last breath I ask her forgiveness for getting Philly the Weeper to slug her jockey, Roy Snakes, and put him out of business. She will find him in Harlem. Tell her I am also sorry I put Washington and Lincoln, the only other jig jocks around, under contract and send them away, but it is necessary for me to win this stake and enough in bets to pay my wife in South Dakota some back alimony I owe her.'

And with this, Mr. Marshall Preston closes his eyes and starts groaning again, and Eddie Yokum remembers about the race, especially as the Honourable Bertie Searles is calling on him to get up, and be a man, and keep going, so Eddie gets up and starts looking around for Follow You, but Follow You is now standing with his head hanging down, and when Eddie climbs on him again, Follow You does not seem inclined for any further action, especially in the way of making another jump.

Well, here is a predicament, to be sure, and as Eddie has no previous experience with balky horses, he scarcely knows what to do, especially as Follow You will not respond to kind words, or to kicks in the stomach, which are advised by the Honourable Bertie Searles, and in fact what does Follow You do but sit down there in the middle of the course, and Eddie slides right off his tail.

Then Eddie runs around in front of Follow You to argue with him face to face, and maybe give him a good yanking by the head, and for the first time since the race starts, Follow You gets a good look at who is riding him, and it seems that between the perspiration that is running down Eddie's face, from his efforts, and falling into the water jump a couple of times, he is now no longer a boogie, but mostly white, and Follow You is not only startled but greatly insulted.

He starts scrambling to his feet at once, and Eddie Yokum is just barely able to climb back on the horse by his mane before Follow You starts running, taking the last jump again in wonderful shape, and then tearing on down the home stretch to finish inside the time limit as the winner of the race, and all that keeps Follow You from continuing on around the course again is the fact that Eddie falls off of him plumb exhausted.

Well, the excitement over this is very great, as Follow You's victory saves the public's money, and they take Follow You to the judge's stand, and put a blanket of roses on him, and Eddie Yokum is also there, holding himself up by leaning against old Ike, when Miss Phyllis Richie comes running up and starts kissing the rest of the burnt cork off of Eddie's face right in front of everybody, and speaking to him as follows:

'Oh,' she says, 'I recognize you when you come out of the water jump the last time, and I say to myself, then and there, I know he will win, because I remember your wonderful ride at the fox hunt. I love you,' she says.

Naturally, Eddie Yokum tells Miss Phyllis Richie that her love is reciprocated, and he does not mention to her that the ride she speaks of at the fox hunt is negotiated on a motor-cycle, because at this time there is further excitement, as it seems The Seldom Seen Kid and Hot Horse Herbie and Big Reds find Philly the Weeper up in the grandstand, and take him out back and give him quite a going over for beating them out of their end of the reward money he collects for the fox hounds, and also remove from his person a batch of pawn-tickets for the jewellery and other valuables he collects at the Oriole Hunts Club and converts into cash to bet on Sweep Forward.

Philly the Weeper says Mr. Marshall Preston permits him to keep the jewellery on condition he leaves a few articles in Eddie Yokum's room, after making a business deal with Philly the Weeper to take care of Roy Snakes in return for Mr. Marshall Preston's kindness in not turning him over to the police when he finds him collecting the knick-knacks.

'Mr. Marshall Preston is a hard guy,' Philly the Weeper says. 'He tells me he starts out making love to Miss Phyllis Richie only with the idea of conning her into withdrawing Follow You from this race, so he can put over a big betting coup. But her having to have a ziggaboo jock makes it easier for him. But only a very hard guy will attempt to use love for such a base purpose,' Philly the Weeper says. 'Can you imagine me trifling with the love of Miss Lola Ledare in such a fashion?'

But Miss Lola Ledare says she is not going to give such a scalawag as Philly the Weeper a chance to trifle with her love any more, anyway, as she is much fonder of the Honourable Bertie Searles; and The Seldom Seen Kid turns the pawn-tickets he takes off Philly the Weeper over to Eddie Yokum, along with ten C's to remove the articles from hock, although he does not mention the sum of money he wins on Follow You with the ten C's.

It comes out that Mr. Marshall Preston is not too badly hurt, after all, so everybody is happy all the way around; but naturally Eddie Yokum is happiest of all, and he is standing around after the races mentioning his happiness to Miss Phyllis Richie, when all of a sudden he is seen to turn quite pale, and out of a clear sky, and as tired as he is, he starts running, and a large guy is observed running after him.

It is some hours before Miss Phyllis Richie sees Eddie Yokum to kiss him again, and to inquire why he seems to be trying to avoid one of her oldest and dearest Baltimore friends, Mr. Barker.

A Story Goes With It

O   NE night I am in a gambling joint in Miami watching the
     crap game and thinking what a nice thing it is, indeed, to
     be able to shoot craps without having to worry about
losing your potatoes.

Many of the high shots from New York and Detroit and St.
Louis and other cities are around the table, and there is quite
some action in spite of the hard times. In fact, there is so much
action that a guy with only a few bobs on him, such as me, will be
considered very impolite to be pushing into this game, because
they are packed in very tight around the table.

I am maybe three guys back from the table, and I am watching the game by standing on tiptoe peeking over their shoulders,
and all I can hear is Goldie, the stick man, hollering money-
money-money every time some guy makes a number, so I can see
the dice are very warm indeed, and that the right betters are
doing first-rate.

By and by a guy by the name of Guinea Joe, out of Trenton,
picks up the dice and starts making numbers right and left, and
I know enough about this Guinea Joe to know that when he starts
making numbers anybody will be very foolish indeed not to

follow his hand, although personally I am generally a wrong better against the dice, if I bet at all.

Now all I have in my pocket is a sawbuck, and the hotel stakes are coming up on me the next day, and I need this saw, but with Guinea Joe hotter than a forty-five it will be overlooking a big opportunity not to go along with him, so when he comes out on an eight, which is a very easy number for Joe to make when he is hot, I dig up my sawbuck, and slide it past the three guys in front of me to the table, and I say to Lefty Park, who is laying against the dice, as follows:

'I will take the odds, Lefty.'

Well, Lefty looks at my sawbuck and nods his head, for Lefty is not such a guy as will refuse any bet, even though it is as modest as mine, and right away Goldie yells money-money-money, so there I am with twenty-two dollars.

Next Guinea Joe comes out on a nine, and naturally I take thirty to twenty for my sugar, because nine is nothing for Joe to make when he is hot. He makes the nine just as I figure, and I take two to one for my half a yard when he starts looking for a ten, and when he makes the ten I am right up against the table, because I am now a guy with means.

Well, the upshot of the whole business is that I finally find myself with three hundred bucks, and when it looks as if the dice are cooling off, I take out and back off from the table, and while I am backing off I am trying to look like a guy who loses all his potatoes, because there are always many wolves waiting around crap games and one thing and another in Miami this season, and what they are waiting for is to put the bite on anybody who happens to make a little scratch.

In fact, nobody can remember when the bite is as painful as it is in Miami this season, what with the unemployment situation among many citizens who come to Miami expecting to find work in the gambling joints, or around the race track. But almost as soon as these citizens arrive, the gambling joints are all turned off, except in spots, and the bookmakers are chased off the track and the mutuels put in, and the consequences are the suffering is most intense. It is not only intense among the visiting citizens, but it is quite intense among the Miami landlords, because naturally if a citizen is not working, nobody can expect him to pay any room rent, but the Miami landlords do not seem to understand this situation, and are very unreasonable about their room rent.

Anyway, I back through quite a crowd without anybody biting me, and I am commencing to figure I may escape altogether and get to my hotel and hide my dough before the news gets around that I win about five G's, which is what my winning is sure to amount to by the time the rumour reaches all quarters of the city.

Then, just as I am thinking I am safe, I find I am looking a guy by the name of Hot Horse Herbie in the face, and I can tell from Hot Horse Herbie's expression that he is standing there watching me for some time, so there is no use in telling him I am washed out in the game. In fact, I cannot think of much of anything to tell Hot Horse Herbie that may keep him from putting the bite on me for at least a few bobs, and I am greatly astonished when he does not offer to bite me at all, but says to me like this:

'Well,' he says, 'I am certainly glad to see you make such a nice score. I will be looking for you to-morrow at the track, and will have some big news for you.'

Then he walks away from me and I stand there with my mouth open looking at him, as it is certainly a most unusual way for Herbie to act. It is the first time I ever knew Herbie to walk away from a chance to bite somebody, and I can scarcely understand such actions, for Herbie is such a guy as will not miss a bite, even if he does not need it.

He is a tall, thin guy, with a sad face and a long chin, and he is called Hot Horse Herbie because he nearly always has a very hot horse to tell you about. He nearly always has a horse that is so hot it is fairly smoking, a hot horse being a horse that cannot possibly lose a race unless it falls down dead, and while Herbie's hot horses often lose without falling down dead, this does not keep Herbie from coming up with others just as hot.

In fact, Hot Horse Herbie is what is called a hustler around the race tracks, and his business is to learn about these hot horses, or even just suspect about them, and then get somebody to bet on them, which is a very legitimate business indeed, as Herbie only collects a commission if the hot horses win, and if they do not win Herbie just keeps out of sight awhile from whoever he gets to bet on the hot horses. There are very few guys in this world who can keep out of sight better than Hot Horse Herbie, and especially from old Cap Duhaine, of the Pinkertons, who is always around pouring cold water on hot horses.

In fact, Cap Duhaine, of the Pinkertons, claims that guys such as Hot Horse Herbie are nothing but touts, and sometimes he heaves them off the race track altogether, but of course Cap Duhaine is a very unsentimental old guy and cannot see how such characters as Hot Horse Herbie add to the romance of the turf.

Anyway, I escape from the gambling joint with all my scratch on me, and hurry to my room and lock myself in for the night, and I do not show up in public until along about noon the next day, when it is time to go over to the coffee shop for my java. And of course by this time the news of my score is all over town, and many guys are taking dead aim at me.

But naturally I am now able to explain to them that I have to wire most of the three yards I win to Nebraska to save my father's farm from being seized by the sheriff, and while everybody knows I do not have a father, and that if I do have a father I will not be sending him money for such a thing as saving his farm, with times what they are in Miami, nobody is impolite enough to doubt my word except a guy by the name of Pottsville Legs, who wishes to see my receipts from the telegraph office when I explain to him why I cannot stake him to a double sawbuck.

I do not see Hot Horse Herbie until I get to the track, and he is waiting for me right inside the grand-stand gate, and as soon as I show up he motions me off to one side and says to me like this:

'Now,' Herbie says, 'I am very smart indeed about a certain race to-day. In fact,' he says, 'if any guy knowing what I know does not bet all he can rake and scrape together on a certain horse, such a guy ought to cut his own throat and get himself out of the way forever. What I know,' Herbie says, 'is enough to shake the foundations of this country if it gets out. Do not ask any questions,' he says, 'but get ready to bet all the sugar you win last night on this horse I am going to mention to you, and all I ask you in return is to bet fifty on me. And,' Herbie says, 'kindly do not tell me you leave your money in your other pants, because I know you do not have any other pants.'

'Now, Herbie,' I say, 'I do not doubt your information, because I know you will not give out information unless it is well founded. But,' I say, 'I seldom stand for a tip, and as for betting fifty for you, you know I will not bet fifty even for myself if somebody guarantees me a winner. So I thank you, Herbie, just the same,' I say, 'but I must do without your tip,' and with this I start walking away.

'Now,' Herbie says, 'wait a minute. A story goes with it,' he says.

Well, of course this is a different matter entirely. I am such a guy as will always listen to a tip on a horse if a story goes with the tip. In fact, I will not give you a nickel for a tip without a story, but it must be a first-class story, and most horse players are the same way. In fact, there are very few horse players who will not listen to a tip if a story goes with it, for this is the way human nature is. So I turn and walk back to Hot Horse Herbie, and say to him like this:

'Well,' I say, 'let me hear the story, Herbie.'

'Now,' Herbie says, dropping his voice away down low, in case old Cap Duhaine may be around somewhere listening, 'it is the third race, and the horse is a horse by the name of Never Despair. It is a boat race,' Herbie says. 'They are going to shoo in Never Despair. Everything else in the race is a cooler,' he says.

[145]

'Well,' I say, 'this is just an idea, Herbie, and not a story.'

'Wait a minute,' Herbie says. 'The story that goes with it is a very strange story indeed. In fact,' he says, 'it is such a story as I can scarcely believe myself, and I will generally believe almost any story, including,' he says, 'the ones I make up out of my own head. Anyway, the story is as follows:

'Never Despair is owned by an old guy by the name of Seed Mercer,' Herbie says. 'Maybe you remember seeing him around. He always wears a black slouch hat and grey whiskers,' Herbie says, 'and he is maybe a hundred years old, and his horses are very terrible horses indeed. In fact,' Herbie says, 'I do not remember seeing any more terrible horses in all the years I am around the track, and,' Herbie says, 'I wish to say I see some very terrible horses indeed.

'Now,' Herbie says, 'old Mercer has a grand-daughter who is maybe sixteen years old, come next grass, by the name of Lame Louise, and she is called Lame Louise because she is all crippled up from childhood by infantile what-is-this, and can scarcely navigate, and,' Herbie says, 'her being crippled up in such a way makes old Mercer feel very sad, for she is all he has in the world, except these terrible horses.'

'It is a very long story, Herbie,' I say, 'and I wish to see Moe Shapoff about a very good thing in the first race.'

'Never mind Moe Shapoff,' Herbie says. 'He will only tell you about a bum by the name of Zachary in the first race, and Zachary has no chance whatever. I make Your John a stand-out in the first,' he says.

'Well,' I say, 'let us forget the first and get on with your story, although it is commencing to sound all mixed up to me.'

'Now,' Herbie says, 'it not only makes old man Mercer very sad because Lame Louise is all crippled up, but,' he says, 'it makes many of the jockeys and other guys around the race track very sad, because,' he says, 'they know Lame Louise since she is so high, and she always has a smile for them, and especially for Jockey Scroon. In fact,' Herbie says, 'Jockey Scroon is even more

sad about Lame Louise than old man Mercer, because Jockey
Scroon loves Lame Louise.'

'Why,' I say, very indignant, 'Jockey Scroon is nothing but a
little burglar. Why,' I say, 'I see Jockey Scroon do things to horses
I bet on that he will have to answer for on the Judgment Day, if
there is any justice at such a time. Why,' I say, 'Jockey Scroon is
nothing but a Gerald Chapman in his heart, and so are all other
jockeys.'

'Yes,' Hot Horse Herbie says, 'what you say is very, very true,
and I am personally in favour of the electric chair for all jockeys,
but,' he says, 'Jockey Scroon loves Lame Louise just the same,
and is figuring on making her his ever-loving wife when he gets
a few bobs together, which,' Herbie says, 'makes Louise eight
to five in my line to be an old maid. Jockey Scroon rooms with
me downtown,' Herbie says, 'and he speaks freely to me about
his love for Louise. Furthermore,' Herbie says, 'Jockie Scroon
is personally not a bad little guy, at that, although of course
being a jockey he is sometimes greatly misunderstood by the
public.

'Anyway,' Hot Horse Herbie says, 'I happen to go home early
last night before I see you at the gambling joint, and I hear voices
coming out of my room, and naturally I pause outside the door
to listen, because for all I know it may be the landlord speaking
about the room rent, although,' Herbie says, 'I do not figure my
landlord to be much-worried at this time because I see him sneak
into my room a few days before and take a lift at my trunk to
make sure I have belongings in the same, and it happens I nail
the trunk to the floor beforehand, so not being able to lift it, the
landlord is bound to figure me a guy with property.

'These voices,' Herbie says, 'are mainly soprano voices, and at
first I think Jockey Scroon is in there with some dolls, which is by
no means permissible in my hotel, but, after listening awhile, I
discover they are the voices of young boys, and I make out that
these boys are nothing but jockeys, and they are the six jockeys
who are riding in the third race, and they are fixing up this race

to be a boat race, and to shoo in Never Despair, which Jockey
Scroon is riding.

'And,' Hot Horse Herbie says, 'the reason they are fixing up
this boat race is the strangest part of the story. It seems,' he says,
'that Jockey Scroon hears old man Mercer talking about a great
surgeon from Europe who is a shark on patching up cripples such
as Lame Louise, and who just arrives at Palm Beach to spend the
winter, and old man Mercer is saying how he wishes he has dough
enough to take Lame Louise to this guy so he can operate on her,
and maybe make her walk good again.

'But of course,' Herbie says, 'it is well known to one and all that
old man Mercer does not have a quarter, and that he has no way
of getting a quarter unless one of his terrible horses accidentally
wins a purse. So,' Herbie says, 'it seems these jockeys get to
talking it over among themselves, and they figure it will be a nice
thing to let old man Mercer win a purse such as the thousand
bucks that goes with the third race to-day, so he can take Lame
Louise to Palm Beach, and now you have a rough idea of what is
coming off.

'Furthermore,' Herbie says, 'these jockeys wind up their
meeting by taking a big oath among themselves that they will not
tell a living soul what is doing so nobody will bet on Never
Despair, because,' he says, 'these little guys are smart enough to
see if there is any betting on such a horse there may be a very
large squawk afterwards. And,' he says, 'I judge they keep their
oath because Never Despair is twenty to one in the morning line,
and I do not hear a whisper about him, and you have the tip all
to yourself.'

'Well,' I say, 'so what?' For this story is now commencing to
make me a little tired, especially as I hear the bell for the first
race, and I must see Moe Shapoff.

'Why,' Hot Horse Herbie says, 'so you bet every nickel you can
rake and scrape together on Never Despair, including the twenty
you are to bet for me for giving you this tip and the story that goes
with it.'

'Herbie,' I say, 'it is a very interesting story indeed, and also very sad, but,' I say, 'I am sorry it is about a horse Jockey Scroon is to ride, because I do not think I will ever bet on anything Jockey Scroon rides if they pay off in advance. And,' I say, 'I am certainly not going to bet twenty for you or anybody else.'

'Well,' Hot Horse Herbie says, 'I will compromise with you for a pound note, because I must have something going for me on this boat race.'

So I give Herbie a fiver, and the chances are this is about as strong as he figures from the start, and I forget all about his tip and the story that goes with it, because while I enjoy a story with a tip, I feel that Herbie overdoes this one.

Anyway, no handicapper alive can make Never Despair win the third race off the form, because this race is at six furlongs, and there is a barrel of speed in it, and anybody can see that old man Mercer's horse is away over his head. In fact, The Dancer tells me that any one of the other five horses in this race can beat Never Despair doing anything from playing hockey to putting the shot, and everybody else must think the same thing because Never Despair goes to forty to one.

Personally, I like a horse by the name of Loose Living, which is a horse owned by a guy by the name of Bill Howard, and I hear Bill Howard is betting plenty away on his horse, and any time Bill Howard is betting away on his horse a guy will be out of his mind not to bet on this horse, too, as Bill Howard is very smart indeed. Loose Living is two to one in the first line, but by and by I judge the money Bill Howard bets away commences to come back to the track, and Loose Living winds up seven to ten, and while I am generally not a seven-to-ten guy, I can see that here is a proposition I cannot overlook.

So, naturally, I step up to the mutuel window and invest in Loose Living. In fact, I invest everything I have on me in the way of scratch, amounting to a hundred and ten bucks, which is all I have left after taking myself out of the hotel stakes and giving Hot Horse Herbie the finnif, and listening to what Moe Shapoff has to say about the first race, and also getting beat a snoot in the second.

When I first step up to the window, I have no idea of betting all my scratch on Loose Living, but while waiting in line there I get to thinking what a cinch Loose Living is, and how seldom such an opportunity comes into a guy's life, so I just naturally set it all in.

Well, this is a race which will be remembered by one and all to their dying day, as Loose Living beats the barrier a step, and is two lengths in front before you can say Jack Robinson, with a third by the name of Callipers second by maybe half a length, and with the others bunched except Never Despair, and where is Never Despair but last, where he figures.

Now any time Loose Living busts on top there is no need worrying any more about him, and I am thinking I better get in line at the pay-off window right away, so I will not have to wait long to collect my sugar. But I figure I may as well stay and watch the race, although personally I am never much interested in watching races. I am interested only in how a race comes out.

As the horses hit the turn into the stretch, Loose Living is just breezing, and anybody can see that he is going to laugh his way home from there. Callipers is still second, and a thing called Goose Pimples is third, and I am surprised to see that Never Despair now struggles up to fourth with Jockey Scroon belting away at him with his bat quite earnestly. Furthermore, Never Despair seems to be running very fast, though afterwards I figure this may be because the others are commencing to run very slow.

Anyway, a very strange spectacle now takes place in the stretch, as all of a sudden Loose Living seems to be stopping, as if he is waiting for a street cab, and what is all the more remarkable Callipers and Goose Pimples also seem to be hanging back, and the next thing anybody knows, here comes Jockey Scroon on Never Despair sneaking through on the rail, and personally it looks to me as if the jock on Callipers moves over to give Jockey Scroon plenty of elbow room, but of course the jock on Callipers may figure Jockey Scroon has diphtheria, and does not wish to catch it.

Loose Living is out in the middle of the track, anyway, so he does not have to move over. All Loose Living has to do is to keep on running backwards as he seems to be doing from the top of the stretch, to let Jockey Scroon go past on Never Despair to win the heat by a length.

Well, the race is practically supernatural in many respects, and the judges are all upset over it, and they haul all the jocks up in the stand and ask them many questions, and not being altogether satisfied with the answers, they ask these questions over several times. But all the jocks will say is that Never Despair sneaks past them very unexpectedly indeed, while Jockey Scroon, who is a pretty fresh duck at that, wishes to know if he is supposed to blow a horn when he is slipping through a lot of guys sound asleep.

But the judges are still not satisfied, so they go prowling around investigating the betting, because naturally when a boat race comes up there is apt to be some reason for it, such as the betting, but it seems that all the judges find is that one five-dollar win ticket is sold on Never Despair in the mutuels, and they cannot learn of a dime being bet away on the horse. So there is nothing much the judges can do about the proposition, except give the jocks many hard looks, and the jocks are accustomed to hard looks from the judges, anyway.

Personally, I am greatly upset by this business, especially when I see that Never Despair pays $86.34, and for two cents I will go right up in the stand and start hollering copper on these little Jesse Jameses for putting on such a boat race and taking all my hard-earned potatoes away from me, but before I have time to do this, I run into The Dancer, and he tells me that Dedicate in the next race is the surest thing that ever goes to the post, and at five to one, at that. So I have to forget everything while I bustle about to dig up a few bobs to bet on Dedicate, and when Dedicate is beat a whisker, I have to do some more bustling to dig up a few bobs to bet on Vesta in the fifth, and by this time the

[151]

third race is such ancient history that nobody cares what happens in it.

It is nearly a week before I see Hot Horse Herbie again, and I figure he is hiding out on everybody because he has this dough he wins off the fiver I give him, and personally I consider him a guy with no manners not to be kicking back the fin, at least. But before I can mention the fin, Herbie gives me a big hello, and says to me like this:

'Well,' he says, 'I just see Jockey Scroon, and Jockey Scroon just comes back from Palm Beach, and the operation is a big success, and Lame Louise will walk as good as anybody again, and old Mercer is tickled silly. But,' Herbie says, 'do not say anything out loud, because the judges may still be trying to find out what comes off in the race.'

'Herbie,' I say, very serious, 'do you mean to say the story you tell me about Lame Louise, and all this and that, the other day is on the level?'

'Why,' Herbie says, 'certainly it is on the level, and I am sorry to hear you do not take advantage of my information. But,' he says, 'I do not blame you for not believing my story, because it is a very long story for anybody to believe. It is not such a story,' Herbie says, 'as I will tell to anyone if I expect them to believe it. In fact,' he says, 'it is so long a story that I do not have the heart to tell it to anybody else but you, or maybe I will have something running for me on the race.

'But,' Herbie says, 'never mind all this. I will be plenty smart about a race to-morrow. Yes,' Herbie says, 'I will be wiser than a treeful of owls, so be sure and see me if you happen to have any coconuts.'

'There is no danger of me seeing you,' I say, very sad, because I am all sorrowed up to think that the story he tells me is really true. 'Things are very terrible with me at this time,' I say, 'and I am thinking maybe you can hand me back my finnif, because you must do all right for yourself with the fiver you have on Never Despair at such a price.'

Now a very strange look comes over Hot Horse Herbie's face, and he raises his right hand, and says to me like this:

'I hope and trust I drop down dead right here in front of you,' Herbie says, 'if I bet a quarter on the horse. It is true,' he says, 'I am up at the window to buy a ticket on Never Despair, but the guy who is selling the tickets is a friend of mine by the name of Heeby Rosenbloom, and Heeby whispers to me that Big Joe Gompers, the guy who owns Callipers, just bets half a hundred on his horse, and,' Herbie says, 'I know Joe Gompers is such a guy as will not bet half a hundred on anything he does not get a Federal Reserve guarantee with it.

'Anyway,' Herbie says, 'I get to thinking about what a bad jockey this Jockey Scroon is, which is very bad indeed, and,' he says, 'I figure that even if it is a boat race it is no even-money race they can shoo him in, so I buy a ticket on Callipers.'

'Well,' I say, 'somebody buys one five-dollar ticket on Never Despair, and I figure it can be nobody but you.'

'Why,' Hot Horse Herbie says, 'do you not hear about this? Why,' he says, 'Cap Duhaine, of the Pinkertons, traces this ticket and finds it is bought by a guy by the name of Steve Harter, and the way this guy Harter comes to buy it is very astonishing. It seems,' Herbie says, 'that this Harter is a tourist out of Indiana who comes to Miami for the sunshine, and who loses all his dough but six bucks against the faro bank at Hollywood.

'At the same time,' Herbie says, 'the poor guy gets a telegram from his ever-loving doll back in Indiana saying she no longer wishes any part of him.

'Well,' Herbie says, 'between losing his dough and his doll, the poor guy is practically out of his mind, and he figures there is nothing left for him to do but knock himself off.

'So,' Herbie says, 'this Harter spends one of of his six bucks to get to the track, figuring to throw himself under the feet of the horses in the first race and let them kick him to a jelly. But he does not get there until just as the third race is coming up and,' Herbie says, 'he sees this name "Never Despair", and he figures

[153]

it may be a hunch, so he buys himself a ticket with his last fiver. Well, naturally,' Herbie says, 'when Never Despair pops down, the guy forgets about letting the horses kick him to a jelly, and he keeps sending his dough along until he runs nothing but a nubbin into six G's on the day.

'Then,' Herbie says, 'Cap Duhaine finds out that the guy, still thinking of Never Despair, calls his ever-loving doll on the phone, and finds she is very sorry she sends him the wire and that she really loves him more than somewhat, especially,' Herbie says, 'when she finds out about the six G's. And the last anybody hears of the matter, this Harter is on his way home to get married, so Never Despair does quite some good in this wicked old world, after all.

'But,' Herbie says, 'let us forget all this, because to-morrow is another day. To-morrow,' he says, 'I will tell you about a thing that goes in the fourth which is just the same as wheat in the bin. In fact,' Hot Horse Herbie says, 'if it does not win, you can never speak to me again.'

'Well,' I say, as I start to walk away, 'I am not interested in any tip at this time.'

'Now,' Herbie says, 'wait a minute. A story goes with it.'

'Well,' I say, coming back to him, 'let me hear the story.'

Old Em's Kentucky Home

ALL this really begins the April day at the Jamaica race track when an assistant starter by the name of Plumbuff puts a twitch on Itchky Ironhat's fourteen-year-old race mare, Emaleen, who is known to one and all as Em for short.

A twitch is nothing but a rope loop that they wrap around a horse's upper lip and keep twisting with a stick to make the horse stand quiet at the starting gate and while I never have a twitch on my own lip and hope and trust that I never have same, I do not see anything wrong with putting twitches on horses' lips, especially the ones I am betting against as it generally keeps them so busy thinking of how it hurts that they sometimes forget about running.

However, it seems that Itchky Ironhat not only considers a twitch very painful to horses, but he also considers it undignified for such a horse as old Em, because while everybody else regards Em as strictly a porcupine, Itchky thinks she is the best horse in the world and loves her so dearly he cannot bear to see her in pain or made to look undignified. To tell the truth, it is common gossip that Itchky loves old Em more than he loves anything else whatever including his ever-loving wife, Mousie.

[155]

In fact, when Mousie tells him one day that the time comes for a show down and that it is either her or old Em and Itchky says well, he guesses it is old Em, and Mousie packs up on him at once and returns to her trade as an artists' model many citizens who remember Mousie's shape think Itchky makes a bad deal, although some claim that the real reason Itchky decides in favour of Em against Mousie is not so much love as it is that Em never wishes for any large thick sirloin steaks such as Mousie adores.

Anyway, it seems that Itchky always goes to the trouble of personally requesting the assistant starters not to place twitches on Em's lip, even though he knows very well that she is by no means a bargain at the post and that she greatly enjoys nibbling assistant starters' ears off and when Plumbuff ignores his request it vexes Itchky no little.

The night after the race he calls on Plumbuff at his home in Jackson Heights and chides him quite some and he also gives him such a going-over that Plumbuff is compelled to take to his bed slightly indisposed for several weeks.

When the racing officials learn of the incident they call Itchky before them and address him in very severe terms. They ask him if he thinks old Em is Mrs. Man o' War, or what, that he expects great courtesy for her from assistant starters and they say they have half a mind to rule Itchky off the turf for life and old Em along with him. But Itchky states that he only acts in self-defence and that he can produce twenty witnesses who will testify that Plumbuff pulls a blunt instrument on him first.

The chances are Itchky can produce these witnesses, at that, as all he will have to do is go down to Mindy's restaurant on Broadway and summon the first twenty horse players he sees. Horse players hate and despise assistant starters because they feel that the assistants are always giving the horses they bet on the worst of the starts and naturally these horse players will deem it a privilege and a pleasure to perjure themselves in a case of this nature, especially for Itchky Ironhat, who is a popular character.

His right name is something in twelve letters, but he is called Itchky Ironhat because he always wears a black derby hat and generally he has it pulled down on his head until the brim is resting on his ears and as Itchky is a short, roly-poly guy with a fat puss he really looks a great deal like a corked jug.

Finally the racing officials say they will not rule Itchky or old Em off this time but that he must remove Em from the New York tracks and run her elsewhere and this is wonderful news to the assistant starters, who are awaiting the decision with interest.

They feel that they are all sure to wind up daffy if they have to always be deciding on whether to cater to old Em at the post or take a going-over from Itchky Ironhat and in fact they say the only thing that keeps them from going daffy on account of old Em long before this is that she does not go to the post often.

She is entered in more races than any horse that ever lives, but just before a race comes up Itchky generally starts figuring that maybe the track will not suit her, or that the race is too long, or maybe too short, or that it is not the right time of day, or that old Em will not feel just like running that day, so he usually withdraws her at the last minute.

Sometimes the racing officials are a little tough with owners who wish to scratch horses from a race at the last minute, but they never argue a second with Itchky Ironhat. In fact, they often give three cheers when Em is taken out of a race, not only because she is so cross at the post but because she is so slow that she is always getting in the way of other horses and inconveniencing them more than somewhat.

It is the way Itchky thinks old Em feels that figures with him in taking her out of a race more than anything else, and to hear him talk you will think she comes right out and informs him how she feels every day. Indeed, Itchky converses with old Em as if she is a human being and he claims she can understand everything he says, though personally I do not believe any horse can understand a slightly Yiddish dialect such as Itchky employs.

[157]

She is a big bay mare with a sway-back and of course she is quite elderly for a horse, and especially a race horse, but Itchky says she does not look her years. She is as fat as a goose what with him feeding her candy, apples, cakes and ice cream, besides a little hay and grain, and she is wind-broken and a bleeder and has knobs on her knees the size of baseballs.

She has four bad ankles and in fact the only thing that is not the matter with her is tuberculosis and maybe anæmia. It makes some horse owners shudder just to look at her but in Itchky Ironhat's eyes old Em is more beautiful than Seabiscuit.

A guy by the name of Crowbar gives her to Itchky at the Woodbine track in Canada when she is just a two-year-old, rising three. This guy Crowbar buys her as a yearling out of a sale at Saratoga for fifty fish but becomes discouraged about her when he notices that she cannot keep up with a lead pony even when the pony is just walking.

On top of this she bows a tendon, so Crowbar is taking her out to shoot her to save the expense of shipping her and he is pretty sore at having to waste a cartridge on her when he meets up with Itchky Ironhat and Itchky asks what is coming off. When Crowbar explains, Itchky takes a closer look at Em and she gazes at him with such a sorrowful expression that Itchky's heart is touched.

He asks Crowbar to give her to him, although at this time Itchky is just doing the best he can around the tracks and has about as much use for a racehorse as he has for a hearse, and naturally Crowbar is pleased to make the saving of a cartridge. So this is how Itchky becomes the owner of old Em and from now on he practically lives with her even after he marries Mousie, which is what starts Mousie to complaining, as it seems she does not care to be excluded from her home life by a horse.

It is no use trying to tell Itchky that Em is nothing but an old buzzard, because he keeps thinking of her as a stake horse and saying she is bound to win a large stake someday and he spends every dime he can get hold of in entering her in big races and on shipping her and feeding her and on jockey fees.

And all this is very surprising to be sure, as Itchky Ironhat is by no means a sucker when it comes to other horses and he makes a pretty good living hustling around the tracks. What is more, the way he can bring old Em back to the races every time she breaks down, which is about every other time she starts in a race, shows that Itchky is either a natural-born horse trainer or a horse hypnotist.

When he is very desperate for a little moolah, he will place Em in a cheap selling race and it is in spots such as this that she occasionally wins. But then Itchky always worries himself sick for fear somebody will claim her, the idea of a claiming race being that another owner can always claim a horse in such a race by putting up the price for which the horse is entered, which may be anywhere from a few hundred dollars on up, according to the conditions of the race and what the owner thinks his horse is worth.

Naturally, Itchky has to run old Em for as cheap a price as horses are ever run for her to win a race, but even then there is really no sense in him worrying about her being claimed as no owner with any brains wants such a lizard as old Em in his barn, and especially after what happens to a character by the name of One Thumb Haverstraw.

This One Thumb is considered quite a joker and one day in Maryland he claims old Em out of a race for eight hundred boffoes just for a joke on Itchky, although personally I always figure the joke is on One Thumb when he gets her for this price.

Itchky is really greatly dejected over losing old Em and he goes to see One Thumb right after the race and tries to buy her back for two hundred dollars over the claiming price, but One Thumb is so pleased with his joke that he refuses to sell and then the most surprising things begin to occur to him.

A few nights later a ghost in a white sheet appears at his barn and frightens away all the coloured parties who are working for him as stable-hands and turns all of One Thumb's horses out of their stalls except old Em and chases them around the country until they are worn plumb out and are no good for racing for some weeks to come.

What is more, every time One Thumb himself steps into the open at night, a bullet whistles past him and finally one breezes through the seat of his pants and at this he hunts up Itchky Ironhat and returns old Em to him for four hundred less than the claiming price and considers it a great bargain, at that, and nobody ever plays any more jokes on Itchky with old Em.

Now the night of the racing officials' decision, I am sitting in Mindy's restaurant enjoying some choice pot roast with potato pancakes when in comes Itchky Ironhat looking somewhat depressed and, as he takes a seat at my table, naturally I tell him I deeply regret hearing that he will no longer be permitted to run old Em in New York, and Itchky sighs and says:

'Well,' he says, 'it is a great loss to the racing public of this state, but I always wish to do something nice for old Em and this gives me the opportunity of doing it.'

'What will be something nice for her, Itchky?' I say.

'Why,' Itchky says, 'I take her many places the past dozen years, but there is one place I never take her and that is her old home. You see, Em comes from the Bluegrass country of Kentucky and I get to thinking that the nicest thing I can do for her is to take her there and let her see the place where she is born.'

'Itchky,' I say, 'how is the bank roll?'

'It is thin,' Itchky says. 'In fact, if you are thinking of a touch, it is practically invisible.'

'I am not thinking of such a thing,' I say. 'What I am thinking of is it will cost a gob to ship old Em to Kentucky.'

'Oh,' Itchky says, 'I do not intend to ship her. I intend to take her there in person by motor truck and I am wondering if you will not like to go with us for company, Old Em loves company. After we let her see her old home we can drop her in a stake race at Churchill Downs and win a package.'

Then Itchky explains to me that he acquires a truck that very afternoon from a vegetable pedlar for the sum of sixty dollars and that he also gets a couple of wide, strong planks which he figures he can let down from the rear end of the truck like a runway so old Em can walk on them getting on and off the truck and that by driving by day and resting by night he can take her to the Bluegrass of Kentucky this way very nicely.

Now it is coming on time for the Kentucky Derby and if there is one thing I wish to see it is this event, and furthermore I never get around the country much and I figure that such a journey will be most educational to me so I tell Itchky he has a customer. But if I see the truck first I will certainly never think of trying to get anywhere in it, not even to the Polo Grounds.

Of course when Itchky tells me the truck costs him only sixty dollars, I am not looking for a fancy truck, but I have no idea it is going to be older than Henry Ford, or anyway Edsel, and not much bigger than a pushcart and with no top whatever, even over the seat.

The body of the truck is not long enough for old Em to stand in it spraddled out, the way horses love to stand, or her hind legs will be hanging out the rear end, so what Itchky does is to push her front legs back and her hind legs forward, so that all four feet are close together under her like she is standing on a dime.

Personally, I consider this an uncomfortable position all the way around for a horse but when Itchky and I get on the seat and Em finds she can rest her head on Itchky's shoulder, she seems quite happy, especially as Itchky talks to her most of the time.

It is no time after we start that we find old Em makes the truck top-heavy and in fact she almost falls overboard every time we take a curve and Itchky has to choke down to about two miles per hour until all of a sudden Em learns how to lean her weight to one side of the truck or the other on the curves and then Itchky can hit it up to the full speed of the truck, which is about ten miles per hour. I will say one thing for old Em, I never see a brighter horse in my life.

[161]

The first time we stop to take her off for the night, we find that the plank runway is all right for loading her because she can run up the boards like a squirrel but they have too much of a pitch for her to walk down them, so finally we drop the tail gate and get hold of the front end of the truck and lift it gently and let her slide down to the ground like she was on a toboggan and I always claim that old Em likes this better than any other part of the trip.

It seems to be a most surprising spectacle to one and all along our route to see a truck going past with a horse leaning this way and that to keep balanced and with forty per cent. of her sticking out of one end of the truck, and twenty per cent. of her sticking out of the other end, and we often attract many spectators when we stop. This is whenever we have a blow-out, which is every now and then. Sometimes there is much comment among these spectators about old Em and as it is generally comment of an unfavourable nature, I am always having difficulty keeping Itchky from taking pops at spectators.

We sleep at night in the truck with old Em tied to the rear end and we use her spare blankets for covering as Em has more blankets than any other horse in the country and most of them are very fancy blankets, at that. It is not bad sleeping except when it rains and then Itchky takes all the blankets off us and puts them on Em and my overcoat too, and we have to sit up under the truck and the way Itchky worries about Em catching cold is most distressing.

Sometimes when we are rolling along the road and Em is dozing on Itchky's shoulder, he talks to me instead of her, and I ask him if he knows just where to find Em's old home in the Bluegrass country.

'No,' he says, 'I do not know just where, but the record book gives the breeder of Em as the Tucky Farms and it must be a well-known breeding establishment to produce such a horse as Em, so we will have no trouble finding it. By the way,' Itchky says, 'Em comes of a very high-class family. She is by an important stallion by the name of Christofer out of a mare called Love Always, but,' he says, 'the curious thing about it is I am never able to learn of another horse of this breeding in this country, though Christofer is once a good race horse in France.'

Personally, I consider it a great thing for this country that there is only one horse bred like Em but naturally I do not mention such a thought to Itchky Ironhat, not only because I know it will displease him but because I am afraid old Em may overhear me and be greatly offended.

The road signs state that we are a few miles out of the city of Lexington, Ky., and we know we are now down in the Bluegrass country, when we come upon a tall old guy leaning against a fence in front of a cute little white house. This old guy looks as if he may be a native of these parts as he is wearing a wide-brimmed soft hat and is chewing on a straw, so Itchky stops the truck and puts on a Southern accent and speaks to him as follows:

'Suh,' Itchky says, 'can you all direct me to a place called the Tucky Farms, suh?'

The tall old guy gazes at Itchky and then he gazes at me and finally he gazes at old Em and he never stops chewing on the straw and after a while he smiles and points and says:

'It is about three miles up that road,' he says. 'It is a big red brick house with some burned-down barns in the background, but friend,' he says, 'let me give you a piece of good advice. I do not know what your business is, but keep away from that place with anything that looks like a horse. Although,' he says, 'I am not sure that the object you have on your truck answers such a description.'

Of course Itchky can see from this crack that the old guy is making fun of Em and he starts to sizzle all over and forgets his Southern accent at once and says:

'You do not like my horse?'

'Oh, it is a horse then?' the old guy says. 'Well, the party who owns Tucky Farms is a trifle eccentric about horses. In fact, he is eccentric about everything, but horses most of all. He does not permit them on his premises. It is a sad case. You may meet a disagreeable reception if you go there with your so-called horse.'

[163]

Then he turns and walks into the cute little white house and I have all I can do to keep Itchky from going after him and reprimanding him for speaking so disrespectfully of old Em, especially as the old guy keeps looking around at us and we can see that he is smiling more than somewhat.

Itchky drives on up the road a little ways and, just as the old guy says, we come upon a big red brick house and there is no doubt that this is the Tucky Farms because there is a faded sign over an arched gateway that so states. The house is all shuttered up and is on a small hill pretty well back from the road and not far from the house are the remainders of some buildings that look as if they burned down a long time ago and are never fixed up again or cleared away.

In fact, the grounds and the house itself all look as if they can stand a little attention and there is not a soul in sight and it is rather a dismal scene in every respect. The gate is closed, so I get down off the truck and open it and Itchky drives the truck in and right up to the front door of the house under a sort of porch with white pillars.

Now the truck makes a terrible racket and this racket seems to stir up a number of coloured parties who appear from around in back of the house, along with a large white guy. This large guy is wearing corduroy pants and laced boots and a black moustache and he is also carrying a double-barrelled shotgun and he speaks to Itchky in a fierce tone of voice as follows:

'Pigface,' he says, 'get out of here. Get out of here before you are hurt. What do you mean by driving in here with a load of dog meat such as this, anyway?'

He points a finger at old Em who has her head up and is snuffling the air and gazing about her with great interest, and right away Itchky climbs down off the seat of the truck and removes his derby and places it on the ground and takes off his coat and starts rolling up his sleeves.

'It is the last straw,' Itchky Ironhat says. 'I will first make this big ash can eat that cannon he is lugging and then I will beat his skull in. Nobody can refer to Emaleen as dog meat and live.'

Now the front door of the house opens and out comes a thin character in a soiled white linen suit and at first he seems to be quite an old character as he has long white hair but when he gets closer I can see that he is not so very old at that, but he is very seedy-looking and his eyes have a loose expression. I can also see from the way the large guy and the coloured parties step back that this is a character who packs some weight around here. His voice is low and hard as he speaks to Itchky Ironhat and says:

'What is this?' he says. 'What name do I just hear you pronounce?'

'Emaleen,' Itchky says. 'It is the name of my race mare which you see before you. She is the greatest race mare in the world. The turf records say she is bred right here at this place and I bring her down here to see her old home, and everybody insults her. So this is Southern hospitality?' Itchky says.

The new character steps up to the truck and looks at old Em for quite a spell and all the time he is shaking his head and his lips are moving as if he is talking to himself, and finally he says to the large guy:

'Unload her,' he says. 'Unload her and take good care of her, Dobkins. I suppose you will have to send to one of the neighbours for some feed. Come in gentlemen,' he says to Itchky and me and he holds the front door of the house open. 'My name is Salsbury,' he says. 'I am the owner of Tucky Farms and I apologize for my foreman's behaviour but he is only following orders.'

As we go into the house I can see that it is a very large house and I can also see that it must once be a very grand house because of the way it is furnished, but everything seems to be as run-down inside as it does outside and I can see that what this house needs is a good cleaning and straightening out.

In the meantime, Mr. Salsbury keeps asking Itchky Ironhat questions about old Em and when he hears how long Itchky has her and what he thinks of her and all this and that, he starts wiping his eyes with a handkerchief as if the story makes him very sad, especially the part about why Itchky brings her to the Bluegrass.

Finally, Mr. Salsbury leads us into a large room that seems to be a library and at one end of this room there is a painting taller than I am of a very beautiful Judy in a white dress and this is the only thing in the house that seems to be kept dusted up a little and Mr. Salsbury points to the painting and says:

'My wife, Emaleen, gentlemen. I name the horse you bring here after her long ago, because it is the first foal of her favourite mare and the first foal of a stallion I import from France.'

'By Christofer, out of Love Always,' Itchky Ironhat says.

'Yes,' Mr. Salsbury says. 'In those days, Tucky Farms is one of the great breeding and racing establishments of the Bluegrass. In those days, too, my wife is known far and wide for her fondness for horses and her kindness to them. She is the head of the humane society in Kentucky and the Emaleen Salsbury annual award of a thousand dollars for the kindest deed towards a horse brought to the attention of the society each year is famous.

'One night,' Mr. Salsbury continues, 'there is a fire in the barns and my wife gets out of bed and before anyone can stop her she rushes into the flames trying to save her beautiful mare, Love Always. They both perish, and,' he says, 'with them perishes the greatest happiness ever given a mortal on this earth.'

By this time, Itchky Ironhat and I are feeling very sad, indeed, and in fact all the creases in Itchky's face are full of tears as Mr. Salsbury goes on to state that the only horses on the place that are saved are a few yearlings running in the pastures. He sends them all with a shipment a neighbour is taking to Saratoga to be disposed of there for whatever they will bring.

'Your mare Emaleen is one of those,' he says. 'I forget all about her at the time. Indeed,' he says, 'I forget everything but my unhappiness. I feel I never wish to see or hear of a horse again as long as I live and I withdraw myself completely from the world and all my former activities. But,' he says, 'your bringing the mare here awakens old fond memories and your story of how you cherish her makes me realize that this is exactly what my wife Emaleen will wish me to do. I see where I sadly neglect my duty to her memory. Why,' he says, 'I never even keep up the Emaleen Salsbury award.'

Now he insists that we must remain there a while as his guests and Itchky Ironhat agrees, although I point out that it will be more sensible for us to move on to Louisville and get into action as quickly as possible because we are now practically out of funds. But Itchky takes a look at old Em and he says she is enjoying herself so much running around her old home and devouring grass that it will be a sin and a shame to take her away before it is absolutely necessary.

After a couple of days, I tell Itchky that I think absolutely necessary arrives, but Itchky says Mr. Salsbury now wishes to give a dinner in honour of old Em and he will not think of denying her this pleasure. And for the next week the house is overrun with coloured parties, male and female, cleaning up the house and painting and cooking and dusting and I do not know what all else, and furthermore I hear there is a great to-do all through the Bluegrass country when the invitations to the dinner start going around, because this is the first time in over a dozen years that Mr. Salsbury has any truck whatever with his neighbours.

On the night of the dinner, one of the male coloured parties tells me that he never before sees such a gathering of the high-toned citizens of the Bluegrass as are assembled in a big dining hall at a horse-shoe shaped table with an orchestra going and with flowers and flags and racing colours all around and about. In fact, the coloured party says it is just like the old days at Tucky Farms when Mr. Salsbury's wife is alive, although he says he does not remember ever seeing such a character sitting alongside Mr. Salsbury at the table as Itchky Ironhat.

To tell the truth, Itchky Ironhat seems to puzzle all the guests no little and it is plain to be seen that they are wondering who he is and why he is present, though Itchky is sharpened up with a fresh shave and has on a clean shirt and of course he is not wearing his derby hat. Personally, I am rather proud of Itchky's appearance, but I can see that he seems to be overplaying his knife a little, especially against the mashed potatoes.

Mr. Salsbury is dressed in a white dinner jacket and his eyes are quiet and his hair is trimmed and his manner is most genteel in every way and when the guests are seated he gets to his feet and attracts their attention by tapping on a wineglass with a spoon. Then he speaks to them as follows:

'Friends and neighbours,' he says. 'I know you are all surprised at being invited here but you may be more surprised when you learn the reason. As most of you are aware, I am as one dead for years. Now I live again. I am going to restore Tucky Farms to all its old turf glory in breeding and racing, and,' he says, 'I am going to re-establish the Emaleen Salsbury award, with which you are familiar, and carry on again in every way as I am now certain my late beloved wife will wish.'

Then he tells them the story of old Em and how Itchky Ironhat cares for her and loves her all these years and how he brings her to the Bluegrass just to see her old home, but of course he does not tell them that Itchky also plans to later drop her in a race at Churchill Downs, as it seems Itchky never mentions the matter to him.

Anyway, Mr. Salsbury says that the return of old Em awakens him as if from a bad dream and he can suddenly see how he is not doing right with respect to his wife's memory and while he is talking a tall old guy who is sitting next to me, and who turns out to be nobody but the guy who directs us to Tucky Farms, says to me like this:

'It is a miracle,' he says. 'I am his personal physician and I give him up long ago as a hopeless victim of melancholia. In fact, I am always expecting to hear of him dismissing himself from this world entirely. Well,' the old guy says, 'I always say medical science is not everything.'

'My first step towards restoring Tucky Farms,' Mr. Salsbury goes on, 'is to purchase the old mare Emaleen from Mr. Itchky

Ironhat here for the sum of three thousand dollars, which we agree upon this evening as a fair price. I will retire her of course for the rest of her days, which I hope will be many.'

With this he whips out a cheque and hands it to Itchky and naturally I am somewhat surprised at the sum mentioned because I figure if old Em is worth three G's War Admiral must be worth a jillion. However, I am also greatly pleased because I can see where Itchky and I will have a nice taw for the races at Churchill Downs without having to bother about old Em winning one.

'Now,' Mr. Salsbury says, 'for our guest of honour.'

Then two big doors at one end of the banquet hall open wide and there seems to be a little confusion outside and a snorting and a stamping as if a herd of wild horses is coming in and all of a sudden who appears in the doorway with her mane and tail braided with ribbons and her coat all slicked up but old Em and who is leading her in but the large guy who insults her and also Itchky on our arrival at Tucky Farms.

The guests begin applauding and the orchestra plays My Old Kentucky Home and it is a pleasant scene to be sure, but old Em seems quite unhappy about something as the large guy pulls her into the hollow of the horseshoe-shaped table, and the next thing anybody knows, Itchky Ironhat climbs over the table, knocking glasses and dishes every which way and flattens the large guy with a neat left hook in the presence of the best people of the Bluegrass country.

Naturally, this incident causes some comment and many of the guests are slightly shocked and there is considerable criticism of Itchky Ironhat for his lack of table manners. But then it is agreed by one and all present that Itchky is undoubtedly entitled to the Emaleen Salsbury kindness to horses award when I explain that what irks him is the fact that the large guy leads old Em in with a twitch on her lip.

Well, this is about all there is to the story, except that Itchky and I go over to the Louisville the next day and remain there awaiting the Kentucky Derby and we have a wonderful time, to be sure, except that we do not seem to be able to win any bets on the horse races at Churchill Downs.

In fact, the day before the Derby, Itchky remarks that the bank roll is now lower than a turtle's vest buttons and when I express surprise that we toss off four G's in such a short period, Itchky says to me like this:

'Oh,' he says, 'it is not four G's. I send the Emaleen Salsbury kindness-to-horses award of one G to Mousie. I figure she is legally entitled to this for leaving me with Em. Otherwise, we will never get even the three and besides,' Itchky says, 'I love Mousie. In fact, I invite her to join me here and she agrees to come after I promise I will never as much as think of old Em again.

'By the way,' Itchky says, 'I call up Tucky Farms this morning and Mr. Salsbury brings old Em into his study and lets her hear my voice over the phone. Mr. Salsbury says she is greatly pleased. I give her your love, but of course not as much of yours as I give her of mine,' he says.

'Thanks, Itchky,' I say, and at this moment I am somewhat surprised to notice a metal ash tray removing Itchky's derby hat from his head and, gazing about, who do I observe standing in the doorway and now taking dead aim at Itchky with another tray but his ever-loving wife, Mousie.

Appendix

Runyon On Broadway, first published in 1950, contained the following stories:

More Than Somewhat

Breach of Promise, Romance in the Roaring Forties, Dream Street Rose, The Old Doll's House, Blood Pressure, The Bloodhounds of Broadway, Tobias the Terrible, The Snatching of Bookie Bob, The Lily of St Pierre, Hold 'Em, Yale!, Earthquake, 'Gentlemen, The King!', A Nice Price, Broadway Financier, The Brain Goes Home

Furthermore

Madame La Gimp, Dancing Dan's Christmas, Sense of Humour, Lillian, Little Miss Marker, Pick the Winner, Undertaker Song, Butch Minds The Baby, The Hottest Guy in the World, The Lemon Drop Kid, What, No Butler?, The Three Wise Guys, A Very Honourable Guy, Princess O'Hara, Social Error

Take it Easy

Tight Shoes, Lonely Heart, The Brakeman's Daughter, Cemetery Bait, It Comes Up Mud, The Big Umbrella, For A Pal, Big Shoulders, That Ever-Loving Wife of Hymie's, Neat Strip, Bred For Battle, Too Much Pep, Baseball Hattie, Situation Wanted, A Piece of Pie, A Job for the Macarone, All Horse Players Die Broke

Runyon From First To Last first published in 1954 contained the following stories:

The First Stories

The Defence of Strikerville, Fat Fallon, Two Men Named Collins, As Between Friends, The Informal Execution of Soupbone Pew, My Father

Stories à la Carte

Money From Home, A Story Goes With It, Broadway Complex, So You Won't Talk!, Dark Dolores, Delegates at Large, A Light in France, Old Em's Kentucky Home, Johnny One-Eye, Broadway Incident, The Idyll of Miss Sarah Brown, The Melancholy Dane, Barbecue, Little Pinks, Palm Beach Santa Claus, Cleo, The Lacework Kid

The Last Stories

Blonde Mink, Big Boy Blues

Written in Sickness

Why Me?, The Doctor Knows Best, No Life, Good Night, Bed-Warmers, Sweet Dreams, Passing The Word Along, Death Pays a Social Call